Alex Gerlis was born in Lincolnshire and for nearly thirty years worked as a BBC journalist. His first novel, *The Best of Our Spies* (2012), has been an Amazon bestseller and is currently being developed for television serialisation by a major production company. The other books in the Spy Masters series of Second World War espionage novels are: *The Swiss Spy* (2015), *Vienna Spies* (2017) and *The Berlin Spies* (2018). *Prince of Spies* – the first novel in the Prince series, commissioned by Canelo – was published in March 2020, followed by *Sea of Spies*, *Ring of Spies* and *End of Spies*. Alex Gerlis lives in London, is married with two daughters and is represented by Gordon Wise at the Curtis Brown Literary Agency.

www.alexgerlis.com

Facebook: @alexgerlisauthor

Twitter: @alex_gerlis

www.canelo.co/authors/alex-gerlis/

Also by Alex Gerlis

Spy Masters

The Best of Our Spies
The Swiss Spy
Vienna Spies
The Berlin Spies

The Richard Prince Thrillers

Prince of Spies
Sea of Spies
Ring of Spies
End of Spies

The Wolf Pack Spies

Agent in Berlin

ALEX GERLIS

AGENT IN BERLIN

CANELO

First published in the United Kingdom in 2021 by

Canelo
Unit 9, 5th Floor
Cargo Works, 1–2 Hatfields
London, SE1 9PG
United Kingdom

A CIP catalogue record for this book is available from the British Library.

Print ISBN 978 1 80032 557 9
Ebook ISBN 978 1 80032 156 4

Look for more great books at www.canelo.co

Printed and bound in Great Britain by Clays Ltd, Elcograf S.p.A.

1

Main Characters

Barnaby Allen (Barney) MI6 officer

Piers Devereux Barney's boss at MI6

Roly Pearson British Intelligence chief

Tom Gilbey MI6 officer

Jack Miller American journalist

Lieutenant Tom Miller US Navy, brother of Jack

Werner Lustenberger German businessman

Sophia von Naundorf Wife of SS officer, Berlin

Karl-Heinrich von Naundorf Husband of Sophia

Tadashi Kimura Japanese diplomat, Berlin

Arno Marcus Jewish man, Berlin

Maureen Holland Briton working at Berlin radio station

Fritz – Ken Ridley Berlin radio

Karl Henniger Gestapo officer, Berlin

Harald Mettler Clerk at Swiss embassy, Berlin

Oberstleutnant Ernst Scholz Luftwaffe officer at Air Ministry, Berlin

Timothy Summers First Secretary, British embassy, Berlin

Noel Moore Passport Control officer (MI6), Berlin

Basil Remington-Barber MI6, Bern, Switzerland

Joe Walsh Editor, the *Philadelphia Bulletin*

Ted Morris Associated Newspapers, New York

Albert Haas Journalist, Berlin

Harald Fuchs (Rudi) SS officer, Berlin

Hiroshi Ōshima Japanese ambassador, Berlin

Kuzumi Kobayashi Japanese Secret Police, *Kenpeitai*, Berlin

Doctor Ludwig Vogt Charité Medical School, Berlin

Air Vice-Marshal Frank Hamilton Head of RAF Intelligence Branch

Cromwell RAF Intelligence analyst

Wing Commander Tim Carter RAF Intelligence officer

Austin US Intelligence officer, London

Joseph Jenkins US Intelligence officer, London

Brookes Foreign Office

The Wolf

The wolf is an unusual creature, feared and revered at the same time.

Many cultures worship the wolf, seeing it as a benevolent animal bringing good fortune. Some Native American tribes believe the Earth to have been created by wolves. Italians cherish the wolf for rescuing Romulus and Remus.

In other cultures, the wolf has a more malevolent reputation; feared as a hunter. In medieval times some Christian cultures saw the wolf as the incarnation of evil; in fairy tales it is resolutely cast as the big, bad wolf.

Norse mythology recognised this paradoxical view of the animal with tales of the wolf chasing both the sun and the moon.

The wolf is a highly social animal, living in packs, which can number in double figures. But the wolf can also operate as a solitary creature – the lone wolf – existing outside the comfort of the pack.

Wolf packs operate within their own territory and commonly travel up to fifty miles a day.

The wolf would make a perfect spy.

Prologue

Pearl Harbor, Honolulu
December 1941

Tom Miller had never had much time for religion. Thankfully his parents hadn't been too bothered by it either and the fact they'd both died by the time he was twenty only confirmed his scepticism about matters of faith.

In so far as this young Naval officer led his life by any credo it was that you should treat other people as you'd like to be treated yourself, and that first weekend in December was a good case in point.

The Pacific Fleet had been on high alert for the past couple of weeks at its base in Hawaii, meaning all overnight shore leave had been cancelled. But that Saturday night it was agreed a dozen junior officers from the *USS Arizona* could have shore leave and Lieutenant Tom Miller was one of the lucky ones when lots were drawn.

One of the unlucky ones was his best friend, Mark Bianci. The two shared a cramped cabin and were the same age and rank, and both from Philadelphia. Mark was devastated at not having been selected for shore leave. He'd recently met a young nurse called Lucy from the Naval hospital and Lucy had managed to arrange for them to have the use of a friend's apartment at Aiea Bay that weekend.

Tom decided that if he were in Mark's position, he'd like someone to do the right thing by him – and as nurses came in groups, Lucy was bound to have friends. So, he gave his shore leave to an unspeakably grateful Mark Bianci, who promised him he'd return the favour one day and said his priority that weekend – which Tom somehow doubted – was to quiz Lucy on her friends and find one suitable for Tom.

Lieutenant Tom Miller's watch wasn't due to start until nine on the Sunday morning so he allowed himself longer in his bunk.

Even at anchor a large battleship was a cacophony of sounds, a consequence of putting thirty thousand tons of metal and fifteen hundred men on the water. It took Tom Miller a few moments to work out what it was that woke him at five to eight that Sunday morning.

The first sound he heard was shouting in the corridor, followed by doors slamming and the wail of the ship's air-raid alarm, and he knew he had to get to the bridge as soon as possible.

There was panic in the narrow passageways: people hurried in different directions, pushing others against the bulkheads; shouts that this was no drill.

Tom Miller made it to the bridge just in time to spot the first wave of a dozen Japanese torpedo bombers swooping in low from the north. He saw guns open fire on the *USS Nevada* on their stern and the *USS Vestal* moored next to them took a direct hit.

Then came the first explosion and his reaction was to notice how everything appeared almost festive, the crackling sounds and the sight of multi-coloured explosions.

For a moment Lieutenant Tom Miller was too shocked to move, then someone shouted at him to head to the bow where a fire was raging. He dropped down a ladder and hit the deck as another torpedo struck the front of the ship.

He came to a few seconds later and glanced at his wristwatch which told him it was eight minutes past eight, and he thought of his father, whose wristwatch this had been and somehow that gave him the strength to get to his feet. He staggered along for a few yards, still thinking of his father, feeling his firm hand guiding him by the elbow.

Lieutenant Tom Miller's final moments soon followed: a blinding light and a volley of deafening sounds, followed by lasting darkness and a perpetual silence.

–

Forty minutes after Lieutenant Tom Miller's death the second wave of Japanese aircraft attacked. Within a quarter of an hour, they'd gone, and the attack on Pearl Harbor was over, leaving much of the US Pacific Fleet destroyed and more than two thousand Americans dead.

Chaos and confusion hung over the island along with the long plumes of black smoke and the acrid smell of destruction.

From his office on North Road, overlooking Quarry Loch, Lieutenant Commander Sam Stein had watched in utter shock as the attack unfolded. He'd fled to the bomb shelter at first and then decided he was deserting his post so climbed the stairs back to his office on the top floor. The windows had all been blown out and he scanned the sky and then the Harbor with his binoculars, doing his best to hold his shaking hands steady, pausing to make notes and wondering whether he should type them up or telephone San Diego.

The end of the raid was marked by a minute or so of a strange silence; a brief pause between the aircraft departing and the onset of sirens and screams. Still in a state of shock, Sam Stein shuffled over to his desk, cleared the debris and – because he couldn't think what else to do – began to write a report. *The sky thick with Japanese warplanes, the surface of the Harbor covered in wreckage, the—*

The sound of footsteps on broken glass caused him to look up. It was Robert Clarke – Robert V Clarke Junior indeed – another lieutenant commander he knew from meetings at Fleet Headquarters. Clarke worked for the Office of Naval Intelligence and had a superior air about him and a faux-English accent, along with a habit of treating anyone not of superior rank with disdain.

'The road's blocked and I can't get near Kuahua. Give me a telephone, Stein.' He seemed surprisingly calm and pronounced

'Stein' as 'Shtein' and then allowed himself a pause and the trace of a smile.

'If you can find one that works, sure. They're all down.'

Robert V Clarke Junior sniffed as if trying to work out what the smell was. He walked around the room, trying all the phones in turn before slamming them down and muttering 'Jesus Christ', looking at Sam Stein as if all this were his fault.

'They've destroyed the fleet,' said Stein. 'From here I've seen the *Nevada*, *Arizona*, *West Virginia* and *Oklahoma* all badly hit. There must have been... what? ... two hundred Japanese planes in each wave?'

Clarke shrugged and lit a cigarette without offering one to Sam Stein.

'Shouldn't we have known about it, Robert? Surely, we must have had some idea, some kind of warning? An attack that size... it doesn't just come out of thin air.'

For the first time Lieutenant Commander Robert V Clarke Junior of the Office of Naval Intelligence looked his fellow officer in the eye and without the condescending manner.

'Oh, we knew all right... we certainly bloody well knew.'

Chapter 1

England and Berlin
May 1935

'Who do you think will win?'

'I beg your pardon?' The wind whistled round the racecourse and Barney Allen hadn't quite caught what the man alongside him had said. He was considerably shorter than Allen and his accent certainly wasn't English: there was something distinctly continental about it.

'I asked who you think will win the Chester Cup?' There it was again, the accent – the 'th' in 'think' sounding not quite right, and 'win' sounding more like 'vin'. 'Cup' sounded a bit like 'cap'. The man looked up at Barney Allen, his eyebrows raised expectantly.

'I hope you don't think I'm being impolite but I'm afraid my job precludes me from being involved in betting or giving my opinion on horses.' Allen was doing his best not to sound too pompous but was aware he came across as more patrician than he intended.

The man nodded his head slowly, apparently impressed that someone could have a job that was so important they could be at a racecourse yet not discuss the big race of the day. After all, the Chester Cup was the most important race held at the course all year.

'And what job would that be, may I ask?' 'Would' sounding like 'vood'.

'Well you see…' Allen moved his hands from behind his back and tried to adopt a less military stance. 'I work for the Jockey

Club. I'm a steward. We're the chaps who oversee the rules of horse racing, make sure everything's in order, so you'll understand that we're not allowed to give tips about who we think will win a race and we're most certainly forbidden from betting on races.'

He was aware he was sounding pompous again so he chuckled and the man responded with a broad smile and held out his hand to shake Barney Allen's and introduced himself as Werner, and Barney said he was Barnaby and was very pleased to meet him and was Werner German by any chance?

Werner said he supposed he was and Barney Allen smiled again and replied in German, apologising if it was somewhat rusty, and said he hoped Werner didn't think he was being difficult in any way but he hoped he understood and he was pleased for an opportunity to use his German.

'Your German is very good and your accent is excellent. You speak a very pure German, as if you're from Hannover.'

And that was how their friendship began. Barney handed Werner his card and asked him where in Germany he was from. Werner shrugged and said he was more German than anything else but his grandparents were Swiss, Austrian, Dutch and French so although he'd spent a good deal of his life in Germany, he regarded himself as European. He also had a Swiss passport, he added. And a French one.

Barney Allen asked what brought him to England and Werner said the atmosphere was far more pleasant than it was in Germany these days and in any case horse racing was his passion and England was the home of horse racing and was it true that this was the oldest racecourse in the country?

'Indeed it is: in fact, the oldest racecourse in the world, would you believe? The first race took place here in 1512, a bit before my time!'

Both men laughed and Werner said the oldest racecourse in Germany was the Horner Rennbahn in Hamburg and that was less than a hundred years old and now that they were friends perhaps Barnaby could tell him who he thought would win the Chester Cup?

Barney Allen hesitated, watching the runners parade past, their flanks already steaming, and peered through his binoculars to study them in more detail. He noticed Werner had moved closer to him and was looking expectantly up at him, waiting for an answer.

'Completely between you and me, Werner, I'd go for Damascus: Foster's a good jockey over this distance. Sired by Transcendent and the dam's Attar, so a decent pedigree. That's the horse, not the jockey!'

Werner laughed and asked his new friend to point out Damascus, which he did before saying he needed to get up to the steward's enclosure now and it was nice meeting Werner and perhaps they'd bump into each other at another racecourse one day – who knows?

As he made his way to the stands Barney Allen shook his head, astonished at how easily this funny little man had managed to persuade him to reveal information he'd normally never dream of divulging to anyone. There was no doubt that as a Jockey Club official he was in a privileged position, picking up inside information – how a horse was likely to run, what injuries another may be carrying. And he knew he was obliged to keep what he heard to himself. Somehow, the man called Werner had got him to do otherwise. It was almost as if he'd been hypnotised.

Barney Allen wasn't in the least bit surprised when Damascus duly won the Chester Cup. As he waited for a taxi outside the racecourse, he felt a tap on his arm and turned round to see the dapper German standing next to him. Werner had a broad grin on his face and gave Barney a knowing wink as he said what a pleasure it had been to meet him and how much he'd enjoyed the Chester Cup in particular. They shook hands once more and Werner said he still had Mr Barnaby's card and perhaps they could meet for lunch in London. He moved closer to Barney Allen and dropped his voice. 'The lunch will be on Damascus!'

-

Just one week later Barney Allen's secretary told him that a Mr Werner Lustenberger had called. 'He checked with me to see which would be the best day for lunch next week: we agreed on Wednesday.'

Barney Allen ought to have been put out at Werner's presumption of friendship, but as with his tipping the winner of the Chester Cup the previous week, he was more surprised at the ease with which the German drew him in. Lunch turned out to be in a small French restaurant tucked in an alleyway in Seven Dials, where the food was superb and the cost of the bottle of Burgundy they drank matched his weekly salary.

By the end of the lunch they'd become firm friends. Werner was so persuasive in a charismatic way that Barney found himself speaking more candidly than he was accustomed to. He talked about his marriage and how it was going through a rocky patch but would be fine; about his money worries and the crippling cost of educating his sons and his regrets at not leading a more… interesting life.

They met on a regular basis after that: sometimes for dinner at Barney's club, other times lunch at a restaurant of Werner's choosing. On those occasions Werner would start by talking about how his recent bets had done: invariably he'd allude to substantial winnings and as far as Barney could tell this was his friend's main source of income. Then it would be Barney's turn and Werner would say little, sympathetic nods and an encouraging word here or there. Talking with Werner Lustenberger had a confessional air to it, his new friend drawing him into areas he'd never dream of discussing with someone else.

It was very rare that Werner revealed anything personal: as far as Barney could work out Werner was in his early thirties and he talked more about his grandparents than his parents. There were occasional references to schools he'd been to – in Switzerland, Germany and France – and he mentioned he was a lapsed Catholic, very lapsed in fact. At one dinner Barney did ask whether Werner was married or had children and was shocked by the response. 'I have to tell you Barnaby' – he always used his full

name – 'I have little interest in women. My preferences are…
different!'

Barney Allen was of course shocked, not least that someone
could be quite so candid about their private life. And he was
surprised, too; Werner was certainly a colourful character, but he
seemed so… normal.

–

That very same month – May 1935 – and in fact in the very
same week as the Chester Cup an altogether different encounter
was taking place in Berlin, where an SS Sturmbannführer and his
wife were leading a party of guests to the veranda of a very smart
restaurant overlooking the Wannsee.

The SS officer was perhaps in his mid-thirties, his wife a good
deal younger. Whereas he was tall and imposing and with an air
of superiority about him, she was slim and attractive – in the way
that caused heads to turn. She wore a fashionable turban-style
hat and its pale colour contrasted with her neat dark hair and her
even darker eyes. Sophia Schaeffer had first met Karl-Heinrich
von Naundorf in 1930 when she joined one of the prestigious
law firms on Fasanenstrasse as a secretary. He was one of the
lawyers there and well-regarded – not least by himself. He was
also interested in Sophia, far more so than she was with him.
He was thirty when they first met, ten years older than her and
not really her type, even though she'd have been hard-pressed to
say what her type was. She would probably have said she'd have
preferred a man more her own age, someone more cultured and
sensitive, perhaps. But her father was charmed by Karl-Heinrich.
'Beggars can't be choosers,' he told her. She and her widowed
father lived in reduced circumstances in Wedding.

They married in 1932 and life was agreeable enough at first.
When it became apparent that she was unable to have children, Karl-Heinrich had been far more understanding than she'd
expected him to be.

But life changed in late 1933, after the Nazis came to power. She'd never known Karl-Heinrich to be political, but now he joined the Nazi Party and in early 1934 he gave up his job as a lawyer and became an SS officer. With it came the trappings of power and privilege. They moved to the apartment in Charlottenburg and she wanted for nothing.

As a relatively recent convert to Nazism Karl-Heinrich was keen to show he didn't lack conviction. He talked about needing to help Germany get out of the mess it was in and was enthusiastic for what he saw as the clear vision of Hitler. He became increasingly unpleasant and prejudiced, blaming the Jews for everything. As her life became materially more comfortable it was also emotionally barely tolerable.

The point at which Sophia realised quite how committed a Nazi Karl-Heinrich was came on that Saturday evening in May 1935. It was one of those evenings when the weather owed more to summer than spring, with a gentle warm breeze and the low evening sun over the lake. It was around the time of her father's birthday and as ever her husband was keen to show off to her father. In truth, it wasn't difficult for her father to be impressed by Karl-Heinrich: as far as he was concerned, his son-in-law could do nothing wrong. He couldn't believe how fortunate his daughter was to have married such a wonderful man and his only regret was that his late wife never met him. Only the previous month her father had joined the Nazi Party at Karl-Heinrich's suggestion.

Without consulting his wife, Karl-Heinrich had booked a table at the very smart restaurant overlooking the Wannsee. Had she been asked Sophia would have said her father would be uncomfortable in such refined surroundings. He preferred plain food and plenty of beer. To make matters worse Karl-Heinrich used the occasion to invite the chairman of their Nazi Party branch, a desperately thin man called Heinrich Röver. Karl-Heinrich insisted he was a good man to be on the right side of. Röver was accompanied by his wife, a nervous type who smoked throughout the meal and hardly ate anything.

But even before they sat down the evening was a disaster. The veranda overlooked the lake, with one row of tables by the lake and another row closer to the restaurant. The table they were shown was one of those by the door. Karl-Heinrich insisted to a mortified maître d' that his secretary had booked a table closest to the lake.

'I insisted she should book one of those tables. In fact, that table there, that was the one I specified.'

Karl-Heinrich pointed to a table with three couples on it. Along with the other diners they'd fallen silent as the man in the SS officer's uniform raised his voice.

'I am afraid there must be a misunderstanding, sir: Frau Roth booked that very table quite a few weeks ago. But please, this table here is very quiet and I would be honoured for you to have a bottle of—'

'Frau Roth, eh?' Karl-Heinrich took a step closer to the maître d' and towered over him, his arms folded high on his chest in a menacing manner. 'You mean to say Herr...?'

'Mann, sir.'

'You mean to say, Herr Mann, that you permit these Jews to take precedence over an SS officer and his guests!' Karl-Heinrich turned to look at the Roth's table. The six people at it looked shocked.

'Well, sir I, I—'

'I, I what, Mann? You are aware of the Citizenship Law, which was implemented last month?'

'Yes, of course, sir—'

'And you still allow these... vermin... to dine in your restaurant, let alone have the best table?'

Sophia looked at the Roth's table. They looked petrified. All the other diners were silent, staring at their plates.

'Darling, perhaps if we sit on this table as Herr Mann suggests and maybe—'

Karl-Heinrich – the man she'd never loved but who had always treated her properly – turned to look at her, his eyes blazing with rage. His waved his hand to beckon her to come closer and when she did cupped his mouth against her ear and whispered into it.

'If you ever – ever – speak like that to me in public again I shall slap you hard across the face. I hope you understand. Now, smile and nod your head!'

Sophia bit her lip and concentrated on fighting back the tears. When she looked up, the Roths and their guests were hurriedly leaving.

She remembered little else of that evening, other than a pervading sense of unpleasantness and her father's embarrassment at ordering from a menu he didn't really understand. All three men got drunk and at one stage in the evening Karl-Heinrich staggered to his feet and insisted every other diner – and the staff – join him in toasting the Führer.

That evening – the point at which she realised quite how committed a Nazi Karl-Heinrich really was – was also her point of no return. She'd made her bed and now had to lay in it. She was paying a heavy price for her own weakness. She did think about leaving Karl-Heinrich but was aware that the consequences for leaving an SS officer could be most serious.

She'd have nowhere to go.

She was trapped

Chapter 2

London
January 1936

'Born 1898, I see...' The man shook his head disapprovingly. 'Thirty-seven makes you a late starter for this business, Allen.'

Barney Allen bristled. 'Actually, I'm thirty-eight but—'

'Old for a new boy, though. And tell me, Allen, why are you suddenly interested in joining the Service?'

Piers Devereux had invested the word 'suddenly' with a degree of sarcasm. He looked up from the file on his desk and leaned back in his chair to face Barney Allen as he prepared to answer. He tilted his head back as if to catch the sun.

Barney Allen hesitated. He thought of the word Tom Gilbey had used to describe Devereux when he heard he was going to be interviewing Barney: disobliging.

'Money, sir.'

The briefest of nods from Devereux and then a gesture with one hand to indicate he should tell him more.

'I had a private income, sir, quite a generous one, enough to enable one to... well, you know – school fees, keeping a place in the country, horses. It was a family trust, sir, and it rather unexpectedly ran out of funds. Quite unforeseeable, and no fault of one's own, I would add...'

'Of course.'

'So to be frank I needed a better-paid job and one with more prospects than I had as a junior steward with the Jockey Club.'

Barney Allen was surprised to see Piers Devereux smile and nod approvingly. His whole demeanour appeared to have changed.

'I was, of course, aware of that and I'm glad you've been straight with me. I'd have taken a dim view had you not been.'

–

Barney Allen's life changed on the afternoon of Christmas Day in 1935. The extended family was gathered as usual at his mother's family home in Gloucestershire. It was a large and still elegant Regency house, its grounds not as extensive or as manicured as they once were but still very much the heart of the family.

The whole family had gathered in the sitting room to listen to the king's Christmas Day broadcast and stood up – some more painfully than others – for the National Anthem, after which his uncle Nicholas asked for the adults to remain in the room and suggested perhaps the children would like to go and play.

Nicholas was his mother's younger brother and now very much the head of the family. He asked the other seventeen adults in the room to be seated and he stood facing them, his back to the enormous fireplace. His mother's eldest sister remarked that the king didn't sound well and his own brother-in-law said he'd heard he was actually quite poorly and then Uncle Nicholas said he had some very grave news to impart, which Barney assumed was about the king.

'I'm afraid it's to do with money,' said Nicholas, who was bouncing on the balls of his feet, his hands firmly clasped behind his back and concentrating his gaze on the rug below him. 'I've endeavoured to deal with this matter to the best of my own ability and with the help of our advisers but I have to tell you that funds in the family trust have all but dried up and—'

One of his cousins asked what on earth that meant and Nicholas snapped that this was exactly what he was trying to explain. The family's stockbrokers – who the family had trusted for many years – had persuaded him to make a series of investments, which had turned out to be disastrous. They were not entirely to blame, continued Nicholas. 'This house needs an awful lot of money spent on it and so I did ask our stockbrokers to see if they could generate more income through our investments, but of course I had no idea they'd be quite so risky.'

He went on to explain that the house would have to be sold and the proceeds of that sale along with what little remained in the trust would just about cover their losses. He was most terribly sorry. He looked as white as a sheet as the room fell into a shocked silence, the only noise that of the fire crackling behind him. The silence was broken by his mother's sister asking precisely what that meant for the family.

Nicholas cleared his throat. 'As you all know, my two sisters and I have received five hundred pounds per annum from the trust and the rest of you' – he swept an arm around the room to indicate Barney, his sister and their four cousins and their spouses – 'received the sum of three hundred pounds annually.' He coughed again and moved his hands in front of him, holding them as if in prayer. 'I am afraid that we will now only be able to afford to distribute one thousand pounds per annum, to be divided between myself, Marjorie and Hermione.' He pointed towards his two sisters and muttered something about how awfully sorry he was again, but—

'Why in heaven's name didn't you tell us before, Nicholas?'

'I felt it only proper to do so after the king's broadcast.'

They left Gloucestershire after lunch on Boxing Day, the earliest opportunity when it seemed decent to do so. It was a short but tense drive back to Oxfordshire and as soon as they arrived home Barney's wife announced that they needed to speak.

She wasn't the least bit surprised, she said. She had always felt – although this was news to Barney – that his family was profligate with money. Nicholas in particular... he was greedy. 'And as a result, Barney, you felt able to indulge your ridiculous passion for horses rather than getting a proper job.'

'It is a proper job Margaret, it—'

'A proper job means a decent salary, Barney. You'd better start looking round for one, hadn't you? We have the boys' school fees to pay, don't we?'

'They're sorted until next summer.'

'And after that? What is going to happen then – they'll go to one of those dreadful state schools?'

Barney said of course not, even though he'd heard that the local grammar school was actually very decent, and after that their discussion became so heated Barney Allen promised he'd look for another job in the new year.

–

Barney Allen kept his promise. Once he was back in London all the talk was of King George's rapidly declining health and he knew that should the king die then all normal life – including horse racing – would be put on hold for a while. So he arranged to have lunch with Tom Gilbey, who'd been in his year at school and with whom he'd remained close friends and who he knew worked for MI6, the Intelligence Service. Barney waited until they'd finished their hors d'oeuvres – in his case a rather rubbery smoked trout – before he mentioned that he wished to move on from the Jockey Club. Were there by any chance any openings at Tom's place of work?

Tom Gilbey swept some crumbs from in front of him. 'You do know that in our field of work we hardly advertise for new recruits in *The Times* or even the *Daily Telegraph*!'

Both men laughed and paused as the sommelier topped up their glasses.

'But you may well be in luck, Barney. There is some talk of new chaps being taken on: some concern at the moment about German rearmament and a feeling we need to do more about it. There's a chap called Piers Devereux who's on the lookout, I hear. Do you know of him?'

'There was a Devereux in the year below us at school, wasn't there?'

Tom Gilbey shook his head. 'Different spelling, I believe. No, his lot are the Sussex Devereuxs. Difficult chap, but very clever.'

'Would you have a word with him, Tom?'

'I could do but it may be better to go through Roly Pearson: remember him – few years above us at school? Seems to look after talent spotting and recruitment.'

–

Roly Pearson was most helpful. Of course he remembered Barney – dear Barney, as he insisted on calling him – from school. 'Always winning cross country as I remember.' Barney nodded. 'Top sets too, bit of an all-rounder, eh?'

Barney said that was indeed true and Tom Gilbey had mentioned that Roly may know of some openings at MI6 – or indeed MI5.

'Languages?'

'French and German.'

'How good's the German?'

'I'd say it's very good actually.'

'Well in that case you may well be in luck, Barney. Tom may have told you about a chap called Piers Devereux at MI6 who's on the hunt for new blood and while I can't promise anything I can promise he'll see you if I ask him to – especially when I tell him you speak German. Get a decent résumé together and I'll see what I can do.'

The king died on 20 January, which meant his meeting with Piers Devereux was delayed until early February. The day before, he met up with Tom Gilbey again.

'Be straight with him, Barney, and don't try to be too clever, eh? He's rather enigmatic and that has led some people to make the mistake of underestimating him. He's a bit older than us – mid-to-late forties I'd say – and no family. His wife died while he was on the Western Front in the war and he never remarried. Maybe that's why he's not an easy sort, Barney. If I was to sum him up in one word, I'd say he was disobliging.'

Piers Devereux became noticeably less disobliging once Barney Allen had been frank about his financial situation. He opened a pack of cigarettes, offered one to the man opposite and after lighting his own looked once again at the file in front of him.

'I see you were in the Guards Division in the war: when did you join up?'

'1916, sir – got out there in time for the Somme Offensive. Passchendaele and the Battle of Cambrai in 1917 and then transferred to the Coldstreams in 1918.'

'Second battle of the Somme?'

'Yes, sir – and Arras of course.'

'Of course.' Piers Devereux stared out of the window and continued to do so for a while, his mind elsewhere, most probably Arras.

'Didn't think of staying on after the Armistice?'

'Not really, sir. I'd remained a lieutenant and wasn't sure there was much of a career there for me. Went to Oxford for three years and then joined my father in the City for a few years but didn't enjoy it terribly and when an opportunity came to join the Jockey Club I was keen to get in the saddle, so to speak!'

A weak smile from Piers Devereux. 'Until the family money ran out.'

'I'm afraid so, sir.'

Piers Devereux tapped the file on the desk. 'I've read all about you, Allen, there's stuff in here even you probably don't know. Tom Gilbey certainly vouches for you.'

'Thank you, sir.'

'And Roly too. He says you speak German. Are you fluent?'

'I wouldn't put it like that, sir, but it's good enough. I imagine if I spent some time there it would come up to scratch.'

'Well you may well be doing just that, Allen. I take it you are keen to join us?'

'Very much so, sir.'

'Well if you're going to do so there'll be no need of the "sir".
I can't abide formality. It'll be first names, eh?'

Barney Allen nodded. He had, it appeared, joined MI6 – the
Secret Intelligence Service. Piers Devereux left his desk and led
his new recruit to a pair of comfortable chairs facing each other
by the window. Devereux leaned forward and beckoned him to
move closer, as if he wanted no one else to hear their conversation.

'The Service is in its twenty-fifth year, you know. You'd have
thought that by now it would have properly established itself, be
more certain about its identity and its role, if you follow my drift.
But… don't get me wrong, we're certainly a fixture in Whitehall
and regarded as important, but I think our problem is…'

Piers Devereux paused and looked at the ceiling as if there lay
the answer as to what the problem is. 'Our problem is that we
operate at the whim of our political masters. Perhaps it's inevitable, but all too often it feels as if we have almost a commercial
relationship with departments such as the Foreign Office, the War
Office, the armed services, even Downing Street. It feels as if we
are their clients and they pay us to tell them what they want to
hear.

'Perhaps as a consequence of this the Service is a most divided
organisation and one fuelled by a good deal of rancour. There
is one group within it which very much takes its lead from the
Foreign Office and from our colleagues in MI5 and the Special
Branch, namely that the focus of our operations should be on
Communists – and specifically on the Bolshevik threat in Europe
and the danger of revolutionaries infiltrating this country from
abroad. This group is currently the predominant one in the
Service.

'There is another group, of which I am very much a member,
which takes the view that actually the main threat to the United
Kingdom comes from Germany. The Nazis have been in power
for exactly three years now, during which time Hitler has shown
a complete disregard for the Treaty of Versailles and has set about
rearming Germany. They've been training pilots, building aircraft
and last year they reintroduced conscription.

'There is something of a struggle within the Service as to what our priority should be. One would have thought we could at least rely on the MI6 station in Berlin to be on the ball as far as German rearmament is concerned but I'm afraid our embassy there doesn't want to do anything to upset our relations with the Germans, would you believe. There's even a certain degree of sympathy for Hitler – they approve of him bringing stability to the place and also approve of him eliminating the Bolshevik threat. As for what he's doing to the Jews, I'm not sure they terribly care. And to make matters worse, there's a view in the Foreign Office that espionage is a distasteful business with which they want as little to do as possible.'

'That sounds hard to believe, Piers.'

'Indeed it does, but I can assure you it is the case. We have a very decent chap called Foley – Frank Foley – running the MI6 station in Berlin but I'm afraid he's treated like something the cat brought in by the embassy. He's based away from the embassy and his cover is as chief passport control officer and they expect him to do that job along with all his intelligence duties and on top of all this they won't even give him diplomatic status. I do sometimes wonder which side the Foreign Office is on.'

Piers Devereux stood up and removed his jacket before unbuttoning his waistcoat and loosening his tie. He was a slim and elegant man though not the type who would especially stand out. Perfect for an intelligence officer.

'This is where I come in, Barney – and you. Do you know Hugh – Hugh Sinclair?'

Barney Allen shook his head.

'Sir Hugh is the Director of MI6 and a good chap, but he has to maintain a difficult balance between the different factions within the Service. I don't think he trusts the Germans any more than I do and I don't believe he's an out and out appeaser but at the same time his job is to fulfil the wishes of organisations such as the Foreign Office, the War Office and the Admiralty – we're very much their clients. Hugh's an admiral himself and the

Navy's position is that the threat to this country comes not from Germany, but from other maritime powers. And then the Service, I'm afraid, very much relies on the Foreign Office for funding, which is pitiful enough as it is. He's therefore not in a position where he can disregard their policies and at the moment, they're convinced the Comintern is going to start a revolution in this country.'

Piers Devereux leaned back in his chair and clasped his hands behind his head, turning towards the window as he did so. 'Look down there, Barney, look around you – do you really think this country is on the verge of revolution?' He laughed sarcastically. 'We British are a compliant lot: this is a conservative and obedient society, and remember, we had our revolution what – a hundred, hundred and fifty years ago: the Industrial Revolution thankfully got that nonsense out of our system.

'So poor old Sir Hugh is rather caught between a rock and a hard place. On the one hand he doesn't want to upset his masters by seeming to ignore what they see as the Bolshevik threat, while on the other hand nor does he want us to be caught out by not having a proper intelligence operation against the Germans. As a consequence, he's asked me to run an espionage operation against Germany that is discrete from anything we're currently running in Germany.'

'May I ask why?'

'Two reasons, Barney. Firstly, he doesn't trust the embassy there if they catch a whiff of any intelligence we gather. They'll start scribbling nasty notes and send them in the bag to the Foreign Office and then there'll be a fuss here. And secondly – perhaps more importantly in my opinion – Sir Hugh takes the view that this country and Germany could well find themselves at war sometime in the not-too-distant future. I know many people regard that as a fanciful and even ridiculous notion, but should that happen – and of course one very much hopes it doesn't – then any agents run by Berlin station could become exposed and most hard to run. We need to have our own agents in place long before this happens.'

Piers Devereux leaned over to his desk and picked up an unopened packet of Player's Medium Navy Cut. He opened the packet and tipped its contents onto the low table between them before removing two of the cigarettes, one of which he placed in his mouth, unlit.

'Indulge me for a moment, please, Barney, I've not lost the plot although it may well look as if I have.' He was quietly counting the cigarettes. 'There we are, eighteen. If each of these cigarettes represents a thousand men then that's pretty much the strength of an infantry division, agree?'

Barney nodded.

'And if we put these five here aside... like so... then that's five thousand men, a brigade. During the Great War the Service was able to persuade some of the military chaps of the value of first-class intelligence – some, but not all. Many remain very sceptical about the value of intelligence. Sir Hugh realised they needed convincing that intelligence actually works: we needed to prove it has an actual value, so to speak. A year or so ago he met an industrialist whose job is to demonstrate to manufacturers how much more efficient machines are than manual workers, how they pay for themselves in the long run. And that's where these cigarettes come in, Barney: a good spy – well placed, absolutely trusted, excellent judgement, good sources – he or she is worth a Brigade and a network of spies is worth a whole bloody division. That's what this industrialist chap came up with – please don't ask me how he worked it out, but it makes the point, doesn't it? It's the same as the way the tank chaps are pushing for more investment in tanks: they say they're the future and far more efficient than infantry.

'Same with our agents: a decent network is worth its weight in gold. Which is where you come in, Barney.'

'In what way exactly?'

'I want you to recruit your own agents, Barney. It will take time to find the right people: you're starting with a blank sheet of paper and because we don't want word of it to spread too far, our opportunities to check your recruits out will be limited – so you'll need to rely on your judgement. Think you're up to it?'

Barney said he was and Piers Devereux held out his hand and Barney Allen stood up to shake it firmly. He agreed he'd hand in his notice straight away and his new boss said in the meantime he'd ensure all the paper work was done and also start thinking about a cover story for him.

'Anything you fancy, Barney?'

'I'm not sure what you—'

'As a cover story? Needs to be something you're comfortable with. Not a travelling salesman though, that's rather over-used, I'm afraid. One other thing before you go, Barney… have a think about recruits, anyone you know…'

Chapter 3

England
March 1936

'You promise me this is a good restaurant, Barnaby?'

Barney Allen waited until he'd finished his mouthful of steak tartare, a dish he'd normally regard as too indulgent as a starter, but Werner had insisted. *Only order the best, Barnaby, I insist!*

'The Ivy is indeed one of the best restaurants in London, Werner, but you really didn't need to push the boat out quite so far.'

'I told you, Barnaby, I had a very good win at Windsor last week and I'd like to celebrate with you!' The German was also eating steak tartare – Barney noticed he always ordered exactly the same as him – but wasn't showing the same inhibition about speaking with his mouth full.

'From what you tell me, Werner, it was more than a very good win... are you going to tell me how much?'

Werner Lustenberger smiled and held his hands out as if modesty was preventing him saying, but soon recovered. 'I bet two pounds, Barnaby – in fact, it was four ten-shilling bets. I didn't want to alert the bookies.'

'And the odds, Werner – dare I ask?'

'Sixteen to one – so I won thirty-two pounds!'

Barney shook his head. It was an extraordinary win but he was beginning to know Werner by now and doubted it was all above board. 'Perhaps it would be better if you didn't go into too much detail about the bet, Werner.'

'Why not, Barnaby? You no longer work for the Jockey Club.'

'No, but—'

'You're a teacher now, aren't you?'

'A lecturer actually but nonetheless, Werner—'

'I know a man called Jack who organises betting opportunities for people he trusts. Jack has a contact at the stables near Newmarket where the two favourites for the race at Windsor are trained. Jack persuaded this person – I'll call him Fred—'

'I'd very much prefer if you didn't call him anything, Werner.'

'Jack persuaded Fred to ensure that these two horses did not run to form on the day: he was to give them something to eat… not poison, you understand, but… but Jack told me it was to help Fred pay for medical care for his child. I contributed two pounds and I also gave the same amount to Jack for the jockey of the horse that won the race to – I'm not sure how to say this – to not win his previous races so he would have better odds in this race. So it was a gamble, Barnaby, and of course it cost me four pounds but as you can see – worth it! It took a lot of organising by Jack so I had to give him one pound and ten shillings from my winnings.'

Barney Allen shook his head and although he hoped he was conveying that he did not approve he was secretly quite satisfied with what he'd just heard. Werner had seemed such an ideal candidate in many ways, offering so much of what he was looking for, but Barney had a lingering doubt as to how much steel he had… whether he'd be prepared to take risks. Those doubts no longer bothered him. He was about to broach the subject he'd been considering when their main courses arrived: inevitably Werner had copied Barney in ordering entrecôte steak – *au point*, please – and they waited as their meals were served.

'You've told me very little about your life in Germany, Werner. I hope you don't mind if I ask you one or two questions? I'm the curious sort you know…'

The German was chewing his steak and used his knife to indicate Barney should go ahead and ask.

'I was wondering if Werner Lustenberger is your real name?'

'Why wouldn't it be, Barnaby?'

'And excuse me for asking this, Werner – I realise it is an awkward question – but have you ever been in trouble in Germany?'

Werner was about to eat a piece of steak but paused and looked up at Barney, a frown on his face. 'Trouble?'

'Have you ever been arrested, Werner?'

'No, of course not, Barnaby – do you think I'm a criminal?'

'Not at all, Werner, but given the political situation in Germany… you know, with everything that is going on, demonstrations and the like… I was wondering whether you'd ever been caught up in any of that?'

'No, Barnaby, I haven't and I've told you before I find the political situation in Germany so unpleasant – that is one of the reasons I came to this country.'

'I thought maybe you fled because you were a political opponent of the Nazis?'

'Well, I'm most certainly not a supporter of them, but I don't have much time for the Communists either, or the socialists. I'm not very political, Barnaby. I prefer to avoid politics – it's easier to do that here. Why are you asking me all this? It sounds as if you're the political police!'

'Not at all, Werner, not at all… but I was also wondering…' Barney leaned across the table and indicated his companion should do likewise '…I'm not too sure how to put this, but you told me that you prefer men' – Barney paused and coughed and looked around – 'to women. That you're…'

'A homosexual?'

'Please keep your voice down, Werner. It's illegal in this country and I can't imagine it's tolerated in Germany exactly.'

'No, but in some cities – Berlin certainly, Hamburg too – it is more common than perhaps you'd realise. What is your point, Barnaby?'

'I was wondering whether these activities of yours have ever got you into trouble?'

'No, Barnaby: I have always been extremely careful and very discreet as far as those "activities", as you call them, are concerned.'

'Good – so you have no police record?'

'No, Barnaby! Tell me why you're asking.'

'Perhaps you'd lower your voice, Werner, I'll tell you in a moment, but can I ask, where have you actually lived in Germany?'

'We moved around: Munich, which I hated, Hamburg, which I loved: I spent time at school, in Switzerland and France and was in Berlin for a number of years.'

'And your work?'

Werner pushed his plate towards the middle of the table and leaned back in his chair, taking his time to light a cigarette. 'This is more than curiosity, isn't it, Barnaby?'

'Quite possibly, Werner – but where do you get your income from, apart from horses of course?'

'My mother's father was French and he had property throughout Europe, mostly in France, Belgium and Germany. The company is now run from Paris by my uncle and I help manage this property. It's not a difficult job, I travel round and check the properties are well maintained and chase up rent if it's due. It gives me a decent income and allows me to indulge my passion for horse racing and for not staying in one place for too long.'

'Is any of this property in Berlin?'

'Not as much as we used to have – so much Jewish-owned property has come on the market in recent years that rents are very cheap. Go on, Barnaby, now you tell me why you want to know all this.'

'I've mentioned my new job to you – the college near here, in Holborn, and along with being head of modern language studies I am also a vice principal and one of my duties in that role is to look for colleges in Europe who may wish to become our partners and we were wondering about Germany. I thought that if you moved back to Berlin you may be able to assist us in that respect. What do you think?'

'I know very little about education, Barnaby.'

'You don't need to: we're looking for a German citizen who's bright, who knows their way around and who can charm people. I'm sure you'll be ideal.'

'I'm not sure, Barnaby. I'm enjoying living in England.'

'We'll pay you fifteen pounds a week along with all your expenses and we'll allow you to continue with your other work so you'll have that income too. What do you think?'

'Fifteen pounds a week – you'll pay that much?'

Barney nodded.

'And what would the expenses include?'

'Rent, travel…'

'Rent?'

'Yes.'

'It's certainly an interesting idea, Barnaby, let me think about it.'

'And there's one other thing to mention, Werner: the Olympics start in Berlin on the first of August. Think of it – more than two weeks of the best sport in the world! What a wonderful time for you to be in Berlin, eh? The principal at the college has very good contacts. We'll be able to get you tickets to as many events as you want. Apparently it's going to be quite a spectacle.'

Werner nodded. 'If I go, Barnaby, there is one condition.'

'And what's that?'

'I can be in Hamburg in July?'

'I don't think that's a problem, but why Hamburg in July?'

'The Deutsches Derby, Barnaby – at the Horner Rennbahn: the biggest horse race in Germany!'

–

'I agreed you should sound him out, Barney, but from the sounds of it you've gone and actually signed him up!'

'I thought I'd better get on with it, Piers. I haven't signed him up as such but I'd certainly say Werner's very interested and I've told you before, I think he'll make an ideal agent.'

'Really?'

'Yes, Piers, really. He's a German citizen with no criminal record and no politics, he's bright and very personable and has no ties so is able to move around the country. My only reservation as I mentioned before is that he's...' Barney Allen paused and coughed.

'A homosexual?'

'Yes, Piers.'

'I'm not sure why that in itself should preclude him.'

'I thought maybe you would—'

'Would what – disapprove? Well obviously I don't *approve* but the point surely, Barney, is that we're recruiting a spy, not someone to go on holiday with. Half the tutors I knew at Oxford were homosexual and that didn't prevent them being bloody good at their job and I fought with a cavalry major at Ypres who we all knew was that way inclined and he was the bravest man in his regiment. In any case, I think it could count in his favour.'

'How on earth do you come up with that?'

'From what you say, Werner is used to concealing a big part of his life: he's clearly done so for many years and has managed it very successfully. That requires a degree of guile and, I'd have thought, not a little courage. We had a chap like that in Vienna for a while. Bloody good at his job, recruited some first-class agents and ran them very effectively. Things rather went wrong when he came back here and had to resign after a most unfortunate incident in Piccadilly Circus.'

'And the betting scam Werner was involved in – is that a problem?'

'On the contrary, his willingness to be involved in it shows he's prepared to break the rules, that he's got some bottle. We can't have agents who are shrinking violets, can we? Look, Barney, when you've been around spies for as long as I have you'll appreciate that they're all flawed characters in some way, otherwise they wouldn't be in this game. Ordinary people with blameless and straightforward lives tend not to become spies. The best ones are people who've been tested by life in one way or the other. People with complications in their lives, who've had to live and survive in what I call the shadows of life – they're the type we're after. The more I think about him, the more I think Werner would be a good recruit. Has he bought your cover story?'

'He certainly seemed to. It sounds so mundane I don't think too many people are going to question it. Even my wife believes it.'

'And you've not told him yet about what he's been recruited for?'

Barney Allen shook his head. 'As far as he's concerned, he's going over to Germany to drum up new business for the college – potential partners.'

'And he seemed happy with that?'

'Happy enough – he certainly likes the salary and the fact we'll cover his expenses.'

'And he wasn't suspicious at all, Barney? I think I'd be, wouldn't you? Chap I've only known for a few weeks suddenly offers me a job I'm not really qualified for on a very generous salary... he bought all that?'

'I think I've got the measure of him to an extent, Piers. For all his bonhomie Werner seems to be rather lonely: he's probably got used to not trusting people. I think he sees me as a friend, certainly as someone he trusts – otherwise I doubt he'd have confided in me about his private life. I think he probably sees my offer as an act of friendship.'

'Well, let's hope so, Barney, let's hope so. Just hope he doesn't smell a rat, eh?'

'When do we tell him what he's been recruited for?'

'Not until he's been in Germany for a while, Barney. We don't want to scare him off. Once he's been over there and he's started to work for us – that's the time to tell him, by which time of course it will be too late for him to change his mind. Whether he likes it or not by then he'll be a British agent. He'll know that the consequences of him pulling out then will be too serious; you'll make that clear to him. You look uneasy about it, Barney?'

'Yes and no, Piers – it just seems like we're press-ganging him into being an agent for us. Is that the best way?'

'It's the way it is, Barney. The longer you work in this business the more you'll appreciate how unpleasant it can be. We exploit people, we trick them, we put their lives in danger and then we often discard them. But always bear in mind we do so for a reason – to protect this country. As I told you when you joined us, there are many in positions of power in this country who don't fully approve of what we do – as if espionage is not quite the done thing. They can look down their noses at us for all they want but I know that we can't afford the luxury of being sensitive to people's feelings. Good intelligence can prevent or shorten wars and save thousands of lives. Always remember that. You'd better get Herr Lustenberger over to Germany, hadn't you?'

'Of course, but there is one other thing, Piers.'

'And what's that?'

'Any chance you could find him some tickets for the Olympics?'

Chapter 4

Philadelphia and New York City, USA
April 1936

'Would you like me to pretend I didn't hear what you said, Jack?'

Joe Walsh was twirling a pencil through his fingers with the well-practised skill of a drum majorette, all the time glaring at Jack Miller on the other side of the desk – daring him to repeat what he'd just said.

Jack said nothing for a while. He knew the charm and quick wit he normally relied on would be wasted on the man sitting opposite him. He also knew his editor wouldn't take kindly to what he'd just told him. Walsh sat with his back to the large window, the bustle of Filbert Street below him, the enormous edifice of the City Hall just visible beyond that. Jack could feel the movement and drama of the newsroom through the glass wall behind him.

'I said I'd like to leave, Joe, and that I'm sorry and it's not personal.'

'Which bastard has hired you, Jack?'

'No bastard has hired me, Joe, I told you that.'

'Because if it's the *Inquirer* or the *Daily News* we'll go over to the crime desk and together we'll wake up Mancini, tell him we're about to give him an exclusive: "Editor kills reporter in case of justifiable homicide"!'

'There'll be no need for that, but if it was the case, I'd like the opportunity to write the story myself. What would be the cause of death?'

Joe Walsh laughed and pushed his spectacles to the top of his head and pulled his tie down. 'Something unpleasant, Jack, possibly involving cement.'

'Like that case in Bella Vista last year?'

Joe Walsh nodded and looked interested in the idea. 'Wet cement, wasn't it, Jack?'

'It was wet when they poured it down his throat. Apparently it was quick drying. Look, Joe, if I was going to another paper, it wouldn't be in Philly, you know that. I wouldn't do that to you.'

'So what is then, Jack? You're not yet thirty and everyone knows you're the best writer on the best paper in the state. You're not doing news desk shifts any more, you're not doing earlies – you get the best stories and the opportunity to write news features. No one can write the way you write, the way you capture the atmosphere of a hard news story, your turn of phrase.'

'Come on, Joe… I've never heard you being so nice to anyone, I've certainly never heard you being so nice to me!'

'I've never had you hand in your notice before, Jack, that's why. Just don't tell anyone though, it'll be no good for my reputation. How many journalists are out there in the newsroom at the moment?'

Jack Miller turned round and shrugged. 'I don't know, maybe a hundred?'

'And I guarantee you that if I went out there now and got them all to shut up for a minute and said "who wants to do the same job as Jack Miller" I'd get crushed in the stampede. So what is it, Jack – the divorce?'

'I guess so, Joe. I thought I'd gotten over it but last week was the first-year anniversary – if that's the right word – and it hit me hard. We'd only been married three years.'

'At least there were no kids, Jack.'

'That doesn't feel like a consolation, Joe. Maybe if we'd had kids she wouldn't have gone for lunch with the lawyer she worked for and—'

'It's happened, Jack. You can't beat yourself up about it. I told you at the time, the only way to cope is to throw yourself into your work and look forward. You've turned out your best articles in recent months, really excellent writing. Look how much we've syndicated!'

'I know, and I appreciate everything, Joe, but I just feel I need to step back from things. Journalism absorbs you too much; it only allows you time to think about the stories you're working on. I need to find time to think about my life.'

'So, what are you going to do, join a monastery?'

Both men laughed. 'I'm not the monastic type, am I? No more than you, Joe.'

'When I was about seventeen, I thought about the priesthood.'

'How long did that last?'

'A couple of months, until I met a girl who was five years older than me. I reckoned I was disqualified after that.'

'I was thinking of going to California.' Jack Miller nodded at the window. Despite it being spring, Philadelphia still looked cold and grey.

'And then what?'

Jack Miller shrugged. 'My kid brother's in the Navy. He's doing his officer training in San Diego. Our mom died five years ago and Dad last year and—'

'I know Jack.'

'I feel responsible for Tom – I'm all he has and I feel I ought to spend some time with him, you know?'

'So you'll join the US Navy too?'

'No – I get seasick.'

'That doesn't sound like much of a plan, Jack. Look, do me a favour – give me a week to see what I can come up with.'

–

What Joe Walsh had come up with was a trip to New York City. He'd even said Jack could travel up the day before and stay overnight in a hotel, but Jack had always disliked the city: too cold in winter and too hot in the summer and he'd never experienced anything in between. And the people: Philly was busy enough but in New York everyone was in a hurry, as if they'd been told to flee the city ahead of an alien invasion.

So he took the first train of the day from 30th Street station and by the time he emerged from Penn station onto 8th Avenue he was pleasantly surprised. It was neither too hot nor too cold, the sidewalks weren't crowded and a couple of people even smiled as he made his way in the direction of Times Square to West 43rd Street, the headquarters of Associated Newspapers.

Jack Miller's own newspaper – the *Philadelphia Bulletin* – was one of four newspapers making up Associated. The other papers were the *Chicago Daily News*, the *Boston Globe* and the *New York Globe* and together they formed something between a co-operative and a syndicate, which looked after the publication of each other's articles, syndicated the best of them to other papers and more recently, organised joint coverage of major events outside of the four cities.

'Ted Morris is a New York Jew,' Joe Walsh had said. 'He may come across as being short with you, as if he's angry. Don't worry about it – it's just the way he is.'

'I'm used to it from you, Joe.'

'He talks fast and is very smart and you have to listen carefully because when he cracks jokes he doesn't smile.'

'I can't wait to meet him.'

'He's now in charge of organising coverage of major events for Associated Newspapers. The group think this is the way of the future and are attaching a lot of importance to it. Ted knows who you are: he likes your articles and he has something in mind for you.'

'What is it, Joe?'

'I've promised I'll let him tell you. Just make sure you don't say no!'

–

Ted Morris looked Jack Miller up and down as he entered his office with views over the Manhattan skyline. He told him to shut the door and sit down and that he could leave his coat on the other chair.

'Joe says you want to leave to go to California.' He shook his head, appalled. 'Are you mad, Miller?'

'No, I—'

'They treat you like a prince in Philly, you're twenty-nine and the best writer on the paper and from what Joe tells me you have a free hand in choosing what stories you write and – do your articles ever get cut, Miller?'

'Well my articles get subbed and—'

'No! You know what I mean, do they tell you to write fifteen hundred words on something and when you turn it in they say they now want it in five hundred and get a drunk sub to edit it – does that ever happen to you?'

'No, but—'

'Look, Miller, I know Walsh told you how much he thinks of you and he's almost as grumpy a bastard as I am. But I feel the same. We don't want to lose you. We have no trouble getting your articles into other papers in the group and we can easily syndicate them around the country. You have the ability to write clearly and simply yet still manage to bring out the atmosphere and colour in a story. Not many journalists twice your age can do that as well as you do, it usually comes with experience. And you also manage to have the sharpness of a news reporter with the insight and depth of a features writer.'

Ted Morris stopped talking and smiled – which Jack wasn't expecting – before lighting a cigarette. He threw the packet to him. 'You like Camel?'

'It's all I smoke.'

'So we do have something in common then. Have you ever covered sport?'

'I tend to keep that for leisure.'

'And you want to give all this up to watch your kid brother playing with boats in California?'

'I had a nasty divorce last year and it's hit me hard. I just wanted to take some time to think about things.'

36

Ted Morris shook his head and leaned forward.

'You speak German.'

'Some, enough to get by, I guess.'

'How come you speak German?'

'It's easier than Irish.'

'Don't mess me around Miller...'

'My great-grandfather was from Germany... my grandfather spoke it with me, I seem to have an ear for languages.'

'Any family there?'

'None that I know of...'

'You Jewish, by any chance?'

'I wasn't the last time I looked.'

'I make the jokes here, Miller, especially the Jewish ones.'

'I'm a good Catholic, don't worry.'

'What kind of a Catholic.'

'Roman.'

'For Christ's sake, Miller... Have you ever been to Germany?'

'I've never left the United States, sir. And I'm not a practising Catholic, if that's what you were after. I had too much practice when I was younger.'

'We have something in mind for you, Miller, but I'll need you to give me an answer today and then commit to it. I asked you about sport... you know what's happening in Germany in August?'

'The Olympics?'

'You've got it in one. We – Associated Newspapers – would like you to go out there for us. We're looking for a series of articles in the weeks leading up to Games, colour pieces – what Germany's really like, the stories behind the news reports and then once the Games start we want at least one feature a day – not sports reports as such because we can get that from the agencies and the wire services, but more articles on people and the atmosphere. What do you think?'

'How long do the Games last?'

'Two-and-a-bit weeks.'

'A feature article each day, you say?'

Morris nodded. 'Is that a problem?'

'Not at all.'

'I don't want to see politics, Miller, steer well away from that. Keep away from all the Nazi stuff as much as you can. That's why I asked if you're Jewish: the Germans don't like the Jews; most of them are trying to get out of the country, not into it. Wouldn't want to send you somewhere you're not welcome. So what do you think?'

'I thought you wanted the answer today?'

'Now will do fine.'

Chapter 5

Berlin
June 1936

'I tell you, my dearest, it was the most wonderful sight to behold, absolutely marvellous. I am almost speechless!'

Sophia von Naundorf sighed as she carried her husband's boots into the hall before returning to sit opposite him in the bay window of their well-appointed apartment on Potsdammer Strasse. They were close to the junction with Schloss Strasse, in the heart of Charlottenburg, and even though they'd been there for nearly two years Sophia still found it hard to believe she was living in such opulence: elegant wood-panelling, four bedrooms for the two of them, along with a dressing room for her, a study for Karl-Heinrich, a library, a dining room and a lounge – and separate living quarters for their maid.

Her husband loosened his belt and dropped his holster on the highly polished walnut table next to him.

'We shall open a bottle of wine, my dearest, and I will tell you everything. Ask Ilse to bring one of the bottles of the French wine that arrived last week.'

Five minutes later he'd poured two large glasses of wine, ignoring his wife's plea for a smaller amount.

'I have some wonderful news to share but I'll start with my trip today.

Sophia nodded, doing her best to look at her husband and smile and avoided glancing out of the window. Karl-Heinrich didn't like it when she failed to pay him her full attention when he was talking to her.

'I was very privileged today to be part of a group visiting the Deutsches Stadion, my dearest.'

He paused and looked at her, waiting for a reaction and she smiled and raised her eyebrows in admiration.

'It is now known as the Olympiastadion and the main events of the Olympics will be held there. Everything is ready. It is more than impressive, it is wonderful – a tribute to German efficiency and planning. No other country in the world could have achieved this. Would you like some more wine, my dearest? You'd better, we soon have a toast to make.'

She allowed him to top up her glass and shifted in her chair so it would be harder for her to look outside.

'You have heard of Werner March?'

'I think he's the—'

'The architect of the stadium? Correct! Werner and his brother Walter themselves were there to show us around. Do you know how many people will be in the stadium, my dearest?'

Sophia shook her head. She'd read in the paper that it would be 100,000 but knew her husband would want to surprise her.

'One hundred thousand – can you believe that?'

She said she couldn't. *How impressive.*

'And let me tell you, my dearest, who else was on this visit.' He coughed and sat up straight and adopted a more solemn tone.

'Theodor Lewald and Carl Diem from the German Olympic committee and Hans von Tschammer und Osten – you've heard of him?'

'Isn't he—?'

'The Reichssportführer! The head of the German Sports Office – a most impressive man. There were also many other officials and SS officers and I haven't told you the most important person there. You are listening, my dearest?'

Sophia turned round, realising she'd been gazing out of the window.

'Wilhelm Frick himself – the interior minister! And not only was he there but he took me aside and spoke with me – what do you think of that?'

Sophia said she was very impressed and leaned over to touch her husband's knee.

'Herr Frick wants me to join a special unit which will be responsible for overseeing foreign visitors to the Olympic Games. Apparently there will be a security side to this role – which is obviously why he chose me – but there'll also be what he described as a diplomatic and propaganda aspect to the job. We are to help ensure that Germany is seen in the best possible light by the many important foreign visitors to Berlin during the Games. All the nonsense that people accuse us of… well this will be an opportunity to show people the overwhelmingly positive work of the Führer. I am to report directly to von Tschammer and to Frick.'

'I am very pleased for you, Karl-Heinrich – you work so hard.'

'And you will have a role too, my dearest. We will attend many social events when the Games begin and indeed before that. We will entertain visitors and charm them and you will be perfect for this position. And now to my special news!'

Karl-Heinrich von Naundorf stood up and after a moment's hesitation his wife did likewise.

'I am to be promoted, my dearest: I am now an Obersturmbann-nführer!'

'That sounds… wonderful, Karl-Heinrich.'

'It means I am the equivalent of a lieutenant colonel. I have been in the SS for just three years and already an Obersturmbann-nführer!'

Sophia forced a smile. The forlorn hopes that she'd allowed herself to indulge in about Karl-Heinrich leaving the SS and going back to law faded in an instant.

'And you, my dearest, will be an Obersturmbannführer's wife!'

–

The apartment was situated at the western end of Tauentzien-strasse, close to where it joined Kurfürstendamm.

When his very good friend Barnaby Allen had made him such an unexpected and generous offer to represent Holborn College in Germany for fifteen pounds a week plus rent and other expenses, Werner Lustenberger had determined that he'd live as close to Kurfürstendamm as possible. It had always been his favourite part of Berlin, with its lively atmosphere, good places to eat, decent apartments and close enough to the centre of the city.

And there was another reason. Along with Schöneberg it had also been one of those areas where as a homosexual he could feel comfortable in the city. Despite Berlin's liberal reputation – even *avant garde* – there were parts of the city which felt anything but liberal, usually those areas where either the Nazi Party or the Communists had held sway.

He'd previously enjoyed the bars and clubs and cafes with a predominantly if not exclusively homosexual clientele, places such as the Zauberflöte, Karls-Lounge, the Cosy-Corner or the Eldorado Cafe. But by 1933 they'd all closed their doors, forced to do so long before the Nazis made homosexuality a criminal offence in 1935. It had been the same all over Germany. It had been one of the reasons Werner Lustenberger had left the country.

He'd last been in Berlin in early 1935 and knew there were still a few bars and cafes in the Kurfürstendamm area in particular where men could meet, usually in cellars or basements reached through closed doors and down dark corridors, or in upstairs rooms, which the barman would allow you to go up to if you knew the right form of words and if he was sure no one he didn't trust was watching.

The apartment Werner found was ideal: on the fourth floor of an elegant block on the north side of the street. Because his apartment was at the rear of the building it was quieter and he had distant views of the Zoological Gardens at the south-western end of the Tiergarten. There were just two apartments on his floor and his entrance was separated from the other one by the lift shaft. It felt very private. The apartment itself was small but decorated in Bauhaus style and with a modern kitchen and bathroom, a brightly lit lounge and a bedroom with a built-in wardrobe, which felt like the height of indulgence.

He'd arrived in the city at the beginning of May, shocked at first as to how much it had changed. It was still Berlin, of course, but there was now a hardness to the city. In one of the bars he'd found on Uhland Strasse he'd heard someone describe the city as being like a military camp. It took him a few weeks to orientate himself, to work out which areas felt safer than others, the places to go where he could trust people, the phrases to avoid and the times when it was best to say nothing and move on.

Barnaby had been vague about the work he'd be doing in Germany. 'Best to get over there as soon as you can, Werner, and get settled in... find somewhere nice to live... get a feel for the place.'

'And then?'

'And then I'll be over in late July: I managed to get some tickets for the Olympics. You can look out for the best restaurants to take me to when I'm over. I can tell you all about the job then.'

That was at his last meeting with Barnaby in London before he'd left. Unusually they'd met not at Barnaby's club or at a restaurant but instead in a sparsely furnished office close to Holborn station, which Barnaby said he was using while his main office was being refurbished. And as the meeting ended – in fact he was halfway out the door – Barnaby had called him back.

'There are a few matters you can get on with in the meantime, Werner.' He waved him back into the room. 'There are some people the college needs to make contact with and you know what the post's like these days!'

Werner said actually his understanding was that the post was more efficient these days, along with most other things in Germany, apparently.

'Nevertheless, we have a few contacts out there we'd like to get in touch with and what with you being over there we thought we could kill two birds with one stone, so to speak, and get you to deliver them by hand. Here we are.'

Barnaby Allen opened a desk drawer and brought a bundle of envelopes and arranged them carefully on the desk top. Three or four of them were quite bulky, the others less so. Barnaby showed each one to Werner. They were all wrapped in sheets of paper attached to the envelope with a paper clip. He was to follow the instructions on the piece of paper about how to deliver each item and was to dispose of the sheets of paper.

Werner looked puzzled as he picked up the bundle. Four of them were to be delivered within Berlin: one to a house in Prenzlauer Berg, another to what seemed to be a shop in Kreuzberg, two more to apartments in Mitte. Then there was a package to be taken to an office in Hamburg, another to a residential address in Würzburg, one to what looked like a factory in Leipzig and the last one to what looked like another office address in Magdeburg.

'I really need to take these in person, Barnaby? I think the post is not at all bad in Germany these days. I could pay for a special postage rate, which I believe is even more efficient.'

'No need, Werner... not while we have you there. It is a bit sensitive because these are clients of the college – some of whom we owe money to, others with whom we dispute what we owe. All in all it would be easier if you delivered them in person.'

Werner nodded and picked up the envelopes, placing them in his briefcase and the two men shook hands warmly.

And by June he was nicely settled in the apartment on Tauentzienstrasse. He'd delivered all the envelopes in Berlin along with the ones in Würzburg and Leipzig. He was planning to take the one to Magdeburg soon, and as for Hamburg, that would wait until he visited his favourite city in July for the Deutsches Derby. Killing two birds with one stone as Barnaby would call it.

It had been a bit odd, he had to say, but there'd been no problems. Maybe that was just the way English colleges worked.

He'd found a very discreet bar called the Saxon on Regensburger Strasse, not too far from where he lived where after a few visits he'd been allowed into a dimly lit bar behind the main one and then in exchange for what amounted to one week's salary from Holborn College he became a member of the Saxon Club, which allowed him to pass through the otherwise locked door leading to the club's premises on the top floor.

Life in Berlin, Werner decided, was not bad at all.

Chapter 6

It often struck Sophia how easily events that so shaped one's life could fade from the memory.

Her mother's death was a good example. She was five years old and while she remembered some aspects of it quite clearly – an aunt dressed in black telling her to stop crying and pull herself together, the muffled silence in the house as the adults left for the funeral, her mother's hairbrush on the mantelpiece with strands of her hair catching the light – she had no memory of how she felt on being told of her mother's death or what she did while her father was at the funeral. A friend told her this could be due to trauma, which was one of these matters people talked about these days, but it was odd how she so clearly recalled some aspects yet not others.

And there were other events too: her first day at school, which she was forever being told saw her being dragged in kicking and screaming, yet which she had no memory of; her first kiss, which a friend remembered her telling her all about but Sophia couldn't even picture the boy, let alone recall his name; the day she was knocked over by the butcher's cart and broke her wrist...

Sophia couldn't recall when she first met her neighbour, Esther. That in itself wouldn't have seemed like an event that shaped one's life but the longer Sophia knew her, the more she realised how significant that meeting had been. They'd moved into the apartment on Potsdamer Strasse in 1934 and it was a few months before she met Esther properly.

She was aware Esther's father was a doctor at the Charité hospital only because one night their neighbour Frau Schmidt slipped at the top of the stairs and someone suggested calling up Dr Goldmann and Karl-Heinrich said under no circumstances should Frau Schmidt be allowed to be treated by that Jew and Sophia was shocked but put it down to the drink, which in those days was her default excuse for her husband's behaviour. After all, when he was sober, Karl-Heinrich was very charming and proper to her.

According to Esther they'd bumped into each other as they entered the apartment building one afternoon: Esther had introduced herself and Sophia – in Esther's words – looked as if she was sleep-walking. But they apparently had a conversation and Sophia had invited Esther up to her apartment for coffee the next day because she recalled answering the door to her and having to pretend that of course she remembered their arrangement and yes, please do come in… through here.

Once Esther's father was sacked from his job at the Charité in 1935 Esther became a regular visitor to Sophia's apartment, desperate to get a break from the tensions of her own small apartment, where the family was now cooped up. Her father would sit in his study, convinced it was just a matter of time before he got his job back, while her mother spent most days weeping in the kitchen and her younger brother started arguments by insisting they leave Germany.

Esther would always come up when Karl-Heinrich was at work and usually when the maid was out shopping. They both knew that was safer.

For Esther, Sophia and her apartment provided a kind of refuge, somewhere she could talk about something other than her troubles and what her family was going to do. Often, they would say little, both relishing the silence.

For Sophia, Esther's visits helped her retain her sanity. Esther was a few years older than her – perhaps thirty – and for a while had studied psychoanalysis in Vienna. She would listen quietly as Sophia opened up: about her doubts over Karl-Heinrich; how she felt she'd been forced into marrying him; how she struggled with his views and... and all the while Esther would listen and let Sophia speak and when she'd finished offer some quiet advice.

She was always reassuring: Sophia must not blame herself for anything, her husband was a cruel man and she was a victim and victims all too often saw themselves as deserving of their fate. Nor did she blame Sophia for not walking out on Karl-Heinrich: that was easier said than done and may well be the beginning of her troubles rather than the end of them.

After the dreadful evening at the restaurant on the Wannsee in May 1935 she'd told Esther that she had to leave, she couldn't stay with Karl-Heinrich any longer.

'He threatened me, Esther: he said he'd hit me! I have to leave but...'

Esther held her hand until Sophia stopped crying. 'Where would you go, Sophia?'

She shrugged. 'I've no idea.'

'You don't speak another language?'

She shook her head. 'And I couldn't possibly stay in the Reich... he'd find me. I have no money, other than the weekly allowance he gives me, but it's not much: he insists on knowing what I spend it on. Even if I saved some of that for a few months it would be so little...'

'Just wait, Sophia.'

'What do you mean?'

'Bide your time, Sophia – understand that the initiative is in your hands, if you see what I mean. One day the opportunity will arise for you to do something – maybe to escape, or to get your revenge. Do you understand?'

Sophia said she did though she wasn't convinced. She couldn't see any way out, she felt trapped and couldn't imagine what opportunity could possibly arise to get her out of this situation.

Then came the election at the end of March 1936, which Jews weren't allowed to vote in because they were no longer proper Germans. The Nazis got 99 per cent of the rigged vote and naturally won every seat in the Reichstag. Although they weren't exactly lacking in confidence, this election result gave the Nazis an even bigger swagger and led to an increase in violence against the Jews.

In the middle of April – a fortnight after the election – Sophia realised she hadn't seen or heard from Esther for a while. She always waited for her to make contact; it seemed safer that way. Eventually she knocked on the door of their apartment and the door opened, but it was on a chain and Sophia couldn't see who had opened it. Eventually Esther asked what she wanted and Sophia said she'd come to see how she was and Esther asked her to go away and then hesitated and asked if it was safe for her to come up to Sophia's apartment – could she promise her Karl-Heinrich wasn't around?

She came up an hour later. Sophia thought Esther had aged in the couple of weeks since she'd last seen her. She seemed pale and drawn and her eyes were red.

'Has something happened Esther? You don't look well.'

Esther gave a brief, sarcastic laugh. 'You could say something has happened, Sophia. We were attacked.'

'Who was?'

'My father and brother. Two days after the election, the last day of March. There were Nazi mobs on Potsdamer Strasse and we didn't leave our apartment for two days, we were terrified. Eventually my mother told my father to go down to our storage cupboard in the basement and bring up some tins of food. When he didn't return after twenty minutes my brother went down to see what had happened. When he didn't return I went down. I saw they'd both been beaten up. My father had a bruised face and broken ribs. My brother had a broken nose and nasty cut on his forehead, which my father had to stitch up.'

'Do you know who did it?'

'A man who said he didn't like the idea of Jews living in the same apartment block as him.'

Esther was silent for a while, looking straight at Sophia in an almost accusing manner.

'It was Karl-Heinrich, Sophia. The man who beat up my brother and father was your husband.'

Sophia felt the room sway around her and her throat tighten. She tried to speak but no words came out so she mouthed the word 'sorry' and then felt tears stream down her face and through them saw Esther shrug in a matter-of-fact manner, as if a dreadful event like this was only to be expected.

This was one of those events that shaped her life that didn't fade in her memory. She clearly remembered how she told Esther she'd do what she could to help and Esther said they had little food because they were terrified to leave their apartment and Sophia went into the larder and filled two large shopping bags with food.

Sophia felt dreadful after that. She realised that her own problems were nothing compared to those of Esther and her family and felt guilty for having talked about herself so much. And then she realised her best course of action was to follow her friend's advice: to bide her time and wait for the time to come when she could escape or even wreak her revenge.

Chapter 7

Berlin
July and August 1936

'Without meaning to sound impolite in any way, Allen, I'd just like to know what the hell you're doing here?'

It was the first time Barney Allen had actually met — as in spoken with — Timothy Summers but he was aware of him through friends and acquaintances. He'd known Timothy's elder brother at Oxford — and had heard of his spikey reputation. 'Always looking to pick a fight,' Piers Devereux had said. Barney Allen certainly knew Summers' type: he was some six or seven years younger than Barney — mid-thirties — so too young to have fought in the Great War and despite having been marked out as a high flyer in the Diplomatic Service nonetheless had a bit of a chip on his shoulder and an ensuing tendency towards rudeness. It perhaps explained why he was the first secretary at the British embassy in Berlin when by now he really ought to have been doing a bit better than that — perhaps minister grade or even an ambassador at somewhere less consequential than Germany.

'I understand Piers Devereux spoke with Sir Eric Phipps in London a fortnight ago and he was perfectly happy.'

Timothy Summers bristled at the mention of his ambassador's name, as if he felt Barney Allen was using it against him. 'It was, as I understand it, a brief conversation at a reception and Devereux mentioned in passing to Sir Eric he was sending you over and asked if that was all right and Sir Eric said it was as long as you didn't queer our pitch and cause any trouble. He also asked that as soon as you turned up you were to come and see me so I could run through the school rules, hence this jolly get together. My brother says you were last heard of doing something with horses?'

'I was working for the Jockey Club: I started working with Piers earlier this year. How is your brother, by the way?'

Summers shrugged. 'Very rich: gave up the idea of the Church soon after Oxford and now makes money doing something frightfully tedious in the City. So, tell me why you're here.'

Barney Allen hesitated and looked around. The British embassy on Wilhelmstrasse had a distinctly English country house feel to it and, but for the side view of the Adlon Hotel next door to Summer's oak-panelled office, could well have been the library.

'Piers has asked me to come over while everyone's got their eyes on the Olympics and see what I can pick up.'

'Pick up?'

'You know… gossip, information, how things are going, who's who… that sort of thing.'

'That's what we do, Allen.'

'Of course… of course… and we're certainly not looking to tread on your toes, absolutely not, but he thought a fresh pair of eyes, a different perspective…'

'I'd have thought we do that perfectly adequately. Are you sure you're not recruiting?'

'No, no… not my job, Summers, I'm more of a – how can I put it? – more of a writing papers type of chap. Probably papers no one will read, but there we are.'

'You're not running any agents over here, are you?'

Barney Allen shook his head, not so vigorously as to look offended by the thought but more puzzled, as if the very idea of him running an agent was something that had never occurred to him.

'So Piers has sent you over on a bit of a jolly, eh? Come over to watch the Olympics, get pally with a few locals, write it all up and it gets filed under "let's be beastly to the Germans"?'

Allen didn't react. The more he looked at Summers the more familiar his thin face and pointed nose was. He thought he may have seen him at a hunt. It was a pity he wasn't the prey.

'Let me tell you something, Allen, and before I do let me assure you I speak with the authority and approval of the ambassador – in fact Sir Eric and I discussed the matter only this morning. It is important you understand that Germany is no longer the enemy of the United Kingdom. We are well aware that there is a school of thought in London to the contrary, one that is determined to see Germany as our perpetual enemy. That, however, is not the case. The Great War finished eighteen years ago and—'

'I do know, Summers, I fought in it.'

Summers' face reddened as he continued. 'The Great War finished eighteen years ago and we signed a peace treaty with them the year after the war ended—'

'Which they're flouting, Summers, they're breaking the treaty left, right and centre as they go about re-arming their forces and—'

'If I may continue, please, Allen? You persist in using confront-ational language. One would expect that seventeen years after the signing of the Treaty of Versailles some of its clauses are less relevant now than they were in 1919. But we see many positive aspects of what is going on in Germany at the present time. Certainly there are some policies of the Nazi government with which we do not see eye to eye and often Herr Hitler's tone is not one we altogether approve of, but then he is talking to a domestic audience, is he not? It is a principle of British foreign policy that we do not interfere with the domestic politics of another country. At the same time we are very aware and indeed grateful that the German government is proving to be a resolute bulwark against the Bolshevik threat which is rampant in Europe. Their policy and approach in that regard is very much in the United Kingdom's interests, Allen. The Germans are in effect a barrier between the United Kingdom and the Bolsheviks in Europe.'

'Out of interest, Summers… this Bolshevik threat… excuse me if I sound naive or perhaps I'm possibly missing something, but really, how serious is this threat to the United Kingdom? I mean, since the Russian Revolution they've hardly swept through Europe.'

'The Comintern are everywhere, Allen!'

'Possibly, but they seem to spend most of their time fighting each other. While one is naturally alert to Bolshevism in the United Kingdom one also has to say it doesn't feel too imminent a threat.'

'What are you trying to say, Allen?'

'That one shouldn't ignore the threat posed by Nazi Germany just because they don't like Bolsheviks.' Barney Allen stopped, worried he'd gone too far. He remembered Piers Devereux's warnings just before he left London.

Try not to be confrontational with the embassy, Barney, don't rile them… they look at things very differently, but remember it is the view that holds sway, even within this building… I thought it best to let them know you're there rather than them spotting you… hopefully that way they won't suspect anything.

'I trust you'll leave your MI6 colleagues on Tiergartenstrasse well alone? We wouldn't want you alerting the Germans by having anything to do with them.'

'I wasn't planning to go there, no. Foley doesn't have diplomatic cover, does he?'

'None of them do, Allen, it's Foreign Office policy. The Passport Control Office is a perfectly adequate enough cover for them, gives them an opportunity to pick up some decent intelligence. We don't seem to view espionage in the same way as you do.'

'Meaning?'

'Meaning we don't think many of the methods employed by those in espionage are entirely… fair. And we are concerned that if any such activities are exposed then it could compromise the United Kingdom, which is why they have no diplomatic cover. That way we can deny any link with your station here if things go wrong. What is your cover, by the way?'

'I represent a college in London, Holborn College.'

'Never heard of it.'

'You wouldn't have, Summers. It's fairly new. We helped fund it so we could use it as a front.'

'And what is your role here?'

'Somewhat vague… looking for partner colleges and the like.'

'Not using your real name, I take it?'

'No, I'm Edward Campion.'

'Sounds rather Catholic but then I suppose half this country is. We've been very strict with MI6 about what cover you chaps use.'

'I'm aware of that.'

'We don't want people posing as journalists or businessmen.'

'Of course not.'

'Or causing trouble.'

'Absolutely not.'

–

Piers Devereux hadn't explained how he managed it but Barney Allen had tickets to the Olympiastadion as a member of the British Olympic Committee, though very much on its periphery – not front row, which suited him fine; he wanted to be in a privileged position certainly, but he didn't want to be too prominent. His pass allowed him freedom of movement around the environs of the Olympiastadion, access to all the Games venues and travel on special buses between the venues and around the city.

He was at the stadium – along with 100,000 others – for the Opening Ceremony, an event that made him deeply uncomfortable with its strident Nazi overtones. He watched the crowd transfixed as Hitler declared the Games open. He returned to the stadium the following day and for the rest of that week to watch the athletics, the highlight being Jesse Owens winning gold for the United States in the Men's 100- and 200-metre sprints.

But the main attraction of the Games was what went on away from the events. At the Olympiastadion there was a reception area for members of the national committees and there were similar facilities at the other venues. He soon realised this was the ideal place to meet German officials, who seemed to be there in large numbers, standing around and waiting to meet foreign visitors and then do their best to persuade them what a modern and sophisticated and cultured country they were visiting: especially the culture.

Tickets for a concert, perhaps, or maybe the opera? That is no problem. Please, let me arrange it for you. Do you have any questions about Germany – there are so many misconceptions I'd be happy to address!

One of these encounters took place at the Olympiastadion on the first Tuesday when he was there to watch the heats for the 1500 metres. He'd gone into the vast reception area for a drink and noticed a small group of uniformed Germans close to him. Within moments one of them had approached him, peering at his name badge.

'Edward Campion from the United Kingdom – welcome!' The man clicked his heels and briefly came to attention. 'And may I ask, Herr Campion, what is your position with the…' He peered again at the badge. 'British Olympic Committee – have I pronounced it correctly?'

The man's English wasn't very good and he looked relieved when Barney Allen – the man he believed to be Edward Campion – replied in fluent German, explaining how he was a *very* senior representative of a *very* important academic institution and how *very* important sport was to our younger generation and how *very* pleased he was to be in Berlin for the Olympics because it gave him an opportunity to see how well everything was run.

He apologised for his German but his companion said not at all, it was truly excellent and it put him to shame, although he didn't appear to be too ashamed. He was a tall man, perhaps in his mid-thirties and wearing the black uniform Barney had come to recognise as that of an SS officer, with the runic symbols on each lapel.

'Obersturmbannführer Karl-Heinrich von Naundorf.' A sharp nod of the head and another click of the heels as he again came to attention and then they shook hands slightly awkwardly and Barney Allen asked him what did he say his rank was and the man said it was Obersturmbannführer, which was the equivalent of a lieutenant colonel in the British Army.

'Did you ever serve in your army, Herr Campion?'

'Too young. I'm not really a military man, I'm afraid: sport and education are more my things.'

Karl-Heinrich said this was no problem and explained that he'd only joined the SS two years previously, before then he'd been a lawyer and Edward Campion quickly invented a brother who was a lawyer so they had something in common and the German slapped him on the shoulder and said yes, fancy that.

'You've been promoted very quickly then, Karl-Heinrich – becoming a lieutenant colonel in two years?'

'Indeed, and I am very honoured. My last promotion was just a matter of weeks ago. To be honest, Herr Campion...'

Barney Allen said please, call me Edward.

'Of course. To be honest, Edward, I think my education and background as a lawyer has been a distinct advantage.' *Edvard*.

They talked a little longer – about horses, how marvellous the organisation of the Games was, and then Karl-Heinrich said there were so many misunderstandings about Germany and Barney said he was sure that was true and in any case, he wasn't terribly interested in politics.

Barney Allen was back in the reception area later that afternoon when the SS officer appeared next to him.

'It was a pleasure to meet you earlier today, Edward.' *Edvard*.

'Likewise.'

'May I have the honour of introducing you to my wife, Frau Sophia von Naundorf?'

He'd not spotted the woman until then when a slim and noticeably younger woman appeared from behind her husband and gently shook the hand of the man introduced to her as Edward Campion. Barney was struck by the contrast: Sophia von Naundorf was quite beautiful, with large dark eyes that demanded attention and an air of refinement and even sophistication about her, quite unlike her husband. Her pale skin was framed and accentuated by the cloche hat she wore. She said in English what a great pleasure it was to meet Mr Campion…

'…Edward, please!'

'Edward: the Obersturmbannführer mentioned you earlier and I'm so pleased to meet you.'

It struck Barney Allen as odd that she referred to her husband by his military rank but he'd puffed his chest out with pride as she did so. Maybe he expected it of her. She'd seemed to shrink slightly when her husband spoke.

'We are having a small dinner party at our home on Thursday, Edward, and we'd be most honoured if you could join us.'

–

Barney Allen had been annoyed that Werner Lustenberger wasn't in Berlin when he arrived in the city. Despite giving him plenty of notice of when he'd be there and promising to meet him on the Friday before the Games began to give him his tickets, the German hadn't turn up to the rendezvous point, a bar on the Unter den Linden.

Werner finally answered the telephone at his apartment on the Wednesday evening, soon after Barney returned to his hotel after watching Jesse Owens break the world record to win the 200 metres. The German crowd had been unamused at the sight of a black man winning another medal in such style. Barney Allen was similarly unimpressed with Werner.

'Where the hell have you been?'

'I had some family business in Aachen, Barnaby, and then my cousin in Paris asked to see me and one thing led to another, but don't worry, now I'm back. What can I do for you?'

Barney Allen did his best not to lose his temper. The last thing he needed at the moment was to get on the wrong side of Werner, especially given what he was about to tell him.

'Let's meet on Friday night, Werner, we need to talk. You find one of those decent Berlin restaurants you were telling me about and I'll give you some tickets for the Olympics. What about the equestrian events? They begin next week.'

Werner replied that he wasn't interested.

'I thought you like horses?'

'I like to see them running, Barnaby, not dancing.'

Werner told him to meet at six at a place called the Saxon on Regensburger Strasse.

–

Dinner at the home of Obersturmbannführer Karl-Heinrich von Naundorf and his wife, Sophia, had been an awkward occasion.

Barney Allen was determined that Edward Campion would come across as a somewhat bemused Englishman, one whose job would be of little interest to anyone, which along with his mild demeanour would mean few people would take notice of him. He was there to observe, to listen, to pick up ideas and who knows whom he may meet?

But from the outset it hadn't felt right. Two of the other guests were fellow SS officers, both accompanied by silent wives. There was a man from the German Olympic Committee and an Austrian journalist who spent most of the evening staring at Barney but saying very little. They'd only just sat down at the dining table in the elegant apartment and were still being served their hors d'oeuvre – cold meats and a potato salad – when the first question was fired at him.

Why are people in England so hostile to the leadership of Adolf Hitler?

He composed himself, allowing himself a moment or two to construct an answer that would seem thoughtful without being confrontational. He didn't have time to answer.

Are you not impressed with the achievements of the Third Reich?

You have Jews in England, Mr Campion – are they not a problem for you too?

The problem with democracy is that it leads to failure and rewards weakness, can you not see that?

Why is your government so tolerant of Bolshevism?

He drank the whole of his glass of a sour Bavarian white in one go – his father would have been appalled – and launched into a lengthy defence of England: people were not necessarily hostile to Herr Hitler, nor to Germany, but surely one should accept that different countries had different ways of doing things and as far as he knew the United Kingdom didn't interfere in the domestic affairs of Germany.

And what about Jews, Herr Campion – and Bolsheviks?

There was a brief respite as the first course was cleared away and Sophia said she wanted no talking while the main course – roast goose – was served. To accompany it was a German red wine and Barney hoped to distract the others by asking about the wine. It was a Spätburgunder, he was told and it was quite pleasant, far better than the white. Not unlike a Burgundy, he commented.

'German wine is at least as good as French wine, Herr Campion. You were going to give us your opinion on Jews and Bolsheviks?'

'I have to be honest, I'm not a terribly… political… person. I'm not sure I have an opinion as such. Could I ask you to pass the potatoes, please?'

'But this is more than politics, Herr Campion,' said the Obersturmbannführer. 'This is about the very future of our countries. Surely you are concerned about the influence and control of the Jews and the Bolsheviks?'

'I understand you have clamped down pretty heavily on the Jews in this country, Karl-Heinrich. You've passed all sorts of laws stopping them going about their daily lives and tens of thousands of them are leaving this country. How many Jews are in your Olympic team? I read in *The Times* last week that you didn't include a high jumper called Gretel Bergmann in your team just because she's a Jew!'

'My understanding, Herr Campion,' said the man from the German Olympic Committee, 'is that she was left out for under-performing.'

'Hah!' Barney Allen laughed. 'Under-performing by holding your national record? Come on!'

'Edward – please, let us not argue, not least because you are a guest in my house and indeed in our country. But you have to appreciate the threat posed to Germany by the Jews. They seek to provoke another war because they will then profit from it as they did from the last one. They control the banks and international finance and they consort with the Bolsheviks, half of whom are Jews anyway!'

'Do you know how ridiculous that sounds, Karl-Heinrich? They either control the banks or are Bolsheviks: they can hardly be both. You need to make up your mind.'

At that point one of the other SS officers spoke for the first time. He saw no point in arguing and they would have to agree to disagree and he understood Herr Campion was interested in horses – was he intending to attend any of the events?

Barney Allen left as soon as he could after coffee. Karl-Heinrich said he'd ask the maid to show him out, but Sophia said she'd do so. He followed her silently down the stairs of the apartment block, the only sound that of their footsteps. It was still just about light as she followed him onto Potsdammer Strasse.

'Where are you staying, Edward?'

'The Kaiserhof on Wilhelmplatz.'

She nodded as she lit a cigarette and offered him one. 'It's a nice night to walk, but you'll find a taxi on Schloss Strasse.' She pointed to her right. He thanked her for a lovely evening...

'It was a dreadful evening, Edward! I'm ashamed at the way my husband and the others speak about the Jews. I have no idea what to do or what to say. I'm in no position to argue with him, but it is too dreadful... to hear you speak like that was so... welcome!'

'I am sorry, I—'

'No – not at all! I cannot tell you how refreshing it was to hear you make them look like the fools they are. If only there was something I could do.'

She looked desperate; her shoulders drawn tight as she held the cigarette to her mouth.

'There's a family on the first floor here – the Goldmanns. Such decent people, their daughter Esther is my best friend. Karl-Heinrich makes their life hell.'

'So, when you said you wish there was something you could do?'

'I have no idea, Edward. What on earth could I do – an SS officer's wife?'

'May I have your telephone number perhaps, Sophia? I visit Berlin from time to time and perhaps I could call you once in a while – to see how you are or if there's anything I could do to help, maybe?'

She swayed slowly, her arms still drawn tightly, staring at the ground and moving her head as if discussing something with herself. Then she looked at him knowingly, as if she had an inkling of something. 'That is very thoughtful of you, Edward, but I imagine I'll be fine.'

'But you never know, Sophia, just a friendly call to see how you are: perhaps we could meet for coffee.'

She looked up at him and smiled. 'It would be so nice to hear from you, Edward.'

Chapter 8

Berlin
August 1936

It was a warm and pleasant evening when Barney Allen left the von Naundorf's apartment on Potsdammer Strasse. The hotel was on Wilhelmplatz which was probably too far to walk, but for the time being he was happy to take the night air as his mother would have put it. The unpleasant atmosphere at dinner had left him feeling tense and angry and he wanted to calm down.

At first he was annoyed with himself for being drawn into an argument. He worried he'd angered them and in so doing jeopardised his cover. But then he remembered Piers Devereux's briefing for the trip – he called it a tutorial and even gave it a title: 'How to behave in the field'.

Always behave as naturally as possible… Don't be too rehearsed… or controlled.

On reflection he realised that he'd probably behaved very much as they'd have expected of Edward Campion: polite at first and even reluctant, but prepared to argue his case and far more likely to take the British position than a German one.

And then there was Sophia. It was always possible of course that this was a set-up, that her husband had spotted him as easy prey at the stadium and her role was to persuade him that she despised her husband's views and he could confide in her. There was certainly something slightly implausible about her behaviour: at the Olympiastadion she'd been every inch the Nazi officer's loyal wife. She'd even referred to her husband by his rank, Obersturmbannführer.

On the other hand, on the other hand… he'd caught sight of her a few times at the dinner table. She seemed to be trying hard not to react and he'd noticed her appearing to go red in the face and her knuckles were white as she gripped her cutlery. She seemed to be sincere when she spoke to him on the street, genuinely upset at what her husband and the others had said. And when he'd offered to call her – he felt it would have been a missed opportunity not to do so – she seemed to realise what he meant.

She may well be a likely source – he'd discuss it with Devereux. Maybe once he had Werner properly on board then he could check her out. She'd mentioned something about having Jewish neighbours – the Goldmanns. That could be verified easily enough, he imagined.

He'd headed east from Schloss Strasse and was now on Kauffmann Strasse, about to turn right into Richard Wagner Strasse. He paused to light a cigarette and stood by a shop window for a moment. The city was much quieter now, with the beginnings of a gentle breeze and the light dropping. He noticed a man standing some twenty metres behind him, just after the junction with Wilmersdorfer. He could have sworn that same man had walked past him earlier.

Barney Allen paused a little longer, allowing himself time to finish his cigarette, adopting the air of a man with all the time in the world. The man behind him was still looking at the shop window. As Barney Allen moved off he stopped suddenly after just a few metres and turned round. The man was closing in on him, now no more than five metres away.

The man smiled and waved his arm in a manner that indicated Allen should keep moving. By now he was alongside Allen and spoke quietly in English.

'We'll keep walking in the direction you were headed – towards Wilhelmplatz presumably? Long bloody way.' Barney Allen had paused, but the man chivvied him along with a gentle pat on the back in a friendly manner. He wasn't standing too close and was on Allen's left-hand side – closer to the buildings; the least threatening position.

Always try and position yourself on the road side if you're walking with someone, Barney: less likely to get boxed in, easier to get away if you need to.

'Let's cross here and head towards Berliner Strasse, eh? I say, can I cadge a cigarette from you?' The man was obviously English, his accent middle class with a hint of the north to it. Grammar school, Barney Allen decided, definitely grammar school.

'There's a bench over there – shall we have a sit down and enjoy our cigarettes?' It was only when they were seated that the man introduced himself, allowing a quick handshake as he did so.

'Moore, in case you were wondering: Noel Moore. I work at the Passport Control Office on Tiergartenstrasse. I trust you understand what that means.'

Barney Allen understood full well that meant the MI6 station in Berlin but he was damned if he was going to admit that to a stranger who'd found him on the street. He shrugged in a manner to suggest no he didn't know what that meant.

'You're Devereux's chap, aren't you? Don't look so worried, we're on the same bloody side. Barnaby Allen, room 476 at the Kaiserhof – pleased to see Devereux's got a budget for the Kaiserhof – here under the name of Edward Campion. Marks out of ten?'

'I beg your pardon?'

'How did I do, Barney… correct names… right room number? Looks like you're not playing my little game… I don't expect you to trust me at the moment but how about you hear me out and then when you speak with Devereux you say you bumped into someone who knows him called Osbourne who works with Walker. He'll soon tell you we're in the same team. Your dinner at von Naundorf's – I presume it was unpleasant, eh? I detest the Nazis, absolutely hate the bastards.'

He said that with such venom that Barney Allen suddenly found him utterly plausible. 'It was quite unpleasant, yes… Do you know him?'

'Know *of* him, that's part of my job – Frank wants us to compile a who's who in the Nazi Party and Frank being Frank he thinks we need to concentrate on the up-and-coming types – those in their thirties, quick promotions et cetera: he calls it talent-spotting. Von Naundorf was made a lieutenant colonel in June so he's very much in our sights. Anything interesting, or just the usual anti-Jew and Hitler hero-worshipping nonsense?'

'Much as you say. When you mention Frank, do you mean—'

'Foley, Frank Foley – Major Frank Foley: head of station here, as you no doubt know but quite rightly won't acknowledge. I'm his number two or three, never quite sure – hierarchies aren't one of his strong points. Frank's absolutely marvellous, quite how he puts up with those bastards at the embassy I have no idea. I hope you'll excuse my language, but they're a bunch of shits, each and every one of them. They'd rather we weren't here and they go out of their way to make it as difficult as possible for us to operate properly. You know they won't allow us diplomatic status?'

'So I hear.'

'Not even for Frank, which is frankly an insult, if you'll excuse the pun. And then they require us to actually run the Passport Control Office, which I can assure you is a full-time job on top of everything else we have to do, but there's the twist – could I cadge another cigarette?'

He waited until they'd both lit their cigarettes. 'They thought squirreling us away on Tiergartenstrasse would be a way of hiding us but in fact it's been damn helpful because it allows Frank to run his own operation, away from those prying eyes at the embassy. Out of interest, who was it you saw there?'

'Summers.'

Noel Moore laughed. 'Odd sort, can't even speak German properly. Probably bullied at school. Anyway, you're probably wondering why have I accosted you in the street?'

'It had crossed my mind, yes.'

'Frank's a genius, knows everything that's going on in this city despite the best efforts of the embassy. He also knows what's going on back at base, hence he knew about you coming over here. He's asked me to be the messenger and the message is two-fold:

firstly, welcome to Berlin – *willkommen* as they say in these parts; secondly, don't approach him or come anywhere near our place on Tiergartenstrasse, please – too dangerous, they watch us like hawks and that's just the embassy! And finally, of course he doesn't expect you to tell us anything or give us even a hint of what your brief is but he suspects Devereux may be setting up his own operation and Frank just wants you to know that he thinks that's a bloody good idea, though Frank wouldn't say bloody – church and all that.'

'Thank you, Noel.'

'Don't mention it. Come to think of it, that was three things. And here's a fourth one while I'm at it. Is there anything we can do to help?'

'There is actually, Noel, seeing as you mention it. Could you see if the von Naundorfs have any Jewish neighbours in their block – and if so their names?'

Noel Moore nodded. 'Wouldn't surprise me, Charlottenburg is a very Jewish area, though lots of them trying to get out now and I can't say I blame them, Frank sees it as a priority to help them. I'll check it out and get a note to you. Oh – there is one other thing.'

Noel Moore looked around and then stood up. He told Barney Allen they should walk.

'Heard of the Reichs-Rundfunk-Gesellschaft?'

'Something to do with radio?'

'It's the main radio outfit here in Berlin, broadcasts in German, of course, through national and regional stations and now they're starting to put out programmes in other languages including English. Based in a rather magnificent purpose-built studios not terribly far from here in Westend, on Masurenallee – you may have passed it on the way to the stadium. It used to be run by the Interior Ministry but now it comes under Goebbels' rather ridiculously named Ministry of Public Enlightenment and Propaganda. The Nazis are putting a lot of money into it, they see radio as one of their main propaganda weapons and one has to be honest and say they're terribly good at that type of thing, even though of course one despises their message.'

They were on Berliner Strasse now, close to the junction with March Strasse. It was surprisingly busy for the time of night, lots of couples out for walks, half of the men in uniform.

'You may want to pick up a taxi soon, but let me get to the point I was making first – I do realise that I tend to give rather a lot of background, Frank says I need to be more concise. Reichs-Rundfunk-Gesellschaft is conveniently abbreviated to RRG, rather like the BBC, eh? Now the point I'm coming to is this. Recently they seem to have attracted quite a number of odd types to work for them from abroad and we've spotted a few of them are British. As far as we can gather some of them are here because they're Nazi sympathisers, others because they happen to be in Berlin – married to Germans, that kind of thing – and for them it's a job.

'Frank thinks they're interesting but we're absolutely not to go within a mile of them – if the embassy found out they'd have the station closed down overnight. As far as they're concerned, we're to have nothing whatsoever to do with British subjects here in Germany, but Frank thinks there's nothing to stop you going to have a look at them.'

'Do you mean going into the radio station?'

'No, no… the radio station's an enormous triangular structure surrounded by three roads, the main one's Masurenallee as I told you. Off Masurenallee is a smaller road called Soor Strasse where there's a bar called *Der Grüner Baum* and they tend to congregate there. One of them in particular has come to our attention – big chap with a florid complexion and a moustache rather like Hitler's. He's as English as you and me but calls himself Fritz and we have no idea who he really is. Many of the others defer to him and we think he may be important there or it could just be bragging. He seems to have difficulty keeping his opinions to himself once he's had a couple of drinks: he's been heard being very pro-Nazi and we'd like to know more about him, find out who he is. If he turns out to be on our side then he's all yours. How does that sound?'

Barney Allen said that sounded like rather a good idea and he may well do as Noel suggested and then he asked Noel how he could contact him and Noel said not to worry, he'd find him easily enough, and they both laughed. By now they were on the corner of Sophien Strasse and Noel said he'd better get a taxi before it was too late and could he have one more cigarette?

–

As soon as he was back in room 476 at the Kaiserhof, Barney Allen sat at the small desk with one hand on the telephone. He'd been amazed to find that every bedroom at the hotel had its own telephone – he'd not heard of that before and wasn't sure he could see the point of it, but now he was grateful. He asked the operator to connect him with a London number.

If you have to call me, Barney, please only do so if it's important – not for a chat about the weather or to see how the test match is going.

'Hello... hello? It's Edward in Berlin. Did I wake you?'

Piers Devereux sounded as if he had indeed been woken and was moving around. 'Hang on a tick. There we are. All well, Edward?'

'Yes, all splendid, thank you, sorry – I hadn't realised it was quite so late.'

'No problem: and how are the Games?'

'Wonderful: these Germans certainly know how to organise big events. Every detail has been thought of, most impressive.'

Assume the Germans are listening in to every word of every call.

'I just thought you'd like to know I bumped into a chap this evening who says he knows you. Goes by the name of Osbourne – he works here with Walker who you apparently know too.'

A slight pause. Piers Devereux would be putting two and two together to work out that Osbourne and Walker were Noel Moore and Frank Foley. His response would be critical.

'Osbourne? Yes – he's an old friend. Walker too. How funny you bumped into him. Do give him my warm regards.'

Barney Allen helped himself to a large Scotch and unusually for him drank it neat. Had Devereux replied that he didn't know them that would have been bad news and had he referred to them as 'acquaintances' that would have been very bad news. But the response couldn't have been more positive.

In Noel Moore's own words, they were on the same bloody side.

–

On the Friday evening Barney Allen arrived on Regensburger Strasse at half past five, allowing himself half an hour to check out the Saxon before going in to meet Werner at six o'clock as they'd arranged.

Get to a rendezvous point early, Barney, allow yourself time to check it out.

See if there are rear or side entrances – watch the type of people who go in and out.

Do this from a point diagonally opposite but do walk past, but not too often.

Don't loiter – walk round the block.

The area seemed to be pleasant enough but the Saxon was certainly not the kind of place he'd had in mind. He was hoping for a decent restaurant but this place didn't look like a restaurant, it was more of a bar than anything else and the word *Klub* on the front didn't bode well. It certainly didn't look like the kind of club he was used to.

He spotted Werner go in just before six and waited another five minutes, just to be sure no one had been with him.

Once inside it took him a few moments to adjust to the dim light and only then did he spot Werner at the end of the bar talking to a younger man. He waited until they'd finished and they exchanged slightly awkward waves of recognition before Werner came over and said – without so much as a 'hello' or 'how are you' – to follow him. He knocked on a door to the side of the bar and once it opened they went upstairs. Barney rather hoped they'd find themselves in a restaurant but the room was wreathed in cigarette smoke with a small bar at one end, jazz playing loudly on a gramophone and a clientele which was exclusively male, every one of them staring at him as if he were an intruder.

'It's my club,' said Werner, his arm sweeping the room in a proprietorial manner.

'Rather different to mine.'

'Does yours allow women in?'

'Of course not!'

'Well then, not too different after all. What would you like to drink?'

Barney said a beer would be nice and do they do food at all?

'No – don't worry, we'll find somewhere else to eat. I thought we could start here. As you can probably guess, it's a very discreet place and you said we need to talk. Let's go through there where no one will hear us.'

They moved into another room, which was far quieter, and sat on their own in the corner, no one within earshot, and for a few minutes drank their beer and exchanged small talk. Werner mentioned the big race meeting in Hamburg and his trip to Aachen and then described his apartment and said Barney really ought to pay a visit and Barney asked Werner to call him Edward while he was in Berlin and then talked about the Olympics and said despite everything it was really rather impressive.

'Why do you want me to call you Edward?'

Barney looked around. The only other men in the room were a couple who at first Barney had thought were father and son but now realised perhaps not: they were very interested in each other and oblivious to them.

'This is what I wanted to talk to you about, Werner.'

'To tell me you have a new name?'

Barney could feel his heart beating fast. He was nervous and had been dreading this moment. He'd assured Piers Devereux that

71

Werner suspected nothing and saw him as a friend and that still appeared to be the case. He worried Werner was going to feel terribly let down: betrayed. He just hoped he wouldn't make too much of a scene, especially in a place like this.

Barney leaned forward, his body now blocking Werner from the rest of the room and closer to him. 'When I hired you to work for me, Werner, I may not have been quite as forthcoming as perhaps I could have been at the time about who you'd be working for.'

'You said for your college, Barnaby. You want me to find possible partners. In fact in Aachen, I found such a college, I even have the name of someone there who—'

'No, Werner, this is the… Look, I'm going to come straight to the point.'

Be clear with him, Barney: make sure he completely understands what you're telling him. Avoid euphemisms!

He hesitated, trying to remember the little speech he'd rehearsed so carefully. If Werner reacted adversely, it would be a disaster, both for the Service and for Barney personally. His cover would be blown and he'd be without an important agent, a man he was trying to build a network around. Werner was looking at him curiously, interested in what he was about to say.

'Please listen carefully and hear me out and if you're going to react, please do so quietly. I work for British Intelligence, Werner. My job with Holborn College is what we call a front, a way of concealing what I really do. We are trying to find out what is really going on here in Germany and to do that we need to have Germans working for us, ones that we can really trust.'

He looked up at Werner who was blinking, but showing no other signs of reaction.

'People like you, Werner. We've recruited you as one of our agents.'

It sounded far too blunt. He'd meant to say 'we'd like to recruit you…'

'Recruited me as what, Barnaby?'

'I've just told you, Werner, as a British agent.'

'Really… you mean…?'

'Yes.'

Remember: don't leave any room for misunderstanding – be emphatic!

'What about if I don't want to be recruited, Barnaby?'

'Edward, please.'

'Edward.'

'Well, I'm afraid it doesn't quite work like that, Werner. You're already working for us. You don't have much of a say.'

'Really? Perhaps you could explain.' Barney was surprised at Werner's tone: more inquisitive than hostile.

'Those packages I gave you in London – the ones I insisted you hand-deliver? I think there were four to be delivered to addresses in Berlin, then to Hamburg, Würzburg and Leipzig.'

'And Magdeburg.'

'That's right. Those addresses were all contacts of British intelligence, Werner. We – you – were passing on messages to them. So, in a sense you've already started working for British intelligence and once you start… well, that's it really. As far as the Gestapo are concerned, you're a British agent.'

'How would the Gestapo know about it?'

Barney shrugged.

'It sounds like I've been blackmailed.'

'That's putting it rather strongly, Werner.'

'I think it's putting it rather mildly actually. Of course, I could pack it all in and return to Britain.'

Basically, Piers, I'll be telling Werner I'm blackmailing him?

Absolutely, Barney!

Won't he be furious, I mean I—

You said he trusts you, that he's your friend?

I doubt he'll be after this.

'That's no longer an option open to you, Werner. We've tightened up who we let in and I think you'll find you'll have difficulties in that respect. Whether you like it or not, you're working for us, but I don't want you to worry unduly… it oughtn't to be dangerous, it's more about keeping your ear to the ground, passing on messages, picking up interesting information and maybe even letting me know if you come across anyone else you may think may be suitable to work for us.'

A long silence during which Barney could have kicked himself for using the word 'dangerous', but Werner looked surprisingly relaxed as he finished his beer and lit a cigarette. When he looked him in the eye there was none of the hostility Barney had expected.

'I did think fifteen pounds a week plus all my expenses was very generous.'

'I was going to tell you that is being increased to seventeen pounds a week.'

'I could say no, couldn't I?'

'By all means, but would you take the risk?'

'I've taken risks my whole life. I could leave Berlin tonight and you'd never find me and I don't believe you'll tell the Gestapo.'

He looked directly at Barney, drawing hard on his cigarette and Barney felt sick. He didn't doubt that would be the case. Werner would politely take his leave and quietly disappear.

'But…'

'But what, Werner?'

'But what you've just told me, Barnaby… Edward… it sounds so exciting! Since I returned to Germany and spent time travelling around and meeting people I've been appalled – it was bad enough when I left, but now… The way people are treated, not just the Jews, but us homosexuals, political opponents… I thought before I left that the Nazis were so ridiculous that sooner or later people would tire of them and they'd go away, but now I realise that's not to happen… I was going to tell you I didn't think I could stand living here much longer but now you tell me there's something I can do about it.'

'So, you—'

'So of course, I'll work for you, Edward – I think it's a marvellous idea!'

Chapter 9

Berlin
August 1936

'Always remember, Miller, journalism thrives on adversity and injustice.'

It was in his first year at the *Philadelphia Bulletin* and Joe Walsh was delivering one of his ad hoc homilies in the middle of the noisy room, where the unremitting sound of shouting and type-writers soon drove some to realise journalism wasn't the career for them. Jack Miller had returned to the newsroom to complain about the injustice of the police refusing to allow anyone back into a rundown apartment block where there'd been a shooting – not even the victim's family. Everyone felt aggrieved.

'But there's your story, Miller – the unfairness and the anger. Look, bad news sells newspapers. Every year some new manager – usually a college-educated kid who's still learning how to shave – arrives on the top floor and once he's looked at the sales numbers, reckons he's got it all worked out. If the paper sells this many copies when it's full of bad news think how many we'd sell if we concentrated on good news: and you know what I tell 'em?'

Jack Miller leaned forward so as not to miss what Joe Walsh would tell the hapless college-educated manager.

'I tell 'em we'd sell less than half the number of copies than when the paper's full of bad news. If you find injustice, you got a story.'

Jack had certainly found his story in Berlin. The city – the whole country – reeked of injustice. The place was fuelled by it.

You came across it on every street and in nearly every conversation.

But he'd arrived in Berlin at the end of June and for the first month he'd kept his head down and concentrated on finding his way around and sorting out his accreditation. Ted Morris in New York wanted a steady stream of colour pieces – the background to the Games, what German trains were like, the food… nothing likely to win him any awards but enough to keep Associated and its newspapers happy. He'd been told to keep away from politics – 'the Nazi stuff', Ted Morris had called it. That was hard to come to terms with because it was obvious to Jack Miller that this was the story. If journalism thrived on adversity and injustice then Berlin was like a seat of higher learning in it.

But that would have to wait until the Olympics. And to his surprise he found a great story of injustice at the Games.

It came on the first Monday, 3 August. It promised to be a good day for the United States: Jesse Owens, Ralph Metcalfe and Frank Wykoff would all be running in the Men's 100-metre final at the Olympiastadion and later on the United States soccer team would be playing Italy – and Jack Miller had worked out a way he could cover both events. The 100-metre final alone gave him plenty of material even before the starter's gun fired. Both Owens and Metcalfe had won their semi-finals and it would be a shock if one of them didn't win the final. And both were black and given that it was apparent the Games had been designed as some kind of festival of Nazism there'd be a wonderful irony if men from what the Nazis termed an inferior race proved to be the best athletes in the world. And as a bonus Ralph Metcalfe was from Chicago, the home of the *Daily News*, one of the Associated newspapers.

Jack Miller wrote 750 words on the final, focusing on the restrained reaction – and some hostility – from the German crowd to Owens' victory, with a couple of paras towards the end on the man from Chicago winning silver. He'd worked in a pun about the Windy City that he was actually pleased with. He filed from the press centre at the stadium and then headed over to the

Poststadion in Moabit where the United States soccer team was taking on Italy.

Until that day Jack Miller hadn't been much of a soccer fan. His sport was baseball – he was a big Phillies supporter. But soccer was popular in Philadelphia, particularly among the city's German community. The city's Philadelphia German Americans team had won the American Soccer League the previous season and that year they'd won the National Challenge Cup. And not only that, eight of the eleven playing Italy were Philadelphia German American players: Ryan, Fiedler, Crockett, Altemose, Nemchick, Pietras, Lutkefelder and Greinert, which would keep Joe Walsh happy, it may even get onto his front page. And three others played in Boston so the *Globe* would be pleased and Bartkus played in Brooklyn and Zbilowski in New Jersey so the New Yorkers would have some interest there.

From the first whistle the game was marked by violence, with the Italians committing a series of fouls, few of which were punished. At one stage in the match Achille Piccini of Fiorentina fouled Fiedler so badly the referee – a German called Karl Weingartner – sent him off. But he wouldn't leave the pitch and Miller watched the Italians surround the referee, some manhandling him, one even holding his hand over the official's mouth. To Miller's astonishment Piccini was allowed to stay on.

The Italians went on to win 1–0, the goal coming from Annibale Frossi of Internazionale. Miller was at once appalled and captivated: soccer seemed to have all the human drama and intrigue one could wish for in a sport. And he had his story: a great injustice, committed against the United States of America and specifically against eight honest men from Philadelphia by a German referee and an Italian team with little regard for the rules of the game. For good measure he added in a sentence about Mussolini and how close the Italian fascists were to the German Nazis, though he fully expected that to be subbed out.

–

A few days after meeting Noel Moore, Barney Allen found Der Grüner Baum on Soor Strasse. He went there after watching the 1500-metre semi-finals at the Olympiastadion and felt that stopping by for a drink was plausible enough.

Der Grüner Baum had low ceilings and dark furniture and in the way of Berlin bars comprised one large room with the bar in the centre, quite unlike British pubs with their different rooms and their nooks and crannies. There were around a dozen men in the front of the bar, all sitting or standing on their own and all silent. On the other side of the bar, he saw a group of people and as he made his way round there, he realised they were talking English. He ordered a beer and remained at the bar, trying to follow the conversation behind him, which seemed to be about the rents in the city and where was the best place to live.

'Schöneberg – are you serious? It's still too expensive.'

'And too close to Wilmersdorf and all those Jews.'

'But not for long!'

There was laughter and Barney Allen glanced round and saw there were five of them, three men and two women, one of whom – a pretty girl perhaps in her twenties – caught his gaze and smiled.

'Where is it you said you were going to move to, Fritz?'

...*calls himself Fritz*...

'I've told you – Pankow. You get far more for your rent than in the fancy areas round here. In fact, I've already found a place!'

'You didn't tell us that, Fritz.'

'You didn't ask – for the same as I'm paying for a single room in Mitte and sharing a filthy kitchen and bathroom with a dozen others, I'm now going to get my own double room with an armchair and a small kitchen area – and I share the bathroom with just the two other people on my floor.'

'Where is it?'

'On Forcheimer Strasse, just off Kissingen Platz. It's a pleasant enough area and there's a U-Bahn station nearby.'

'You sound like an estate agent!' The man had said that with a mock Jewish accent and the others laughed and so did Barney Allen, turning round and raising his glass at the small group.

'You understand?'

'I would jolly well hope so, I've only been in Berlin a couple of weeks, not long enough to forget my English!'

They invited him over and Barney insisted on buying a round – *no please, I insist, my pleasure* – and then joined them and there were the introductions, first names only: Clarice, Jean, Norman, Donald and Fritz. Fritz was almost exactly as Noel Moore had described him: a large man with a florid complexion and a moustache a bit like Hitler's, though that was stretching it a bit. He was certainly the dominant character of the group – the one with the loudest voice along with an impressive capacity for drink. No sooner had he finished one large glass of the strong Bavarian lager than he'd signal for another.

Barney Allen had introduced himself as Ted and said he was from London where he was a teacher and had saved up for two years to come to the Olympics because he loved sport and all things German and here he was – 'very boring, I'm afraid.' They said not all and what did he think of the Games and he replied he was very impressed and then went into tedious detail about the different events he'd been to – who came first, second – their times, the conditions and he noticed the others' eyes glaze over as they made mental notes not to ask him any more questions.

'And what do you all do?'

Norman explained they worked for German radio which was based round the corner and they were employed on the English language section and Ted appeared very impressed and asked if they were famous and Donald said not really and in any case Clarice and Jean were only secretaries and Norman was the only one who you'd hear on the radio while Fritz was an engineer, at which point Fritz got a bit angry and said Donald knew full well he was more than that and in any case without engineers...

Clarice and Jean announced they really must be going and when they left, Norman explained they were both married to Germans and said he was too. Barney ordered another round and this time asked for a bottle of schnapps with it, which was a bit of a risk because they may wonder why he was being so generous, but they didn't seem to worry about that and the schnapps had the effect he was hoping for, certainly with Fritz, whose face reddened even more and when he stood up to go to the toilet, he seemed to sway in the manner more noticeable in men of his size.

When he returned, Norman announced reluctantly that he too had to leave as his wife would wonder where he was and Ted should know that German wives are more prone to give a piece of their mind than English ones and they all laughed, Barney topping up Fritz's glass as they did so.

Donald was barely awake but Fritz was still alert and Barney asked him if he was German and Fritz seemed surprised and said 'of course not' and asked whatever made him think he was, couldn't he hear his accent?

'Of course, but your name – Fritz.'

'It's a nickname, obviously.'

Barney laughed and said he was sorry and filled up Fritz's glass and Fritz said not to be sorry because there was nothing wrong in being German and Barney said of course not, in fact from what he'd seen over the past fortnight the Germans were a very impressive people.

'So you don't believe all this nonsense the British papers write about the country?'

'I take people as I find them and I find the German people to be very... impressive.'

Fritz nodded approvingly.

'What is going on here under Herr Hitler – it is wonderful, Ted. He's turning a defeated, downtrodden country into the best one in Europe: Britain would do well to take a leaf out his book!'

Barney Allen replied that he wasn't political at all but he could see Fritz's point and, please – here, do finish the schnapps, it's gone straight to my head and Fritz said he didn't mind if he did.

'If Fritz is your nickname what's your real name then?'

It was a bit blunt but Barney was counting on the other man's defences being down thanks to the amount he'd drunk.

'It's very boring…'

'Can't be more boring than Ted!'

'Ken, Ken Ridley – told you it was boring!'

–

It was the last Saturday of the Games and Barney Allen had been at Döberitz to watch the equestrian cross country and by the time he returned to the Kaiserhof and had his bath he couldn't decide where to eat that night. Since their meeting at the Saxon Klub a week or so earlier he'd gone to dinner with Werner on a few nights. To his delight, Werner had thrown himself into his new role with an enthusiasm he'd not expected. Tonight, Werner was meeting a Kriegsmarine officer who'd been heard talking about how merchant ships were being armed.

Barney had thought about going for a walk up Wilhelmstrasse to the Unter den Linden and finding somewhere to eat but decided to stay at the hotel. He went to the smallest of the hotel's bars, which overlooked Hitler's Chancellery. With its leather club chairs and near silence it reminded him of his own club in London.

But as he entered the room – the steward at the door bowing very slightly as he did so – all was not silent. At the far end of the bar an argument was going on. A tall man – quite young and speaking good German but with a foreign accent – was talking in a raised voice. A shorter, older man was standing next to him but the argument appeared to be with the barman and a man alongside him dressed in a formal suit of a hotel manager.

'I don't care what you say, Herr Haas is a friend of mine and he's my guest and it says very clearly in the reception that residents in this hotel are permitted to bring their guests to any of the public areas of the hotel, including this bar!'

Barney Allen moved closer. The older man – Herr Haas presumably – was tapping him on the elbow and saying it didn't matter, really.

'I am afraid, Herr Miller, that regrettably this particular guest is not welcome in this hotel.'

'Why, what has he done wrong – trashed the place, eh?'

'Please, Herr Miller, I ask you not to cause a scene, I—'

'I want to see the manager.'

'I am the manager.'

'No, I meant the real manager, not the undermanager!'

A phone call was made and within moments another man in a formal suit appeared in the bar.

What appeared to be the problem?

Barney Allen listened as the undermanager spoke to the more senior manager. *Mr Miller insisted on bringing this guest to the bar but this guest is… a Jew… and there were regulations strictly prohibiting that and…*

The senior manager looked around and caught Barney Allen's eye and returned his awkward smile with an embarrassed nod of the head.

There are indeed such regulations, but during the Olympics… and only during the Olympics… we are expected to exercise some discretion… for the sake of appearances, you understand… the authorities don't want our laws, as necessary as they are, to be misunderstood by foreign visitors.

'Excuse me…' Everyone turned round to look at Barney Allen. 'My name is Edward Campion and I too am a resident in this hotel, room 476 if you care to check. I couldn't help overhearing you and although my German is not perfect I rather got the impression that my fellow guest here, who I do not know' – he nodded in the direction of the other man – 'wishes to entertain a Jewish friend and your colleague here is declining to serve him.'

'I am afraid it is a complicated situation, Herr Campion, we—'

'Please.' It was the German friend of the tall man, the one he'd referred to as Herr Haas. 'I wish to leave. Please do not let there be any unpleasantness on my behalf. Jack, please allow me to leave and maybe we will make contact tomorrow. Good evening.'

Herr Haas hurried out of the bar, everyone else remaining silent in his wake. The senior manager said he was sure this had all been a misunderstanding and he could only apologise and perhaps the gentlemen would accept a drink on the house? Barney Allen was about to say he'd rather check out than take a drink from them but the other man spoke first.

'Make it dinner.'

'I beg your pardon, sir?'

'Dinner on the house for this gentleman and myself: whatever we want from the menu.'

The senior manager looked furious but agreed. The other man turned to Barney.

'English?'

'Indeed: Edward Campion.'

'Jack Miller – United States of America.'

The previous day – Friday 14 – Barney Allen woke to find a slip of paper under the door that had certainly not been there when he went to bed. On it was the name of a cafe on Ritter Strasse and underneath it *9 a.m. – Osbourne.*

The cafe was ten minutes' walk from the hotel and Noel Moore was sitting at a table against the wall facing the door with a napkin tucked into his collar and a plate of eggs and sausages in front of him. He patted the seat next to him for his guest to join him.

'No one can overhear us like this. Not got long. Will you eat?'

'I'll just have a coffee.'

'They seem to have plenty of decent coffee these days, must be the Olympics. No thank you, I tend not to smoke when I eat – you go ahead, please.'

They waited as the waitress poured Barney's coffee.

'Two items on the agenda, then. You asked me to check out whether the von Naundorfs have any Jewish neighbours in their block on Potsdammer Strasse. Well, you're in luck: Frank has terribly good contacts in the Jewish community and one of his most trusted sources knows a family called Goldmann in that very block – father was a doctor at the Charité hospital until he lost his job. Frank's contact had a word with them – very carefully, naturally – and according to them Karl-Heinrich von Naundorf is a complete bastard, dyed in the wool Nazi, but Sophia von Naundorf is very much the opposite – as sweet and as helpful as possible but of course only when her husband isn't around. It seems that Sophia and Esther Goldmann are jolly good friends. Does that help?'

'It does, Noel, thank you.'

'And a big thank you to you too – the intelligence you picked up on Fritz turned out to be spot on. His real name is indeed Ken Ridley and he's just moved into rooms on Forcheimer Strasse in Pankow. Thanks to what you told us we were able to check him out, in so far as we're able to without the embassy catching wind of what we're up to. We'd rather hoped he'd turn out to be a useful source for someone like you in the Service – an agent inside German radio would be terribly useful but...' He paused as the waitress asked if they wanted more coffee?

No, thank you.

Or toast?

No, thank you.

'But the answer is not to touch him with a bargepole, steer well clear et cetera et cetera to mix one's metaphors, though not sure it is actually. Turns out he's a Nazi sympathiser who's desperate to do what he can to help the Germans and is offering himself all over Berlin... the Abwehr – the intelligence service – turned him down as they felt he's unreliable, and even the Gestapo regard him as a drunk, which is a bit rich coming from them. If you could be so good as to alert MI5 and Special Branch about him when you get home at least that will get him on a watch list. Until then I imagine he'll be a thorn in our side here in Berlin. Still, at least we now know, don't we?'

–

Barney Allen's dinner with Jack Miller turned out to be a thoroughly enjoyable evening, not least because it was courtesy of the Kaiserhof Hotel and both men were of the view that it would be quite in order for them to order the most expensive items from the menu and indulge in the very impressive wine list.

Jack Miller was excellent company. During the first course he told the very charming Englishman his life story – including the divorce – and how he'd come to be sent to Berlin and how wonderful it had been covering the Olympics.

'But the shadow of what's going on here – that has hung over me. I'm a journalist, Edward, I like writing hard news stories at length and what's going on here in Germany – well it has to be the biggest news story around, you agree? Certainly beats bank heists in Philadelphia, I can tell you. I just wish I could stay, but I doubt it… and the sport, you know what's surprised me?'

His companion said he didn't know.

'Soccer – not a sport I really cared about back home but the Olympic soccer tournament – it had everything! The Italy v USA match was like watching gladiators in the Colosseum in Rome. I was at the final this afternoon where Italy beat Austria 2–1. You a soccer man, Edward?'

Edward said he was more rugby and in any case we call it football and Jack Miller laughed.

'I'd love to cover soccer in Europe: the guy in the bar with me was Albert Haas, best soccer journalist in Germany according to everyone you ask, but since the Nazis came to power he's banned from all games because he's Jewish. I've been paying him a retainer to give him advice and information and he's been wonderful. He's desperate to get out with his family but he's got problems getting an exit visa as his wife's from Poland and I'd love to do what I can to help. He really wants to go to Britain, home of soccer, he says. He keeps talking about a team called Arsenal United, could that be right? Anyway, do you know anyone who could help him?'

Barney Allen said he may be conflating two separate teams but as a matter of fact he may well know someone who could help

Herr Haas and if Jack wrote down Herr Haas' details, he'd do what he could. It was around this time it began to occur to him that Jack Miller showed some potential. He had a perfect reason for being in Germany and as a reporter specialising in sport, he'd attract less attention… He was clearly anti-Nazi and he spoke good German and was unattached and had a certain something about him that was hard to put into words… charisma certainly, guts possibly, enthusiasm definitely. By the time they were on to dessert – and their second bottle of excellent Bordeaux (*none of this German stuff, are we agreed, Edward?*) – Barney decided to take the plunge. He was due to return to London in a couple of days and didn't want to miss the opportunity.

'No promises, Jack, you understand, but I have some good newspaper contacts in London and they're always on the lookout for talent and in fact one of my friends did say to me before I came out that he was looking for freelance journalists in Europe who could write decent English. If you were minded to stay out here I may well be able to put some work your way. No promises, of course, but if you want I can ask some questions in London and then come back to you.'

Jack said he was indeed interested, very interested in fact. He'd already been thinking about staying out here and if Associated wouldn't let him stay as a staff reporter he'd go freelance.

Edward promised he'd be in touch.

–

Barney Allen left Berlin the following Tuesday, but not before attending to one important matter. He'd sent a message to Noel Moore and they met on the Monday lunchtime in the Tiergarten.

'You said Frank's helping a lot of Jews with their exit visas?'

'We all are.'

Barney slipped a piece of paper into Noel Moore's hand. 'Chap called Albert Haas, Jewish journalist. Desperate to get to Britain and it would help us to help him, if you see what I mean. Apparently his wife's Polish: is that a problem?'

'It is a bit: how important is it to get him out?'

'Very – think you can manage it?'

'Consider it done.'

Three years later...

Chapter 10

London and Berlin
February 1939

The headquarters of MI6 – head office as Piers Devereux insisted on calling it – was situated alongside St James's Underground station and St Ermin's Hotel at 54 Broadway, between Victoria station and the Houses of Parliament, with Buckingham Palace to the north and the two cathedrals of Westminster just to the south. The entire establishment conveniently on their doorstep: the State, the Monarchy and the Church.

As with so many London buildings constructed that century there was little to distinguish it aesthetically, which was just as well as its purpose was anonymity rather than architectural admiration. The façade was bland enough to ensure few people afforded the building a second look, and those who did would have spotted a brass plaque by the main entrance indicating this was the offices of the 'Minimax Fire Extinguisher Company'.

In the unlikely event of a passer-by bothering to attempt to enter the building to enquire about fire extinguishers they would have got no further than a pair of tall metal doors which remained closed until the moment they were used. Had the passer-by interested in fire extinguishers managed to get a glimpse inside the building they'd have been none the wiser. The entrance hall was dark and they may have just made out quite a few uniformed guards, but that would have been for no more than a second or two, certainly not long enough for anything to have registered.

One of the many peculiar features of 54 Broadway was a degree of uncertainty as to how many floors it actually had. From the outside it was unclear quite how high the first floor extended and within the building the network of corridors and concealed staircases created a maze-like effect. This air of confusion was shared by many who worked there and was amplified by the way most of its floors were arranged. As more people came to work for the Service, extra office space was created by the hasty erection of partitions, meaning many offices had no natural light and had to do with low-voltage lightbulbs and such light as the internal windows allowed.

The uncertainty as to how many floors there were was fuelled by the nature of the building. Unless one was of a very high grade there were restrictions as to which floors one could visit. That usually meant the floor one worked on, Registry of course, the library and research office and the administration floor.

There was talk of hidden floors, of secret lifts and even tunnels. Some secretaries even perpetuated the rumour that there was a floor deep below the basement – a dungeon – where prisoners were held and from where in the early hours of the morning the most dreadful sounds could be heard.

This inclination to gossip was perhaps an inevitable consequence of working for a covert organisation where staff were prohibited from discussing anything about their work with anyone other than those they worked with. This led to a sometimes-febrile atmosphere within the building and a form of office politics of the most rancorous kind.

But by the middle of 1939 such office gossip as Barney Allen was the subject of was delivered in revered tones, admittedly with a degree of reluctance by some of those on the same grade as him.

Who'd have thought it of such a late starter? Terribly bright... decent chap too...

...he'll be running this place sooner or later... Apparently, he's managed to recruit an agent in every German city! No, he's France actually... nothing to do with Germany

...I heard the Soviet Union – or maybe the Baltics. Lucky chap: in the right place at the right time...

Few knew what Barney Allen actually did, which of course was very much to be expected in 54 Broadway; it would have been unusual had more than a handful of people been au fait with his work. But it was generally known that Barney Allen was a high flyer, had something to do with Germany and that whatever it was he was doing was going remarkably well.

Tom Gilbey was one officer at the same level as Barney Allen for whom envy was not an issue. For a start, Tom Gilbey himself was doing pretty well and in any case the two men were old friends – they'd been at school together – and Gilbey had been instrumental in Allen joining the Service. As a result, people assumed he'd allow them an insight into Barney Allen.

But Tom Gilbey said little.

'Let's just say that Barney has the Midas touch: let's hope it lasts, eh?'

–

The three years since the summer of 1936 had been remarkably successful for Barney Allen. He'd been assiduous and resourceful in recruiting a network of agents across Germany, though 'agents' was a word he'd come to be circumspect about. Few were actual agents in the sense that Werner Lustenberger – for example – was an agent. Most were what he'd call sources – people in different parts of Germany and in different jobs and with different degrees of access to information. Some were committed anti-Nazis and sympathetic to Britain, others were prepared to trade information for money, some didn't even realise they were supplying Britain with intelligence – the sources who didn't even know they were sources.

Barney liked to think of his network as a collection of sources and contacts, held together by a small number of agents. Some sources would only be active for a short while, others would then take their place. Some supplied intelligence on a one-off basis. In the early days – certainly until the middle of 1938 – a high proportion of his network were committed anti-Nazis, either political opponents of the regime or Jews. But as the Nazis' grip tightened these people began to leave Germany.

Or disappear.

Replacing them was far from easy. In some areas like Hamburg it was easier to find sources, in other areas next to impossible. Some people lost heart or were too afraid or stopped when they felt that they'd gone as far as their luck was going to take them.

But in general, the task that Piers Devereux had set Barney Allen in January 1936 had been achieved. He'd established a network independent of the MI6 station in Berlin and this was vindicated as tensions between Britain and Germany increased on a daily basis. Few conversations failed to mention the possibility of war.

–

The enthusiasm with which Werner embraced his role as a British agent astonished Barney Allen. His initial decision back in March 1936 to try and recruit Werner had been based on a gut feeling that he could be the right man for the job but also, if he was totally honest, was as much out of a sense of desperation. Piers Devereux had told him to recruit his own network and he was struggling. Werner was a gamble.

He'd never anticipated how good Werner would be. He wasn't just competent: he was intuitive and good at using his own initiative as well as following instructions. He was sociable but also adept at giving away little of himself: he was enthusiastic too, and committed, motivated by a growing hatred of the Nazis and the sense that in this role he could do something about it.

Every time he and Barney met he would say how grateful he was for having been given this opportunity. And he liked the money too, which at first caused Barney some concerns that he was being too mercenary but Piers Devereux told him in fact this was reassuring: wanting to be properly recompensed for one's services was perfectly natural.

'How much are we paying him now, Barney?'

'Twenty pounds a week, sir.'

'The agents I worry about are the ones who have no interest in money. In fact, I'd distrust them. It's not natural not to be interested in money, is it?'

Barney travelled regularly to the Continent, usually to Germany though not always. Sometimes he met Werner or his other agents across the border, in the Netherlands or France, occasionally in Belgium or Switzerland. And over time he began to understand why Werner – his codename was Robert – was quite so effective.

'You know, Barnaby, I'd not realised how my whole life had in many ways been a perfect preparation for this role – it was as if I'd been trained for it without realising.'

It was a wet spring evening in 1938 and they were in the St Pauli district of Hamburg, on the upper floor of a cafe in an unlit side street between the Reeperbahn and the Elbe. They could hear the former and smell the latter.

St Pauli had retained some of its air of anarchy: in other times it would have felt dangerous and a place to avoid at night. Now that menace somehow made it feel safer. In the past few months Barney had found it easier to slip across the border from Denmark to Hamburg. He was even getting used to the city's low German dialect.

'What do you mean?'

'Once I became a teenager and then in my twenties... being a homosexual here in Germany wasn't a big problem as long as one was careful about it. Even though it was illegal – section 175 of the Civil Code, to be precise – it was more or less tolerated, more so than in many other countries in Europe. But since the Nazis took over things have become much worse; it was one of the reasons I left. The Nazis hate people who fail to conform to their view of society and since 1935 the sentence for homosexual activity has increased from six months in prison to five years and now they're starting to send homosexuals to these awful prison camps. The point I'm making, Barnaby, is that my whole life I've learnt to conceal an important part of it, to present a front, if you like, so people see me without realising what secrets I have. Working for you is an extension of this. People see me as a happy-go-lucky chap moving round Germany representing his family business and Holborn College, perfectly sociable and with no interest in politics. I'm a good listener, I don't get into arguments with people and I try not to draw attention to myself in any way.'

'Which all goes to explain why you're so effective, Werner.'

-

It was at their meeting in Hamburg in the spring of 1938 that Barney had told Werner that as well as he was doing, the view from London was that they needed him to move up a gear. Werner had looked at him confused and slightly hurt.

'What London means is that it is all very well recruiting middle-ranking or lower officials across Germany – not that one isn't very grateful, of course – but there's a limit as to how much intelligence we can get from these people.'

He'd looked up and saw how disappointed Werner looked. 'No reflection on you, good heavens, no – we're very grateful and it's all very useful – but what I think London means is that we need a higher grade of intelligence, probably the kind best found from within the higher echelons in Berlin.'

When he was giving difficult instructions, Barney did have a tendency to invoke 'London', which was partially true anyway but it was also a way of hinting it wasn't a view he entirely concurred with: an attempt to reassure Werner he was on his side. The two of them against London.

'When you say "higher echelons"…?'

'I mean senior Nazi Party officials, civil servants, military… diplomats… I appreciate that's easier said than done but maybe concentrate on Berlin for a while and see how you get on?'

Werner said fair enough – as long as it wasn't a reflection on how he'd done so far and Barney said absolutely not, this was simply reflecting how much more serious the situation had become.

'I mentioned diplomats, Werner: London also has a particular thing about countries who are likely to end up on the same side as Germany.'

'What does "a particular thing" mean, Barnaby?'

'It means they want to know more about them. At the moment it's all a bit unclear as far as the Foreign Office is concerned, they seem to change their minds every week and their country desks aren't always reliable. A bit like our embassies, they often go native and aren't as frank as they ought to be. We want to know more about Italy: Mussolini's obviously a natural ally of Hitler but every schoolboy can tell you that. We need to know more. There are rumours about a formal military pact between Italy and Germany. They've already got the Anti-Comintern Pact, of course, but anything you can pick up there.'

Werner nodded and said the Italian embassy was on Hildebrandstrasse opposite the Bendler Block, the Army headquarters, and Barney said thank you very much but he had in mind something better than an address and it was a moment or too before Werner realised that was meant as a joke and laughed.

'And there are the other countries that may pal up with Germany: Spain, Bulgaria, Romania – Hungary. Anything you can find on them would be most gratefully received. No need to give me their embassy addresses though! And then there's the country that worries us the most at Broadway: Japan.'

Barney paused and looked at Werner, who wondered whether he was to respond that yes, he had indeed heard of Japan.

'Very strong militarily, currently at war with China, big powerful navy, air force growing by the day, already an ally of Germany. But while we know they're on Germany's side we need more specific intelligence: we're not sure what their intentions are. Bloody hard to get anything out of Tokyo. Who knows, you may be able to pick up something in Berlin.'

Werner said it would be difficult and Barney said of course, he didn't for a moment imagine it would be easy, but it was an example of what he meant by higher-grade intelligence.

'One thought I've had, Werner, that may help you – who knows – is to join the Nazi Party.'

'Seriously? I thought you said I was to appear disinterested in politics.'

'I know, but there is a feeling that in the long run it may be a good idea: an insurance policy, if you like. No need to be active, going to meetings and all that, but perhaps if you joined sooner rather than later that could stand you in good stead.'

And Werner had indeed joined the Nazi Party. When they next met – in Berlin in January 1939 – he'd shown Barney his *Mitgliedskarte*, his party membership card, and said it had made some difference, actually; it seemed to open one or two more doors. It had given him a degree of confidence.

His *Mitgliedskarte* certainly came into its own in February 1939. Werner was concentrating his efforts on finding better contacts as requested by London, which was proving to be difficult and more than anything else was very hard work – out all the time meeting people, sticking to his cover story, trying to assess how important people were, how sympathetic they may be and how useful they would be in the unlikely event of them becoming a source of information.

He was still living in the apartment on Tauentzienstrasse but it was now more difficult to find a social life. The Saxon Klub on nearby Regensburger Strasse had been closed down by the Gestapo – it was surprising it had remained open as long as it had. But then he found a new bar through a most unlikely source. It was a late February Tuesday afternoon and he'd had lunch with the business manager of a college based in Moabit in the north-east of Berlin. She didn't seem terribly interested in the idea of a partnership with Holborn College, but she was happy to be taken out for lunch at the smart place Werner had suggested just north of the Unter den Linden, quite close to the Reichstag. Werner was cultivating her because her husband was a senior civil servant at the Finance Ministry and at the social event where they'd first met she'd rather unwisely let it be known he was someone who didn't approve of politics, which was code these days for saying he wasn't a Nazi.

That, of course, was still a long way from turning someone into a source but it was how one started. He suggested that maybe her husband would like to meet for dinner one evening – he was rather hoping she'd invite him to their home – but she was non-committal. After that he decided to walk back to his apartment, but it was one of those February afternoons when it was surprisingly light even at three o'clock so he decided to try his luck and walk through the Tiergarten and sure enough he'd not gone very far – off the main path and down a narrow track in the bushes near the lake – when he saw a tall young man leaning against a tree.

An unlit cigarette hung from his mouth and he was wearing a dark brown suit with a dark shirt and no tie – Werner worried he may be cold without a coat – and a long green scarf was draped over his shoulders and he appeared camouflaged against the tree. His eyes caught Werner's and he asked if he had a light and Werner said of course and as he held his lighter the man held his hand. He had dark blond hair with deep blue eyes and a face that looked almost delicate. They remained like that for a moment – the flame still licking from the lighter – and then it started to rain, one of those showers which very quickly goes from light to heavy. He said his name was Rudolf – Rudi – and Werner said he was Josef – Joe – and Rudi asked if Joe had a place nearby and Werner, who didn't like bringing anyone back to his place said unfortunately not so Rudi said he had a room in Neukölln and they could go there if Joe paid for a taxi.

Afterwards they stayed in the room in Neukölln for a while, which was a good job as Werner was quite exhausted. It was very comfortable – fully carpeted with its own small bathroom and perfectly warm and cosy. Rudi said he was from Lübeck but was now based in Berlin – he didn't say what he did – and his parents were paying for the room because they wanted him to be comfortable and they both laughed at the thought of his parents seeing just how comfortable he was now.

'Where do you go in the evenings, Joe?'

'I don't much these days – they've closed everywhere down. I used to go to the Saxon Klub on Regensburger Strasse.'

'There's a new place, but you need a recommendation.'

'Where is it?'

'In Schöneberg – on Reppich Strasse, between Belziger Strasse and Hauptstrasse. I could get you in.'

'What's it called?'

'It doesn't have a name.'

'What about the Gestapo, aren't they a problem?'

Rudi laughed sarcastically and suggested they meet the night after next and Joe would see what he meant.

'There's a cake shop on Reppich Strasse: meet me outside it at nine o'clock. I'll be coming from work.'

Werner said that sounded good. He'd look forward to it.

'One thing, Josef, as well as requiring a personal introduction the club is also very discerning.'

'Of course.'

'It doesn't want... how can I put it, undesirables.'

'I'm not sure what that means.'

'It means people who'd be regarded as a problem for the Reich. Are you a civil servant or an official anywhere... or do you have a Nazi Party card?'

'Of course I'm a Party member!'

'That is no problem then.'

–

The night after next was a Thursday and following a few almost spring-like days Berlin had settled back into its traditional bitterly cold weather. That evening an odd kind of mist had fallen over the city, an unpleasant and stifling mixture of dense, light rain and the ubiquitous coal fumes. As Werner walked down from

Tauentzienstrasse into Schöneberg the city was deathly quiet, the buildings looming out of a light brown haze as if cast in sepia. He'd noticed that since the turn of the year there were fewer people on the streets. Tonight, there were hardly any.

He arrived outside the cake shop on Reppich Strasse just before nine and waited for Rudi in the shelter of the doorway. He ought to have arrived earlier and walked round the block and checked the area, looking for alleyways and the connecting passageways that linked blocks and streets in this part of Berlin, but he was tired and cold and, in any case, he'd taken the view that this was his night off, even Barnaby would allow him that.

Despite the chill he was relaxed, looking forward to the evening and seeing what the club that didn't need a name was like and also looking forward to seeing Rudi again. He was younger than Werner was normally interested in but he did have a certain boyish charm. He'd keep him amused for a few weeks.

The silence of night was broken by sharp footsteps approaching from the direction of Hauptstrasse. The mist was low and quite dense so he didn't see the person until they were just a few feet in front of him and even then, it was hard to make out anything other than a tall figure in black.

When he realised the black was the uniform of the SS he felt himself sway and he gripped the wall next to him.

'Follow mc.'

He looked round and was as sure as he could be there was only one of them, which seemed unusual but it was still the SS and they were telling him to come with them and for the life of him he couldn't think what mistake he'd made or who'd informed on him and how could he get a message to Barnaby that he was very sorry but he'd been arrested by the SS?

The man was still a few feet away from him and now sounded impatient.

'Come on now!'

Chapter 11

Werner turned towards the man in the black uniform. The white runic flashes on the lapel just stood out in the gloom but little else. For a moment or two he pondered making a run for it. It was dark, visibility was no more than a few feet and he knew the area. But even though he was quick he doubted he was quicker than the man in uniform and he certainly didn't fancy seeing whether the Luger semi-automatic pistol was as lethal as the newspapers claimed it was.

'Are you coming?' The tall man moved even closer. 'What on earth's the matter, Joe – you look terrified?'

A moment's silence. Werner's breathing seemed to fill the street.

'Rudi, my God, is that you?'

'Who else had you arranged to meet outside a cake shop on Reppich Strasse at nine o'clock on a Thursday night? Come, let's go. Have you got your *Mitgliedskarte* with you?'

'I didn't know you were in the SS.'

'You didn't ask, Joe. I was off duty the day we met.'

'I know, but it would never occur to me that you—'

'That I what… that I like men and am in the SS? You sound naive, Joe. This is Berlin, where you can get away with anything as long as you're on the right side.'

'I don't understand, Rudi, I—'

'I've just been commissioned as an Untersturmführer – that's a lieutenant – and now I'm based at the SS headquarters on Prinz-Albrecht-Strasse for a few months. After that I'll return to Lübeck and hopefully get command of my own unit. I'll marry Else and I imagine we'll keep the Aryan race going, but in the meantime… I can have some fun.'

'And being in the SS, it's not a problem here?'

'It adds to my appeal, Joe.'

–

The club was on the top floor: narrow with a series of dimly lit corridors with rooms off them, most with their doors closed. Rudi had told Werner to wait at the entrance while he spoke with the man behind the desk who then beckoned him forward, holding out his hand for the entrance fee: it appeared he was paying for Rudi too.

It was only as Werner showed him his *Mitgliedskarte* that he realised the card was in his real name, Werner Lustenberger. Rudi knew him as Josef. He glanced at Rudi but he seemed to be paying no attention, but as they turned from one corridor into another and towards what looked like a bar area the SS man turned round.

'So you're real name is Werner something?'

'Sometimes I use the name Josef.'

The younger man laughed and leaned over conspiratorially. 'And sometimes I use the name Rudi!'

–

A dozen men milled around the bar, a few in uniform but mostly men on their own watching the room like hawks, moving furtively around the perimeter and occasionally approaching another man. Once paired up the couples disappeared into the corridor.

Rudi brought him a drink and said he'd seen someone he knew and he was sure Werner – he pronounced Werner very deliberately – would understand and perhaps he'd see him later.

Werner moved to the far end of the room and sat at a small round table. There was something about the place he didn't like: the club with no name had a furtive atmosphere, a distinct air of menace. The uniforms didn't add to its appeal and he was uneasy that Rudi – whose name wasn't Rudi – now knew he was Werner and he doubted he'd have much trouble in discovering his full name and address.

Nonetheless, Rudi had told him he was an officer at the SS headquarters. The information he could get from him could be priceless. He needed to think of the best approach. He looked up as a short figure slipped into the chair opposite him. It took him a moment or two to realise in the low light but the man was clearly foreign, possibly oriental.

'May I ask if anyone is occupying this seat?'

'No, please – you may sit here.'

'It is just that I saw you enter with a friend and I observed him buying you a drink.'

He'd been watching. He spoke impeccable German, in a slow and deliberate manner and with the formal touch often used by foreigners.

'Yes, a friend, but you know… it seems I'm not his only friend here!' Werner laughed but the other man nodded as if grateful for the information but perhaps feeling awkward that he'd pried. The man lit a cigarette and then looked up, addressing Werner through the anonymity afforded by the smoke.

'Have you been here before?'

'No, this is my first time. And you?'

The man shrugged. 'My second time. I visit many places through my work. Does your work bring you to a place like this?'

Werner wasn't sure how to reply to a question like that: whose work brought them to a place like this – unless they were in the Gestapo, which this man plainly wasn't.

'No, I'm just here… socially. Where do you work that it brings you here?'

Werner was intrigued by the man: nothing in his manner suggested he was interested in him; indeed, he edged his chair slightly further away. He was talking to him but avoiding eye contact.

'I work on Graf Spree Strasse, just off Tiergartenstrasse. Do you know it?'

'I do, yes. You work in the Japanese embassy there?'

'How did you guess?'

Werner moved so he could see the man's face more clearly. 'Graf Spree Strasse isn't a very long street with three embassies on it and, with respect, you don't look like you work at either the French or Italian ones.'

Werner laughed and was relieved when the man joined in. Werner leaned over and offered his hand, which the other man grasped quite firmly and then the man bowed his head as he shook Werner's hand for a while longer than he needed to.

'My name is Werner, Werner Lustenberger. I'm a businessman.'

'Tadashi Kimura: I am the second secretary at the Japanese embassy.' He was still shaking Werner's hand.

Werner smiled and thought of what Barnaby had told him a few months before.

Bloody hard to get anything out of Tokyo. Who knows, you may be able to pick up something in Berlin.

'You do understand what kind of club this is?'

The diplomat nodded. *Of course.*

'And your work brings you here?'

'It is important I'm familiar with all aspects of German life.' He watched for a reaction from Werner and then winked. 'Yes, of course I know. I was based here from 1931 to 1934 as a naval attaché, I used to be an officer in the Imperial Japanese Navy. I found this aspect of life in Berlin to be most... how can I say, most refreshing, quite unlike anything I'd ever experienced or imagined in Japan. I returned to Japan and joined our diplomatic service and last year I was posted back here: I was very pleased to return to Berlin. The Japanese government values its relationship with the German government very highly and the fact I learnt German during my first spell here was seen as a big advantage.'

The two men talked for an hour. The diplomat said he was impressed Werner could pronounce his first name and Werner said 'Tadashi' wasn't difficult.

'You'll be surprised: most people here assume any non-European name is unpronounceable. You seem to be – how can I put it? You seem to be a very... open-minded person?'

'Because I'm in a place like this?'

'No, not just that – but the way you talk, Werner. You've travelled, you don't seem to have a problem with me being so obviously foreign – you talk with me as if you're interested in me rather than treat me as an object of curiosity.'

As they talked Werner was thinking about Barnaby's echelons and how high a Japanese diplomat would come in them. Quite high, he thought. Maybe he'd be in line for a bonus.

'I come here for company, Werner, to meet people and relax. Japanese society is very formal and you're expected to be very conformist and within our diplomatic community here in Berlin it is a very narrow life, that's how I'd describe it. It can be quite suffocating.'

'Have you met anyone at the clubs, Tadashi?'

His companion watched him through a haze of smoke and said nothing for a while. 'I'm married, you know, Werner.'

'You hardly look old enough.'

'Thank you, but I was forty a few weeks ago, can you believe! It was easy enough to avoid being married while I was in the Imperial Navy but when I joined the Diplomatic Service it was suggested I marry and that was the wish of my family too, so I married a woman in 1936.'

'And do you have children?'

Tadashi shook his head vigorously.

'Is she here with you in Berlin?'

'No, no... it is not expected that the wife of a second secretary would accompany her husband. My wife remains in Kyoto: her father was an important official and she helps look after her elderly mother.'

'You must be quite lonely, Tadashi.'

Another pause, another cigarette – the lighting of it an intricate ceremony. 'Not as lonely as you may think, Werner.'

They carried on talking, Werner giving away as little as possible – he was a businessman, it was very uninteresting, no he wasn't married, he travelled a lot and wasn't interested in politics – all the time trying to work out Tadashi. He was unsure of how genuine he was and he found it hard to read him. He knew that the description he'd so often seen of Japanese people being inscrutable was probably a prejudiced one, but there was no doubt Tadashi gave little away.

But the Japanese were getting very close to the Germans, their ambassador, Hiroshi Ōshima, was regarded as one of the most powerful diplomats in the city: he was close to von Ribbentrop and had Hitler's ear too. And Barnaby had specifically asked him to get intelligence on Japan.

'Did you hear me, Werner?'

'I beg your pardon?'

'I don't think you heard what I said.'

'I'm sorry, Tadashi, I missed it.'

'I said I like that you're more… sympathetic than other Germans.'

Werner replied that he liked to think he was open-minded and he also enjoyed meeting different people and then said something about being a loyal German. Tadashi replied that it was getting late and he had an early meeting at the embassy but he would very much like to meet Werner again and how about this coming Sunday?

–

The Japanese diplomat had slipped away from the club soon after that – Werner had gone to the bar, to the toilet and when he returned the table was empty so he decided to leave. He was on Reppich Strasse heading towards Belziger Strasse when he heard footsteps closing in on him and before he could turn round felt a heavy slap on his shoulder.

'Running away, Werner?'

'I'm going home, Rudi, I'm tired.'

'Do you live near here?'

Werner reflected how exhausting it was having to be so alert, having to be careful about any slip. Now he'd made the error of mentioning his home and it was the very last place he wanted to take the SS officer to.

'No, Rudi, it's not near here and in any case I live with my mother and—'

'Ah, your mother! There's always a bloody mother. Fortunately my bloody mother's in Lübeck. Come, we'll go back to my place.'

It was an order rather than a suggestion, but Werner was happy enough to go along with it: he'd decided he'd need to cultivate Rudi as a source and now seemed as good a time as any to start.

They found a taxi to take them to Neukölln, the young SS officer spending the journey complaining loudly that the damned Jews had forced up taxi fares, which Werner realised made no sense because Jews weren't permitted to use taxis, but he allowed an occasional grunt in agreement and when they arrived outside Rudi's apartment a clearly nervous driver refused to take any money, insisting it was his way of serving the Reich.

Rudi was clearly drunk and once they were in his room, he insisted they finish a bottle of schnapps and then he went into the bathroom. Werner undressed and climbed into the bed: when Rudi came out of the bathroom he asked Werner if he minded if he continued to wear his uniform and at that moment Werner would have gladly been anywhere else but managed to make what he hoped sounded like a non-aggressive suggestion that perhaps Rudi would at least undo his holster and leave his pistol on the side in case there was an accident, which he did, though with a degree of reluctance.

He kept his boots on though and when they'd finished, he lay next to Werner in a state of undress as they both smoked and Werner hoped Rudi wouldn't spot his hands were shaking.

'You said you work at Prinz-Albrecht-Strasse?'

The SS man nodded.

'A friend of my family works there – Hans Schmidt, do you know him?'

'For heaven's sake, Werner, do you know how many people work at Prinz-Albrecht-Strasse – and with a name like Schmidt?'

'He's a major, if that helps.'

'You mean a Sturmbannführer: that hardly narrows it down. Which department is he in?'

'I don't know – I could get my mother to ask his mother and—'

'Don't bother. Are you cold? You seem to be shaking.'

Werner replied that he was a bit chilly and pulled the covers over him and Rudi drank some more schnapps, this time straight from the bottle. He blew smoke from his cigarette into the bottle and watched in fascination as it swirled around and turned the remaining schnapps cloudy.

'Which department do you work in, Rudi?'

'It's very boring.'

'I'm sure it's very important.'

'Why do you want to know?'

'Because I'm impressed, Rudi, I feel I ought to have done something for the Reich and I admire the work people like you do.'

'It is boring but of course it is important. I'm part of the Waffen-SS, which is its military branch as you know and you wouldn't believe how quickly we're recruiting at the moment. I work in the office that is creating a structure for all these soldiers as they're allocated to existing divisions and then we're creating new divisions and deciding where they're based and of course all the time we have to make sure the fucking British and the fucking French think we're just boy scouts and… Christ, Werner, are you really interested in this?'

'I'm impressed, Rudi, you must be important.' He leaned against him, the uniform coarse against his bare skin.

'It certainly keeps me busy. Look…' He pointed to a tan briefcase on the floor. 'Full of work I have to bring home. At this rate I'll never get back to Lübeck. Else will have to wait, eh?'

–

The diplomat had been precise with his instructions.

Do you know Lessingbrücke – the bridge over the Spree?

Of course.

And may I ask, do you go to church on a Sunday?

No.

Very well: let's meet on Holsteiner Ufer close to the bridge at 10.30. We will then stroll across and head towards Kleiner Tiergarten. Let us hope the weather is agreeable!

It was a sunny morning – cold but not one that could be described as crisp because there was a dampness in the air, especially by the river. Barnaby would have been pleased with the precautions Werner had taken. At ten o'clock that morning he'd crossed to the north bank of the Spree on the next bridge – the Moabiter – and watched Holsteiner Ufer from there. It all seemed clear to him and when Tadashi appeared just before 10.25, he was on his own and no one appeared to be following him. Werner hurried back across the Moabiter and only just regained his breath by the time the two men met, five minutes late.

They shook hands, Tadashi again holding the grip and bowing his head. It was a fine morning; they would be able to have a good walk. Most of the conversation revolved around Tadashi trying to find out about Werner. Where did he live, where was he from, what kind of business was he involved in?

Werner had no problem answering the questions. Most of his story – his legend as Barnaby insisted on calling it, which made him sound like a medieval knight – was based on his real life. He spoke of his love of horse racing and his job, which was to represent the business interests of an English college in Germany.

'So you speak English?'

Werner said he did and French too.

'And have you been to England?'

Werner nodded. They were entering the Kleiner Tiergarten but it was quiet, most families would still be at church.

'I have much respect and admiration for Britain: when I was with the Imperial Royal Navy and then when I was based here as a naval attaché, I had many dealings with the Royal Navy. The links between the two navies were traditionally very strong, but now of course... but I visited England three times and loved it: a very civilised country.'

Werner didn't reply. He wasn't sure what point Tadashi was making, if indeed he was making one. He appeared to be reminiscing more than anything else.

Let the other person talk as much as possible, Werner: try not to ask leading questions; be subtle, nudge them once in a while.

So Werner said how much he loved London and Tadashi said he'd had a very wonderful time in London in 1932 and he'd been to Portsmouth too, did Werner know it and Werner said he only knew places in Britain if they had a racecourse.

They'd found a quiet spot with a dry bench and the two men sat with neither saying anything for a while. Werner had noticed how comfortable Tadashi seemed with silence. It didn't feel as if the air needed to be filled with conversation. When he finally started to speak he hesitated and moved his hands in front of him as if they'd help him form the right words. 'The other night, Werner – in the club. Do you remember you said that I must be quite lonely?'

'I hope you don't think I was being rude, Tadashi, it just seemed to me—'

'I'm not lonely, Werner. That's the point. It's why I wanted to see you today.'

'I'm not sure I understand, I—'

'Are you busy today?'

'Well, not especially, no... it's Sunday.'

'Could I ask you to accompany me to my apartment? It's not far from here – and there's someone I'd like to introduce you to, Werner.'

Chapter 12

Berlin
February 1939

At the same time as Werner met the Japanese diplomat on Holsteiner Ufer, Sophia von Naundorf was flirting with danger elsewhere in Berlin.

Since her friend Esther had fled Germany with her family the previous year there'd been an enormous void in her life. No longer did she have a shoulder to cry on and no longer could she listen to her friend's wise advice.

Life with Karl-Heinrich became increasingly intolerable and Sophia felt trapped. She often found herself thinking of the Englishman called Edward, who she'd first met in 1936. He'd said he'd like to keep in touch and had been as good as his word. Every so often – once or twice a year – he'd telephoned her and said he happened to be in Berlin and perhaps they could meet for coffee? And each time she felt her body quiver with a mixture of excitement and fear, because although she couldn't put her finger on it, there was something illicit about this Englishman. She sensed that once she met him there'd be no going back. She'd reply that now wasn't a good time, but perhaps soon. She was now regretting not meeting with him.

That Sunday in February Sophia was travelling to Wedding to visit her father, which she did every Sunday when her husband wasn't in Berlin.

But this visit had a clandestine edge to it.

The previous Sunday she'd been returning to her car after visiting her father when she'd heard her name called from the dark end of an alley on Malplaquetstrasse.

Sophia!

It was a man's voice and he moved forward far enough for her to see his face before returning to the shadows and beckoning her to follow him.

It was Kurt, who'd lived in the same street as her when they were children and with whom she'd been good friends. It was years since she'd seen him.

'I need your help, Sophia.' He held both her hands with his as he talked urgently.

'I became mixed up with politics: if the Gestapo catch me, I'll end up in one of those prison camps. I'm terrified Sophia. I need to get out of Berlin: I have friends in Denmark.'

He told her that although his family had left the area he'd been hiding in the basement of a friend's house, from where he'd spotted her visiting her father the previous Sunday. Now he had a plan.

'That Mercedes of yours: I could hide in the boot and you could you drive me out of Berlin?'

'Where to Kurt?'

'As close to the Danish border as possible. Maybe to Flensburg?'

She shook her head and said that was too far. They started to negotiate. She suggested Oranienburg and Kurt shook his head.

'That's hardly leaving Berlin Sophia. How about Schwerin?'

'That's still too far Kurt. It would need to be somewhere closer, so I can be back in Berlin before dark.'

They settled on Perleberg, a hundred miles north of Berlin.

That Sunday she visited her father earlier than usual and left after just half an hour, telling him she felt unwell. She stopped by the alley on Malplaquetstrasse long enough for Kurt to climb into the boot and they were in Perleberg by noon. She left him by a bus stop outside the town.

She drove straight back to Berlin, anxious to be in the city before nightfall. She was terrified, angry with herself for being talked into something so reckless. But by the time Berlin came into view she realised she hadn't been followed and gradually her feeling of fear was replaced by a sense of exhilaration.

Perhaps she wasn't trapped after all.

–

They walked in silence, back across the Lessingbrücke onto Lessingstrasse and Werner noticed how Tadashi altered their pace, crossed the road, and glanced behind them. On one occasion he stopped to light a cigarette, allowing a man who'd been walking behind them to pass. At the junction with Flensburger Strasse he paused, as if uncertain which way to go, before turning left and hurrying along to the end of the road. Wherever they were going, they were taking a roundabout route to get there.

Just before Bellevue U-Bahn station they turned right onto Brücken Allee, a very pleasant residential avenue, with smart detached houses on one side and on the other – the one backing onto Schloss Park – Bauhaus-style apartment blocks set back from the road with well-tended front gardens behind stylish wrought iron railings.

Tadashi opened a side gate, which took them down the side of one of the apartment blocks to a doorway at the rear. They climbed to the fourth floor where Tadashi paused outside the door of an apartment.

'I'm very fortunate – just four apartments in this block use the side entrance: this is very private.'

The door opened into a large room, a window to their left opening onto a balcony and beyond that the park. In the middle of the room was a dining area and at the other end – with a window looking out over the street – was a comfortable lounge.

'Wait, I'll be one minute.'

Moments later he returned, but not alone. A nervous-looking young man was at his shoulder, his eyes anxiously sizing up

Werner. He was European, with black hair and dark eyes. The two of them sat down close together opposite Werner.

'In the park, Werner – when I told you I'm not lonely and that's why I wanted to see you – I may have sounded somewhat… cryptic – is that the right word?'

Tadashi patted the knee of the young man who then moved closer to him. Tadashi's hand stayed on his knee.

'This is Arno – he's the reason why I'm not lonely.'

He nodded at Werner and said nothing and Werner sensed it was the start of another long silence. The young man watched Werner carefully, almost suspiciously.

Werner was about to say he was very pleased that Tadashi wasn't lonely and it was a pleasure to meet Arno, but he'd started to get the measure of these periods of silence and they were clearly to be respected.

Eventually Tadashi muttered something to Arno who left the room. Tadashi lit another cigarette and when Arno returned, he was carrying a tray of tea. Once he'd poured them each a cup he leaned forward and spoke: there was a hint of Berlin to his accent, but it was more of a refined accent than anything else. He spoke in a soft voice and Werner had to lean forward to catch all he was saying.

'My name is Arno Marcus and I am twenty-five years old.' He paused and gestured to Tadashi who handed him his own half-smoked cigarette.

'I met Tadashi last June, was it?'

'It was the fourteenth June, Arno, a few weeks after I returned to Berlin. We met in one of those clubs, not the one we were in the other night!'

'I am Jewish, from Berlin, and I was a medical student until I was thrown out of Charité Medical School three years ago along with all the other Jewish students. I should have left Germany then but I hesitated – like a fool I thought they may let medical students at least back into university, God knows what possessed me to imagine that. In late 1937 my mother died – she'd been ill for many years – and I felt I couldn't leave my father alone and by the middle of 1938 it was becoming increasingly difficult for Jews to leave. I mean… it was possible to get out but you needed to have the correct papers and money and somewhere to go.

'Then last May I got into trouble. Jews are required to have special identity cards with the letter "J" stamped on it to indicate the religion, it's on our passports too. I met a man who was recommended by someone I knew, who in return for an outrageous amount of money promised to prepare a completely new identity for me, that of a non-Jewish person. My plan was to use it to smuggle my father to Amsterdam where we have family and from there I'd go to England: it's my dream to go there. I speak English and hoped I could resume my medical studies – one of our Jewish professors at the Charité had found a post at a place called Leeds and I had his details. I don't know exactly what happened – whether the man producing the documents was betrayed or whether he'd conned me – but the upshot is that the Gestapo found out about me. They turned up at my father's house and fortunately I was out. I had to go on the run: the Gestapo were now searching for Arno Marcus and my new identity was worse than worthless, it was a liability.'

'What happened to your father?'

'He was arrested, beaten up and then released. The following day he killed himself.' Arno talked in a very matter-of-fact way.

'I stayed at friends' houses – never more than two nights at a time – anywhere I could find. I thought about escaping from Berlin but it felt too risky, I kept thinking I'd give it another week… then another week… then I met Tadashi in a club in Pankow, a real dive of a place actually, but places like that could be useful: if I was lucky I'd find a man who'd pay me to spend the night with him, maybe two, and… that's how we met.'

'I assure you I didn't pay Arno to spend the night with me; I'd heard on the grapevine about this place that had opened in a basement in Pankow and I thought I'd try it, but as soon as I went in I regretted it because it was not my kind of place at all, quite unpleasant and it felt threatening and people muttered nasty things to me as I walked past. I was about to leave when I saw Arno pushed up against a wall by a huge man who was pawing him and so I went up and we pretended we knew each other and… here we are!'

'It wasn't as straightforward as that, of course. I couldn't tell Tadashi who I really was but I did tell him I had nowhere to go and hadn't eaten for two days and he said I could come here. He was very proper: I slept on this sofa and it was only a few days later that we…'

'Became more than friends I think is how you'd say it, Arno. He was very distrusting, Werner – I think you can see that – and who can blame him? But I realised he was a fugitive and it wasn't too hard to guess that he's Jewish.'

'So you've been here since the middle of last June, Arno?'

Arno nodded. 'Eight months.'

'And no one knows?'

'No one needs to know. I hardly ever have visitors: if I entertain people, I do so at a restaurant. I have a cleaner who comes in twice a week and I tell her I keep my study locked because of embassy business. So, for two hours on a Monday and a Thursday Arno stays in the study.'

'It's nearer two and a half hours, actually, but it's fine. As you will have seen, this apartment more or less has a private entrance, though the staircase is shared with the three other flats on that side of the block. If someone ever tried to enter when Tadashi is out I'd have time to hide in the wardrobe in the main bedroom, but that's never happened before. It's a perfect place to stay.'

'But being in here all this time – how do you cope?'

'Tadashi works long hours and, in the winter, when it was dark it was hard, but Tadashi managed to get hold of a lot of second-hand medical textbooks and English language books for me – I study very hard: it's not quite the same as being at university, but I think in the last six months I've covered well over a year's theory. My anatomy is now excellent!'

'Your anatomy is indeed excellent, Arno!'

Their laughter subsided into another long silence. The sun streamed in from the large window and in the distance a dog barked.

'Arno is safe here as long as he doesn't leave, and remember, I'm a diplomat so even the Gestapo would think twice about bursting in. This apartment is in many ways ideal, but I do sometimes wonder if we're riding our luck. It's very quiet, and people don't hear him and people can't see in from the street but...'

Another silence and Werner became aware of tension between the two men.

'But what happened the other week is my fault, Werner; I know that and I take full responsibility. Once or twice a week I go out for a walk for just thirty minutes, usually at dusk: if I didn't, I'd go mad. I pause at the top of the stairs and if I hear no sound, I hurry out. Last Tuesday I was leaving when I bumped into a Frau Sauer who lives in the apartment on this side on the second floor. It was awkward because we came face to face and she said good evening so I had to reply. I was a bit shaken by that so I stayed out longer than I usually do...'

'...you can say that again: in fact I was so worried I went out to look for him and...'

'...I was coming back into the block just as Werner was coming out so we literally bumped into each other. He asked me where the hell I'd been and...'

'...I didn't say it like that, Arno, I—'

'Actually, you did, Tadashi, I'm not making this up – but we exchanged words in a harsh manner and were still doing so as we climbed the stairs. When we passed Frau Sauer's door she was standing in her open doorway and clearly saw us together.'

'Whether she was waiting there or heard something I don't know but she certainly saw us and said "good evening" in an unfriendly way and of course we replied and she then watched us and we had no alternative but to carry on upstairs.'

'And has anything happened since?'

'No, but it's still been a worry – it shows us that we're on... what was the phrase you used the other day, Arno?'

'Thin ice.'

'It shows us what thin ice we're on. Clearly Arno can't stay here. He needs to escape.'

'I'm a Jew in Berlin, Werner, which is dangerous enough, but on top of that I'm also a fugitive: I'm damned if I stay here and I'm damned if I try to leave.' He was looking down at the ornate rug between them. 'Tadashi relies on his instinct a lot and he tells me he instinctively trusts you. But I don't – I don't distrust you either, it's just that I don't know you well enough to say I trust you but Tadashi insists we should seek your help and after all he's the important diplomat and I'm only a student and we're...'

'...desperate, Werner, we're desperate.'

The familiar silence returned and Werner understood exactly what it was about. 'I'd like to do what I can to help. Can you give me a week or two?'

–

Werner had arranged to return to Rudi's on the following Saturday, 25 February. The SS officer said he'd be working there on papers all weekend so his visit would be a welcome diversion.

Werner prepared carefully for the evening. He knew a store on Zimmerstrasse where they sold *palinka*, the Hungarian version of schnapps, which tasted more or less the same but was far stronger. He decanted it into an empty bottle of German schnapps – one from Bavaria, which he counted on Rudi being less familiar with.

From under his floorboards he removed one of the metal boxes hidden there: inside was a bundle wrapped in a small towel that contained a cardboard box and within that was a tiny camera, which Barnaby had brought to Berlin about a year after Werner started working for the British.

'It's a Minox Riga, Werner: best little camera in the world by a long chalk, no competition. Clear this table and I'll show you how it works.'

It was an extraordinary piece of equipment, excellent for photographing documents and easily concealed. The strips of film each contained fifty frames and were around a quarter of the size of 35-millimetre film. It also came with a set of four legs which screwed in to make it easier to photograph documents, but Werner found them too fiddly and avoided using them.

The final ingredient of his plan required meticulous attention to detail – not too much, certainly not too little, and even then he couldn't be sure. Its effectiveness would depend on luck as much as anything else and that was a big risk, but one he had to take.

He arrived at the apartment in Neukölln just before nine o'clock. Rudi said he'd been working all day – he pointed to the table covered with papers – and was exhausted. Now he wanted to relax: he'd have a drink and then he'd be ready. Werner produced the bottle of schnapps and poured them each a large glass and Rudi said it was good, a slightly fruitier taste than he was used to and Werner said it was Bavarian and Rudi said he approved and yes, of course he'd have more!

By eleven o'clock Werner himself was exhausted, amazed by Rudi's stamina. He'd been drinking far more than Werner but only now was beginning to flag. Werner suggested maybe he should have a bath and offered to run it for him. Rudi seemed happy to go along with that.

He knew he needed to move fast once Rudi got into the bath, not knowing whether Rudi was someone who got into the bath and then out within a matter of minutes or whether he'd stay longer. He removed the vial from his jacket pocket and slipped it into a full glass of the schnapps.

He'd prepared the chloral hydrate the previous night, carefully crushing the tablet into a fine powder and was relieved to find it didn't markedly affect the taste or appearance of the schnapps or create any noticeable residue in the glass. He stirred it vigorously and did so twice more before Rudi emerged from the bathroom, naked and still wet and saying he wanted to go straight to bed.

'Let's have a drink first.'

'After.'

'One before and one after!'

He knocked the drink back. Werner reckoned it would take around thirty minutes for the sleeping draught to work: he'd given him quite a high dose, but not so high that he'd be suspicious when he eventually woke up.

The effect was quicker than Werner had anticipated. Rudi was unable to perform and became irritable, saying he didn't know what the matter was with him and it was Werner's fault and Werner said he should relax and have another drink and within ten minutes Rudi was fast asleep, snoring loudly.

He moved quickly. He stared at the table for a while, memorising which papers were where so Rudi wouldn't notice they'd been moved. He searched through the documents: there were about a dozen of them, all appeared to be drafts on which notes or corrections had been made by hand. Some seemed to be incomplete or of little interest – one was something to do with the manufacture of uniforms. It became clear Rudi's real name was Harald Fuchs and he was indeed an Untersturmführer. That was useful to know, it would help verify the material.

He selected two documents: one ran to twenty-three pages and was marked 'For the attention of General von Brauchitsch' who Werner knew was the head of the OKH, the High Command of the German Army, so he put that to one side. The other document he selected was a longer one and appeared to be a directory of sorts, densely typed lists of names and ranks with what seemed to be their military units alongside most of them. Heinrich Himmler's name was on the front page. He was the head of the SS: Werner decided he'd photograph this document too.

Photographing the two documents proved to be a nerve-wracking job and far more time consuming than Werner had anticipated. Every few minutes he went over to check Rudi then returned to put a new page in position, use an ink bottle to hold it in place, angle the lamp to ensure there was optimum light on the sheet, take the photo, move to the next exposure, position the next page, check Rudi…

The directory turned out to be thirty pages long, but the text was on both sides of the page so in total he had to photograph over eighty pages. When he finished it was one in the morning and he was about to select another document when Rudi stirred.

He'd moved the Luger semi-automatic to the table and reached over for it as he turned to look at the young SS officer. He was still asleep but had turned over and his nose appeared to twitch and Werner decided he couldn't risk another photograph. It took him fifteen minutes to get everything back in its place.

He hardly slept that night. At eight o'clock Rudi work up, announcing he had a terrible headache. 'That schnapps must have been strong, Werner – but it is good!'

Werner said he really ought to leave.

'I'd normally persuade you to stay, but look at the table there – I have so much work to do! I'm going to make a strong coffee and get on with it.'

He asked Werner if he'd see him soon and the British spy said he very much hoped so. It had been such an enjoyable visit!

–

'Are you sure this isn't too good to be true, Werner?'

'I seem to recall that you once told me, Barnaby, that just because something appears to be too good to be true doesn't mean it isn't.'

'I suspect something may have been lost in translation there, Werner.'

It was a Monday, 27 February – just over a week after Werner had met Arno – and now he was in Cologne, in the office of a lawyer who was one of Werner's sources. He was trustworthy and it was a safe place to meet: Barney could take the train from Brussels and return the same day. Barney's back was to the window with the enormous Gothic expanse of the cathedral behind him.

'Tadashi Kimura is indeed the second secretary at the Japanese embassy on Graf Spree Strasse, I was able to check that out,' said Werner. 'He is also listed as being a resident at the apartment on Brücken Allee. I also looked into Arno Marcus – that was more difficult, to be honest, I felt I was exposing myself more enquiring about a Jewish fugitive, but I did find an old telephone directory that showed a family called Marcus living in Wilmersdorf, in the same street he told me they lived. I also checked at Charité Medical School and there was a student there called A Marcus who had to leave in 1936 along with the other Jewish students.'

'I think one accepts they're genuine, Werner. I also asked our chap who liaises with the Royal Navy and they're seeing whether they have any record of him, but he did say that up until a few years ago the links between our navy and the Japanese one were indeed very close. If we assume this is a genuine approach and we're not being set up then this would seem to be a perfect opportunity to recruit Tadashi.'

'Without him knowing, Barnaby?'

'I think this is going to be one of those occasions, Werner, where you can afford to be explicit with him. He's desperate for Arno to escape from Berlin. You should promise not to only get Arno out of Berlin but also ensure he gets to England and is looked after there – and in return we want Tadashi to supply us with intelligence. You said he was pro-British anyway, didn't you?'

'He said something along the lines of admiring and respecting Britain, whether that—'

'How tricky will it be to get Arno out of Berlin?'

'Depends where to, Barnaby.'

'France would be my suggestion: the Germans are very strict about their Swiss and Dutch borders these days. Get him into France and I'll take over from there. Go back and talk to them. But we'll want something from him first, some intelligence to know he's genuine.'

Werner said fair enough, he'd get on with it and he was thinking he'd definitely need to find some kind of fake identity for Arno and what with the cost of smuggling him out of Germany...

'How much? In pounds, shillings and pence, please, Werner.'

'The equivalent to twenty-five pounds, I would say, perhaps even thirty pounds.'

'As much as that?'

'I think you'll find it's good value for money.'

'Let's hope so – and in your message you said something about having a surprise for me?'

Werner removed his jacket and with a penknife unpicked the material lining the inside pocket. A moment later he removed a small envelope and when he opened it he took out a cardboard sleeve and ceremoniously pushed it towards Barnaby, telling him to be very careful with it.

'What is it, Werner?'

'Your surprise, Barnaby.'

'Please, Werner, I'm not—'

'Two strips of film, Barnaby. I suggest you get them developed as soon as you're back in London. I think you'll find them most interesting!'

–

The following day – the last one of February – was a Tuesday and Werner waited across the road from the apartment block on Brücken Allee until he saw Tadashi approach it at a shade after seven in the evening. He hurried across the road and caught up with him as he opened the side door to the block.

Tadashi appeared calm and beckoned for Werner to follow him upstairs. Five minutes later the three of them were sitting in the lounge as they had done some ten days before.

'Tell me, Werner, are you able to help Arno?'

It was Werner's turn to hesitate and he was silent for a while as he pondered the best approach. He'd have preferred to speak with Tadashi alone, but he hadn't been able to think of a way of doing this other than approaching him on the street, which didn't feel right.

'Can I ask you a question first, Tadashi?'

'Of course.'

'At the club, when we first met… how come you confided in me? I don't understand why you approached me.'

'I've already told you, we're desperate and I didn't know where else to go – because I stand out, I have to be careful. These clubs – because they're illicit – somehow, they feel the kind of places where I could find someone who may be able to help. You came across as a... sympathetic kind of person, even though I knew nothing about you.'

Werner glanced at Arno. He still viewed Werner suspiciously but now more than anything else he looked nervous, even frightened. His right foot was tapping on the floor and he twisted his signet ring round his finger.

'I can help you: I can get Arno out of Berlin and away from Germany. My plan would be to smuggle you into France and from there I know people who can get you to England – that's where you wanted to go?'

'More than anywhere else, yes... but in England – would I also be a fugitive there?'

'No, you'd be treated as a legitimate refugee and be given proper papers. You should even be able to resume your medical studies.'

Arno's head dropped and his shoulders heaved. During the now familiar silence Werner could just make out the sound of the young man sobbing.

'You would really do all this, Werner?'

'Yes – but I would want something in return, Tadashi.'

'Don't worry, Werner, I have money, that wouldn't be a problem.'

'I don't want money, Tadashi. I want information from you, from the embassy – information that the British government would be interested in. The people I know who would get Arno from France to England and who'll look after him there, they would do all this in return for information – once they know it's genuine.'

'Secret information?'

Werner nodded and the silence that followed was charged with tension. Arno – his eyes filled with tears – looked anxiously at

Tadashi who for the first time since Werner had met him seemed unsettled.

'You want me to pass secrets to you?'

'Yes.'

'For the British – do you understand what you're asking me to do?'

'I do, Tadashi, and in return I'll get Arno to safety. Isn't that a price worth paying?'

'But if I get caught I—'

'But you won't get caught, Tadashi. I know what I'm doing. I've been doing it for three years now. You pass on copies of a couple of documents to me and a few days later Arno will be in England.'

'What kind of documents, Werner?'

'Your job, Tadashi, what areas do you cover?'

'Mostly relations with the German Foreign Ministry, because of my ability to speak German I mainly work on agreements between the Japanese government and the German government.'

'So you have copies of agreements between the governments?'

'Of course.'

'And how easy is it to obtain copies of these?'

'It is possible, but it could take time. If I'm very careful I could copy a document one evening when I work late and bring it home and then another one the next night, but I can only do this when I'm certain no one else is around – I share my office with two other second secretaries and if I'm caught... Is there really no other way, Werner?'

'When you leave – are you searched?'

'Sometimes – I'd also need to choose a night when security is lighter.'

During the long silence Werner barely breathed as he waited for Tadashi to give his answer, but when he looked at Arno and noticed him smile for the first time, he knew the young man had already sensed what the answer would be.

'I don't have any choice, do I, Werner?'

Chapter 13

Gelsenkirchen and Berlin
March 1939

Even Jack Miller had to acknowledge that by March 1939 travelling around Germany had become so much easier. He was sick and tired of being told that Hitler had built wonderful new roads and under him the trains were running on time but he had to admit that travel had improved, although he wished that also applied to the trams in Berlin.

Getting to Gelsenkirchen in the heart of the Ruhr was a case in point. When he'd first started going there – his first trip must have been in late 1936 or possibly early 1937 – it took the best part of two days travelling via Münster and Dortmund.

Now it was much easier: Berlin to Münster and then a reliable connection to Dortmund where he stayed at a small guest house on Kessel Strasse, not far from the station. The place was very clean and his room had its own bathroom: it was run by a war widow and her daughter, Irma, an extraordinarily beautiful girl in her early twenties who could barely look at him when he first visited but on his second visit slipped into his room when her mother left for Evening Mass and returned when her mother went for Morning Prayers.

When he arrived in Dortmund, he'd make a telephone call from the station before walking to the city centre where he'd wait inside the entrance of a small shopping arcade opposite the main hospital on Beurnhaus Strasse and watch as a tall doctor left the hospital. If the doctor turned left the meeting was off and he'd hurry to the guest house. Turn right and Jack would walk through the arcade and eventually meet up with the doctor in the back room of an ironmongery on Johannes Strasse.

The doctor was a precise man, not so much unfriendly but someone with no small talk. Jack called him by the code name 'Arthur' and knew little about him, other than that he was a surgeon and his first name was perhaps Wilhelm.

Not much news since your last visit, though my contacts at the marshalling yard have produced this list of train movements, please note the incidence of wagons arriving under armed escort... My source at the police station is still promising that list of Nazi Party members, I hope to have it next time... I have the plans here from the Dortmunder steel engine assembly plant in the east of the city, which I think will be useful... and the Willmann boiler factory in the same area, I hope to make a contact there too.

He'd hand everything over and then inevitably remark that life was becoming more dangerous by the day and he may reach a point where this – he'd gesture at Jack and around the room as if to show what he meant by 'this' – may be their last meeting. Jack would say he quite understood and give the doctor an envelope, which he'd refuse at first but then accept when Jack insisted: *To cover your expenses.*

The following morning – after Morning Prayers, of course – Jack would walk back to the station accompanied by Irma who'd tell her mother she needed to post a letter. They'd have a largely silent coffee in a cafe by the station before Jack caught the train to Gelsenkirchen.

He always had the same sense of a city that had come from nowhere: there seemed to be something very sudden about the place, like towns he sometimes came across in the United States. It was no surprise really: fifty years before, Gelsenkirchen had a population of less than ten thousand. Now it was one of the largest cities in Germany with over 330,000 inhabitants – all thanks to the discovery of coal and the explosion of industries that came in its wake.

This was why Gelsenkirchen was so important. It wasn't just that the city produced so much coal, it was what they did with it that was of so much interest. There was the Gelsenberg factory at Nordstern for converting coal to synthetic oil, and also the Scholven factory, which produced aviation fuel from coal. Operations like this were springing up all over the area: each time the train from Dortmund approached Gelsenkirchen Jack Miller would spot something new and make a mental note to check it out and within minutes of arriving in the city he had an opportunity to do so.

Lotte was the best of them: unlike so many of the others she was uncomplicated, not given to moods or inclined to share any worries with him. She was smart, efficient and highly motivated; an audit clerk who'd risen to be a finance manager at the factory turning coal into aviation fuel and as such she had access to every detail one could wish for on the company's operation. And she had contacts too at similar plants in the city. Jack was never quite sure of how she got them but intelligence was of the highest quality.

He'd find Lotte in the station cafeteria where to any observer they'd appear to be two strangers sharing a table. When they were as sure as they could be it was safe, she'd explain what she was handing over. She'd be very concise and when she'd finished, she'd nod and he'd lean under the table where she'd pass an envelope to him, which he'd slip into his bag, and then they'd each smoke a cigarette and leave, their farewell being as cursory as one would expect from two people who'd apparently only met minutes earlier.

And then Jack Miller would go to work.

–

His presence in Gelsenkirchen could not have been more legitimate.

By March 1939 Jack was a well-established freelance journalist, based in Berlin but travelling all over Germany for the stories he was covering. He wrote some travel pieces – the American papers seemed to like those – but he mostly concentrated on sport and especially football: a dozen newspapers in Britain were keen for anything he sent them.

Gelsenkirchen was the home of Germany's top football team, FC Schalke 04. When the Nazis came to power in 1933, they'd taken over football in Germany and organised the country into sixteen regional leagues, or Gauligen, to correspond with the Gau or the new administrative regions they'd brought in.

FC Schalke 04 were in Gauliga Westfalen and from the league's inception in 1934 had won every year, which meant they qualified for the German Championship Finals, a knock-out tournament for the sixteen teams that had won their own Gauliga.

Schalke dominated this tournament too: they'd been national champions in 1934, 1935 and 1937 and runners-up in 1936, losing 3–4 to Hannover 96 in an exciting final in front of one hundred thousand spectators in Berlin. They were already set to win this year's Gauliga Westfalen and everyone agreed they were favourites to win the national finals once more.

And all this gave Jack Miller a perfect excuse to visit Gelsenkirchen: why would a football journalist not visit the home of the country's top football team?

From the station he'd make his way to Schalke's ground, the Glückauf-Kampfbahn. Today's game was an important one – a local derby against VfL Bochum who were second to Schalke in the Gauliga and an interesting team in their own right. They'd only been formed the previous year when the authorities had forced the three teams in Bochum to merge. It had been a controversial move and one that Miller hoped to work into his match report: *the team the Nazis created*. The British newspapers would like that.

They seemed to like most of what he sent them.

–

He returned to Berlin the day after the match. It was a long day: first train out of the city and as soon as he arrived back in his apartment, he wrote up his story. By late evening he was in a reflective mood and as was often the case these days he thought how funny it was the way his life had turned out.

It had all turned really on his own obstinance: that last Saturday of the Olympic Games in August 1936 and his insistence that he'd take Albert Haas for a drink at the Kaiserhof to thank him for all the help he'd given with the coverage of the Olympic football tournament.

Haas had been characteristically modest and said it was really not necessary: Herr Miller had been very kind and most generous and he was happy to pass on his knowledge of football and, yes, of course it was a shame he'd not been able to attend any of the matches, but that was Germany these days… it was the least of his problems.

But Jack insisted and so Haas met him outside the hotel on Wilhelmstrasse and seemed slightly hesitant when Miller said to come in and then when they entered the bar all the trouble had started, with the barman and his manager both insisting they wouldn't serve a Jew.

He was ashamed he didn't make more of it, but Albert Haas had seemed so worried that Jack realised continuing the argument wasn't going to do him any good. Then the very pleasant English gentleman had intervened and the long and the short of it was they had an extremely good dinner with three bottles of excellent and very expensive Bordeaux followed by some superb vintage Port and he felt he'd wreaked some kind of revenge on the hotel.

Once he recovered from his hangover, he did feel bad about poor Albert Haas but then two days later he heard from him. *Could they meet, as soon as possible?*

He feared he was in trouble for what had happened the other evening, but not at all: Albert wanted to share some wonderful news and couldn't wait to thank him enough. Did Jack recall he'd told him how hard it was for his family to get an exit visa and papers to allow them to settle in Britain?

Of course.

With a flourish he produced an envelope with all the papers. They were leaving the following day. A very nice man called Mr Moore at the British Passport Control Office on Tiergartenstrasse had called him in and sorted everything out in a matter of minutes and told him it was all due to Jack Miller!

A week later Jack was still trying to work out quite how this had happened when he received a telephone call. It was the charming Englishman, Edward Campion, who unexpectedly found himself back in Berlin and was at a loose end and perhaps they could meet for dinner, though maybe not with quite as much wine as before?

They met at a Swiss restaurant just off Behrenstrasse and Edward Campion was less jolly than when they'd met before, but then without three bottles of Bordeaux and vintage Port that was hardly surprising.

Did Jack remember that he'd expressed an interest in remaining in Germany as a working journalist, ideally covering football?

Jack said he did recall that. In truth, he'd been thinking of little else. Associated Newspapers in New York hadn't been very keen on the idea of him remaining in Germany and on their payroll and were asking when he was returning. Jack had been trying to work out how feasible it was to remain in Germany as a freelance journalist.

'Well, I think you may be in luck, Jack – here, have another rosti, I'm full already. It seems there's quite an appetite for coverage of football in Germany from someone who can write decent English. Are you still interested, by any chance?'

Jack Miller didn't want to appear too keen because there was bound to be a catch so he said, yes, thank you very much, Edward, he would have another rosti and, yes, he was indeed very interested.

'Well, looks like you may be in luck, Jack. I don't know how it works in the United States but in Britain we have three different types of newspapers. There are the national newspapers like *The*

Times and the *Daily Telegraph* and then we have local newspapers – most cities and towns in the country have those. But there is another category of newspaper and these are what we call regional newspapers and the difference between them and local newspapers is firstly that they cover a larger area and secondly, they are published in the morning like the nationals and unlike the local papers, which tend to be published later in the day.

'I was at school with a chap whose family own a couple of these regional papers and I remembered he told me a while back that they sometimes struggle for the right kind of articles because they're less parochial than local papers but without the clout of the nationals. I thought you may be just up their street and... well... to come to the point, I had a word with him and he put me in touch with one of his editors and he said they'd be terribly keen to look at what you can send them – no promises, of course, until they see something. Even better, because the regional newspapers don't compete with each other they sometimes share the same article, helps with the cost and all that. And as far as the articles go, they're rather keen on sports-related stuff, especially football. They say they get plenty of political material from the news agencies. How does that all sound?'

Jack Miller – who thought it sounded a bit too good to be true – said he thought it sounded... interesting. He hoped Edward didn't think he was being too blunt, but what kind of fee would be involved?

'As far as I gather, you'll be paid around three pounds per article, which I gather is around eleven dollars. Hope that doesn't sound mean. Apparently, you'll get more if more than one of the newspapers takes the same article.'

Jack said it didn't sound mean at all and... when should he start?

Edward Campion had replied that there was no time like the present so why didn't Jack start right away, which is pretty much what happened. Jack resigned from the *Philadelphia Bulletin* but promised Joe Walsh at least one article a month and Ted Morris in

New York was agreeable to Jack sending him articles to syndicate across his newspapers.

He found an apartment on Sächsische Strasse that had a second bedroom that he turned into his office and he even had his own telephone. Edward Campion had put him in touch with various editors and soon he had a stable of papers with a surprisingly keen interest in his articles. His main clients were the *Western Daily Press*, which was based in Bristol; the *Eastern Daily Press* in Norwich; the *Yorkshire Post* in Leeds; the *Evening News* in London; the *Western Mail* in Cardiff and the *Scotsman* in Edinburgh.

He was in his element. He loved the independence of being a freelance journalist; no editor coming up with crazy ideas and telling him to write something in a thousand words when he didn't think it merited two hundred, if any at all.

He seemed to do well too. He placed at least two articles a week in his British papers and perhaps one a week in the American ones. On that income he was able to live comfortably. And living in Berlin was proving to be an extraordinary experience, though one with an undoubted unpleasant edge to it. He had a palpable sense of watching history being made by the day and the sheer menace of the Nazis and the danger and horror that was all round made life difficult though fascinating at the same time, if often very hard to come to terms with.

His instinct as a journalist was that the brutality of the Nazis was what he should be covering rather than sport, but he'd got to know some of the American and British reporters based in the city and for a start there were plenty of them covering that story and then they all seemed to operate under the same fear: that it was only a matter of time before they'd annoyed the authorities so much that they'd be thrown out.

Nonetheless he did discuss this with Edward Campion on one of his frequent visits to Berlin. Edward had become something of a mentor to him: Jack found he could discuss almost anything with him and he was proving to be a useful sounding board. Jack had mentioned to Edward that perhaps he ought to switch to politics and the activities of the Nazis, but Edward suggested – rather forcibly in fact – that he should stick to football.

So he did stick to football and then in November 1937 Edward had telephoned him and asked if he'd be his guest in London for a few days and he'd send him a first-class ticket and it would be a good opportunity to meet some of his editors.

–

'Are you sure it isn't too soon, Piers?'

'Of course I'm sure, Barney: how long has he been on the books now?'

'Well over a year.'

'Well, there you are, that's long enough without him doing anything useful from our point of view. Bring him over here and we'll get him started. One thing though, Barney... you understand we'll need to be absolutely sure and you know what that entails?'

Barney Allen said he had heard but was it really necessary in the case of someone like Jack Miller?

'All the more necessary.'

So Jack Miller turned up in London on a filthy day in early November and for a week he had the time of his life: a bit of sightseeing, a couple of agreeable dinners with Edward Campion and daytrips to meet some of his editors, though for the *Scotsman* he had to stay overnight in Edinburgh, which seemed to be no imposition.

At dinner he broached with Edward the subject of why Edward had brought him to London and that was when Edward turned rather serious.

'It may well be that I want you to do some work for me, Jack.'

'But you're nothing to do with newspapers, Edward.'

'It may be work of a different nature, Jack.'

Jack was none the wiser and Edward was evidently not about to tell him but he did say that if Jack was interested in finding out more then he'd like him to meet a couple of his colleagues for a chat and after that all would become clear and Jack – who was of course most intrigued by now – said why not?

The following day a colleague of Edward's picked him up from his hotel in Victoria and drove him to meet Edward's colleagues. Jack had imagined this would be in London but it turned out to be a good hour and a bit's drive. It was difficult to know where he was going but he did spot a sign for Oxford shortly before they came off a main road and then they turned into a road that seemed too narrow for the car and at the end of a bumpy lane there was a rather handsome house situated behind high gates.

Things moved very quickly after that. Jack was taken into a room on the first floor with the curtains drawn and asked to sit at a table with two men on the other side, who he assumed were the colleagues Edward had mentioned.

It was very business-like at first as they checked out where he was born, his family, his ex-wife, who he'd worked for and where he'd lived. He did feel that they knew far more about him than he'd ever told Edward and even then, it was information he'd told him in passing more than anything else. He did ask if they could explain what the work Edward had in mind was and why had he come out here to talk about it but they ignored him: *A few more questions, if you don't mind.*

Jack did mind actually but it was becoming clear he wasn't going to be able to do too much about it. He thought about getting up and walking out but when he turned around, he noticed a large man standing in front of the door very much like the men who'd stand guard at the Italian bars in South Philly where he'd go to follow up crime stories.

When he turned back the mood abruptly changed from business-like to threatening.

Who exactly was he...? How come he was just writing about sport...? Why did he avoid politics...? Which of his German friends were Nazis...? Which of his German friends weren't Nazis...? What about Karl Hofmann... and Martin Köhler... and that woman Frieda Lehmann...?

'It's not Martin Köhler, it's Matthias Köhler.'

'Very well then, what about him?'

'I'm not sure why you're asking me all these questions? You're treating me like a fucking Nazi spy!'

'Matthias Köhler is a member of the Nazi Party, Mr Miller, and so is Karl Hofmann.'

'Jesus Christ... I have no idea what the hell this is about and if you'll excuse me I think I'd like to leave, but Matthias is a member of the Nazi Party because otherwise he'd lose his job as a sports reporter on the *Berliner Morgenpost*. He's the least Nazi Nazi Party member I know. Karl Hofmann I had no idea was a member of the Party: he lives in the apartment below mine and we meet socially once in a while for him to help improve my German and for me to help improve his English.'

'And Frieda Lehmann?'

'I had no idea her surname is Lehmann, that's how well I know her: she's a woman I sleep with from time to time. Are you going to tell me she's a Nazi?'

The men on the other side of the table looked slightly shocked at the American's frankness but soon recovered their composure. Jack Miller had decided by now he wasn't interested in whatever work Edward had in mind.

I'm a sports reporter... Berlin doesn't need another American covering the Nazis... and none of this is any of your business anyway...

The questioning went on for half an hour: Jack Miller found it impertinent and intrusive but was intrigued to see what they knew about him and what this was all about. There were questions about his contacts in Berlin, trips he'd made out of the city, his social life, and then one of the men handed him a sheaf of papers, which turned out to be copies of his statements from the First National Bank in Philadelphia.

Perhaps Mr Miller could explain where some of the larger deposits had come from?

'Some of these are to do with my divorce; this is back pay from the *Philadelphia Bulletin* and some of the more recent ones are because I bill newspapers every month or two rather than when my articles appear and… Look, I've had enough. I don't know why the hell I'm telling you all this. I'd like to know how the hell you got hold of my financial details from the States and how you know everything else and if you don't mind finding the man who drove me here I think I'll head back to London.'

A long silence followed and Jack Miller could hear his heart pounding and realised he was perspiring profusely. He noticed the two men glance at each other and both nodded before one picked up the telephone and muttered something and moments later a door opened in the wood panelling behind him and through it emerged Edward Campion who greeted Jack with a sheepish smile and then came to join the two men at the table.

'I imagine you've been wondering what on earth that was all about, Jack?'

'Well, it had momentarily crossed my mind, yes.'

'I'm an officer with British Intelligence. We've had our eyes on you for a while Jack and—'

'You seriously think I'm a Nazi, Edward – really?'

'Goodness gracious, no, Jack, quite the opposite: what I mean is we've had our eyes on you for a while as someone who may be suitable to come and work for us. We recently came to the conclusion that you would be suitable, but the final part of the process was to subject you to the somewhat rigorous questioning you've just undergone with my two colleagues. Please be assured that we just needed to be sure we could trust you, which I personally never doubted and—'

'You mean you want me to be a British spy?'

'Well, yes… I—'

'I'm a journalist, Edward.'

'Indeed.'

Jack Miller was unsure what to say. His instinct was to tell Edward – he now doubted that was his real name – to go to hell and he'd stay as a freelance journalist in Berlin thank you very much but then he realised all the British newspaper contacts had come from Edward and now he knew why. He had no doubt if he turned them down all those commissions would dry up.

But there was something else stopping him telling Edward to go to hell. He'd felt increasingly compromised in Germany just covering sport and travel. He'd been deeply affected by everything he saw going on as the Nazi's implemented their terrible policies. One reason he'd remained in Germany was that he was fascinated by it, but he was doing nothing about it. He was not covering it as a journalist, he was just a bystander. Now he was being offered the chance to be more than that.

He began to speak and then stopped himself. He knew that from the moment he said 'yes' there'd be no going back.

'Take your time, by all means, Jack.'

'I'll do it, Edward.'

'Really?'

'But I stay in Germany, yes? Spying against the Nazis, that's what I'm signing up for... not helping you run your empire.'

Edward said of course. He looked relieved and delighted and got up to come over and shake Jack's hand.

'Now you see why I steered you away from covering anything controversial, eh, Jack? Didn't want you coming to their attention, did we?'

Chapter 14

London and Berlin
April 1939

From their earliest schooldays Tom Gilbey had always rather looked up to Barney Allen.

Barney had been one of those boys who excelled both academically and at sport, which would have been annoying had he not also possessed the kind of charm that caused others to want to be his friend, which had continued into adulthood. Tom had been only too pleased when Barney had approached him some three years earlier to ask about the possibility of him joining MI6. He'd been happy to make the introductions and was delighted when Barney joined the Service. He was even more delighted at what a success Barney was evidently turning out to be: he couldn't help thinking this ought to reflect in some small way on him.

The two men were walking through St James's together, heading towards Pall Mall and a mutual friend's birthday dinner. They were walking in step, their umbrellas swinging in unison.

'I hear it's all going splendidly, Barney.'

'Thank you, Tom, yes...'

'I was covering for Pearson at the Europe heads meeting the other day and Piers was singing your praises.'

'Good of him.'

'He said you've set up a network in Germany, independent of the Berlin station. He said that it raised eyebrows when you started out but appears to have been vindicated what with events out there...'

Barney grunted something but was reluctant to say more, even though Gilbey had full clearance.

'And you have some decent agents, I hear?'

Half a nod from Barney, as if to show he'd heard that too.

'Do you have a full team?'

'I beg your pardon, Tom?'

'I meant are you looking for more agents, or do you have all you need?'

'Always on the lookout for the right recruits, Tom, you should know that.'

'It's just that I may have someone for you… she's a walk-in though.'

'I thought we weren't touching walk-ins these days?'

'I think we're taking the view that we should be very sceptical of them but not dismiss them outright. Want to hear more?'

'Go on.'

'An English woman in her forties walked into Kensington police station a fortnight ago and asked to see a senior officer about a matter of national importance, as she put it. Happens quite often, so I'm told, particularly women who are having problems… you know, the type that think people are following them and all that. However, she seemed to be perfectly sane and told an inspector her name is Maureen Holland and she's lived in Berlin for four years and now works for the English language section of German radio.'

They were turning into Pall Mall now and their pace slowed down.

'She said she was appalled at what the Nazis were up to and horrified at the thought that this country and Germany could go to war so she wanted to offer her services to this country.'

'In what capacity?'

'She wasn't specific but talked about her contacts in Berlin, how in the course of her work she came across a lot of confidential material and she felt it was her duty as a patriotic English woman to do what she could to help this country, despite any risk that may pose for herself. The inspector took the view that as she did not seem to be certifiably insane, he ought to refer the matter to Special Branch and when they sent a couple of chaps to interview her at Kensington police station they were rather impressed with her. They checked her out and as far as they could tell every aspect of her story appeared to be true so they passed the matter on to our colleagues in MI5 and it happened to land on the desk of Chilvers – don't know if you remember him from school, year above us, terribly useful medium-pace bowler, bit of a stutter?'

Barney said the name rang a bell.

'Chilvers contacted me because this is someone possibly of interest to us, which is decent of him, and he wanted to know if I'd like to meet her but when I heard the word Berlin, I thought of you and… here we are!'

Barney said he was certainly interested and perhaps if Tom put him in touch with Chilvers then he'd take it from there.

–

'Of course I remember you, Barney – weren't you cross-country champion? My brother Arthur was in the year below you. Good that the old school connection transcends the unfortunate tension between our two organisations. Never completely understood them myself.'

Barney said he didn't either and maybe Chilvers could tell him about Maureen Holland.

'One of my juniors interviewed her and he thinks she's worth talking to further, which was also Special Branch's view. I would suggest we bring her in for a chat then we can see what we both make of her.'

Maureen Holland was asked to come to a large office block in Clerkenwell. It was a building MI5 used from time to time – it contained various government departments of an imprecise nature and had enough floors and endless corridors to ensure the necessary degree of anonymity. When Maureen Holland was shown into the room, Chilvers said his name was Mr Purcell and introduced Barney as Mr Walton and perhaps Miss Holland could start from the beginning.

She told her story and Chilvers then went through the details and asked about her life, checking dates, schools, home addresses, parents, former colleagues – an interminable amount of information, which Barney felt wasn't completely necessary. When Chilvers finished, he asked if Barney had any questions?

'Can I just clarify something, Miss Holland: you're currently working for Reichs-Rundfunk-Gesellschaft?'

'That's right.'

'And do you intend to remain there?'

'Oh yes, indeed.'

'Why did you not approach the British embassy in Berlin?'

'Because I understand the Gestapo watch the place the whole time as they also do the Passport Control Office in Tiergarten-strasse.'

'You could have been going in on consular matters.'

'One didn't want to take the risk. I was here on leave and thought it would be safer to make an approach away from Berlin.'

She was what Barney Allen's wife would describe as a sour sort, a face unused to smiling, a minimum amount of make-up applied to it, and dressed formally but not very well. Drab would have been another word Mrs Allen would have used.

He carried on for a while – what kind of confidential material did she have access to and had she brought any with her? She said of course she'd not brought anything with her, but some of it was very sensitive indeed, even military material.

Barney had wanted to push her on this but Chilvers thanked her very much for her time and said they'd be in touch. Once she'd been escorted out of the building Chilvers asked Barney what he made of her.

'I'd want to know more. I'd have appreciated more time with her, to be frank.'

'I understand, but we find in these circumstances it's best we pause to take stock. If we decide she's a plant there's a risk in exposing ourselves by showing we may be interested. Personally, I'm not sure I trust her. She's too rehearsed, had all her facts and dates right there, not a moment's hesitation: who remembers the exact dates they were at school unless they've planned it? My instinct is she's not genuine. Her story seems too convenient and there's no sign of any... how can I put this... motivation there. If she was a passionate anti-Nazi she'd have said so and if she wanted money then she'd have found a way of bringing that up, but how long were we with her – an hour – and during that time there was no hint of why she wants to work for us.'

'She said she was a patriot.'

'That sounded rehearsed, I'm afraid: one assumes a British citizen is a patriot. If she's such a patriot why is she working for German radio, which I understand takes a strong anti-British line?'

'Having someone already in Berlin... working there at the radio station, it would be terribly useful. You're not suggesting we drop her, are you?'

'I'd suggest setting Miss Holland a test to see how genuine she is. Do you have someone in Berlin who could be potentially sacrificed in the cause of testing her?'

Barney Allen moved his head in a non-committal manner, which Chilvers nonetheless took as confirmation.

–

Maureen Holland was clearly very pleased with herself when she arrived at another anonymous building, this one on the Gray's Inn Road. She looked slightly more relaxed than two days previously and seemed to have made more of an effort with herself, the most notable feature of which was bright red lipstick.

'I'd very much like to take you up on your offer to work for us in Berlin, Miss Holland,' said Barney Allen. 'We appreciate it is a patriotic gesture and one which you have not taken lightly.'

Maureen Holland allowed a brief, thin smile accompanied by a slight bow of the head. Her handbag had been on her lap but now she placed it on the floor and folded her hands and patted her hair as if to ensure it was in place.

'I would like you to return to Berlin. Am I correct in thinking you work at the main Reichs-Rundfunk-Gesellschaft studios in Westend, on Masurenallee?'

'Indeed.'

'I have to tell you we already have a very trusted agent working there and it would be splendid for you to work with him. I have here an envelope for him. It contains some money along with some instructions. Say it's from Walton in London. You're to follow whatever instructions he gives you. There's another envelope here for you, which contains five pounds to cover your expenses. I'm sorry it's not an awful lot but we will make those payments on a regular basis.'

Barney Allen passed the two envelopes to her. 'His name's written on the first one. I presume you know him?'

The wide-eyed and shocked look on Maureen Holland's face assured him she did indeed know the man.

The trap had been set.

–

Maureen Holland returned to Berlin two days later. Special Branch had followed her in London and reported she did nothing to arouse their suspicion other than a shopping spree at Dickins and Jones in Regent Street, which included the purchase of an expensive coat.

The day after her return to Berlin she woke early, made a call from a telephone box and then went to the Witzleben Park. She walked along the perimeter of the lake until she spotted the man she knew as Karl, his raincoat folded over his arm meaning she could approach him.

'I thought you were coming back yesterday.'

'I was – I mean, I did.'

'So why did you only call this morning?'

'I was tired when I got back and I didn't think you'd want to meet up so late and—'

'In future you'll let me decide that. How did you get on?'

Maureen told the man everything, apart from the five pounds the British had given her, with which she'd bought a good coat and some leather gloves that would help her get through the Berlin winter. She told him how she'd gone into a police station and then met various people – all the time sticking to the story they'd agreed. Eventually she met two men who seemed to be important and who believed her story. At their second meeting the man calling himself Walton said they'd very much like her to work for them and told her they had a very trusted agent working inside Berlin Radio and he gave her an envelope to give to him.

'You have the envelope?'

She removed it from her handbag and handed it to him. 'His name's on the envelope.'

'I can see that. But we know of this man – they say he's a British agent?'

'Yes.'

Karl spent another hour going through her story, trying to find out as much as he could about the people she'd met and where she'd met them. He pushed her on the one called Mr Walton and she said it was difficult to describe him but said she'd know him again if she saw him.

Karl told her to leave matters with him but to say nothing and certainly not approach the man – the British agent in the radio station.

'I'll deal with him.'

–

They arrested Ken Ridley – the man known to colleagues as Fritz – at their favoured time of six o'clock the following morning, which in Berlin had become known as Gestapo Time.

A dozen of them arrived at Ridley's rooms on Forcheimer Strasse in Pankow and broke down his door. Ridley was still in bed and looked terrified as he was dragged from it and made to stand against the door. A small puddle emerged from his pyjama trousers.

He was taken to a dungeon on Prinz-Albrecht-Strasse and kept there for much of the morning, dressed only in his urine-soaked pyjamas and no shoes. Early in the afternoon Ridley was brought to one of the interrogation rooms where the guards beat him up for a couple of minutes, nothing too serious but enough to ensure he was in no doubt about the seriousness of his predicament.

Karl had used the time between meeting Maureen and the arrest to check matters out. The Abwehr station in London confirmed the addresses in London were ones they believed British Intelligence occasionally used to meet people, but they said they had no idea who Mr Purcell or Mr Walton were. Karl had checked Ken Ridley's file: he claimed to be a Nazi sympathiser and had been offering his services around Berlin, but no one trusted him. The Gestapo view was that he was an unreliable drunk.

The evidence though appeared to be damning. He'd been named in London – presumably by someone from MI6 – as a trusted British spy. The envelope the woman had handed over contained instructions about where to meet other agents, a letter saying how delighted they were with him, some questions on a previous intelligence report he'd submitted, some names and another note that said although he was to keep up the pretence of being a drunk, he was to be careful about overdoing it. There was also a considerable amount of money in the envelope.

They interrogated Ridley for the rest of the day and well into the night. Karl told him it was obvious his being a Nazi and a drunk was an act, a charade, a façade – whichever word he preferred. If he was honest and told them everything then he'd be dealt with more leniently.

Ridley denied everything and was far more resolute than Karl imagined he'd be. He was thrown back in the dungeon and they resumed the interrogation the following morning. Ridley stuck to his story: *I have no idea what you're talking about… these notes and documents mean nothing… I have no idea who Walton is… I'm a committed Nazi and would never think of working for the British…*

At lunchtime Ridley was allowed a meal and then subjected to an afternoon of torture. Every hour or so he was given the opportunity to confess but each time he insisted he had nothing to confess to.

'If I did I promise I would tell you everything!'

They broke him some time in the early hours of the following morning. By now Ridley was hanging naked by his fingertips and subject to bouts of electric shocks. He was brought down, wrapped in a coarse blanket and brought back to the interrogation room where he sobbed like a child.

'What is it you wanted me to tell you?' he looked at Karl through badly bruised eyes, blood and phlegm dripping from his face and his whole body shaking. Dried vomit covered his torso.

'I want you to tell me the truth, Ken.'

'Then you'll stop?'

Karl nodded.

'Then I'm a British spy. It's all true.'

They shot Ken Ridley, nickname Fritz, at dawn two days later, Gestapo Time. But something which he couldn't put his finger on made Karl uncomfortable. Maybe subconsciously he wasn't sure about the confession, but his boss had been delighted with it and was very pleased with Karl and Karl – who was up for promotion – was hardly going to argue with that.

They found nothing incriminating in Ridley's rooms in Pankow, which was unusual. He was obviously a very smart agent.

There was the question of what to do with the woman Maureen. Karl hadn't been too sure about her but she had brought him Ridley. On the other hand, when the British found out that Ridley had been arrested so soon after Maureen's return to Berlin they would assume she'd betrayed him.

Maybe he'd made a mistake arresting Ridley so quickly.

Maureen would be discarded, he decided. They'd put her in cold storage as they called it in the Gestapo: keep an eye on her and wait to see if the British contacted her and tried to activate her as an agent, which he very much doubted.

—

A week after Ken Ridley's death Werner Lustenberger took the U-Bahn to Pankow Vinetastrasse and walked from there to Forcheimer Strasse. Barnaby had been insistent: find out what had happened to Ken Ridley.

Finding that out was surprisingly easy. Ridley had lived in a large house with around a dozen rooms to rent, three of which were vacant and the landlady was eager to show a prospective tenant round. They came to one set of rooms, which still looked occupied.

'Isn't this taken?'

She shook her head and then closed the door and took him further into the room. 'It was an Englishman here. I thought he was a good man, he always paid his rent on time. But you know what? The other week the Gestapo came for him – he was a spy!'

'What was the man's name?'

'I shouldn't really be telling you this but he was called… Herr Ridley though he liked people to call him Fritz. My brother was called Fritz.'

'And what happened to him?'

'What do you imagine they do to spies?'

She ran her finger slowly across her throat in case her potential lodger was in any doubt.

Chapter 15

Barney Allen had only met Basil Remington-Barber once before, in the late autumn of 1938 when the MI6 director Sir Hugh Sinclair had started to think seriously about the prospect of war with Germany and had called all the European heads of station to London for an emergency meeting. Most of the senior officers from 54 Broadway were there too, which meant that along with a few Foreign Office types and people described by Piers Devereux as hangers-on there were well over fifty people present. They met next door to Head Office, in St Ermin's Hotel, and it was a chaotic affair with people talking over each other and too much shouting.

After a particularly ill-tempered session just before lunch Barney found himself in a corner of the dining room with Tom Gilbey. It was a buffet lunch and both men were struggling to eat from their plates while holding drinks and generally complaining about the event. At that point an older man strode up to them. Barney had spotted him in the meeting but hadn't caught his name. He was stylishly dressed in a three-piece suit and looked like he could do with a haircut. Barney took him to be one of the hangers-on.

'Ah, Basil – how are you – do you know Barney – Barney Allen? He's working with me. Barney, this is Basil Remington-Barber, he runs our operation in Bern.'

'I don't think I do, I'm glad to meet you, Barney.' Basil Remington-Barber allowed a pleasant smile and carried on eating. He seemed altogether more relaxed than most others in the room, with his quiet voice and calm manner. Barney now recalled Piers talking highly of him: *Basil's very reliable... no side to him... been in Bern a long time and knows the place inside out... comes across as a bit too clubbable but actually he's razor-sharp.*

He'd very much taken to Basil that day at St Ermin's Hotel. When he did speak in the afternoon it was noticeable that he did so with a quiet authority and even a sense of humour and they had a long chat over drinks that evening and again at lunch during the session the next day.

'Do let me know if there's anything I can ever do to help, Barney. Switzerland may seem to be a backwater but I can assure you that if we go to war with Germany, it will become terribly important.'

–

Barney Allen had travelled to Paris on the Monday and stayed there for a couple of days, supposedly to liaise with Paris station but they seemed to resent how little he could tell them about his own work and he left the city with the feeling that he really need not have bothered. On the Wednesday he took an early train from Gare de Lyon, arriving in Geneva at one o'clock to allow a nostalgic couple of hours in a city he'd first visited as a seventeen-year-old: an encounter with a considerably older woman who was staying in the same guest house as him ensured the city would always occupy a place in his heart.

He walked around the Old Town for a couple of hours, stopping to eat in one of the cheap cafes he frequented and particularly enjoyed because his mother would have been appalled to see him eating in places like that – but then his mother would have been appalled at much of what he got up to in Geneva.

He found Cour de Saint-Pierre and from there worked out where the narrow road was but the guest house had been replaced by a lady's hairdresser. Barney stood for a while on the cobbled street staring wistfully at the top floor window and for the briefest of moments wondered if one of the women in the salon was the woman herself but then snapped out of it and took a circular route back to the station to allow him to walk past the lake.

He caught the three o'clock train to Lausanne and waited an hour for the connection to Bern. He should have spent the journey admiring the spectacular scenery but his thoughts remained in the narrowed cobbled street in Geneva's Old Town.

It was seven o'clock when the train pulled into Bern. Basil Remington-Barber was there to meet him. He greeted Barney like an honoured guest who'd unexpectedly accepted an invitation to a remote country house. Basil shepherded him out of the station and across Bahnhofplatz to the Schweizerhof.

'In my opinion, Barney, this is possibly the best hotel in Switzerland, let alone Bern. Wonderful place. Not many of our visitors stay here – budgets and all that – but I persuaded the ambassador's secretary that you need to be here because' – he tugged Barney's coat sleeve to stop him, indicating he should come closer – 'the Germans have started putting guests up here. Their embassy on Willadingweg is becoming quite the hive of activity and it's useful to have an excuse to pop in and out of the hotel to see who else is here.'

Half an hour later they were in a restaurant in an ancient building on Kreuzgasse. On the short walk there, Basil told him this was his favourite restaurant in Bern – in Switzerland in fact – the food was wonderful, the wine list 'a work of art' and it was as if it had been designed as a meeting place for spies.

Barney could see what he meant. They had to ring a bell in an unremarkable doorway to be admitted and then a maître d' guided them along uneven floors through the low-ceilinged building to their table, which was in its own alcove and completely private from any other diners.

The service was discreet and unobtrusive and the food excellent, though Barney found himself worrying about the bill and quite how Piers Devereux would view his expenses claim but Basil must have sensed his concern because he said not to worry, this meal was on the embassy and Sir George was a terribly decent sort even though he was technically an envoy rather than an ambassador.

'Can you see us avoiding war, Barney? I gather you spend a good deal of time in Germany.'

'Not as much as I'd like, Basil, one has to be careful these days. I ration my visits but I am going on to Berlin from here – after Zurich.'

'Good idea: the train from Zurich is probably the best way in, assuming you're not on any list. What cover are you using?'

'I'm diplomatic here but in Germany I'm Edward Campion, representing a college in London. Not sure how much longer I'll be able to use that though, these days no one is interested in coming to study in England – apart from the Jews, and they struggle to get out.'

'This could be one of your last visits there… I say, here's the *côte de boeuf*, looks splendid – deserves it's very own bottle of red, wouldn't you agree?'

They returned to the subject of war. Barney said he was by no means certain either way whether there would or wouldn't be a war. 'I'm a betting man, Basil, and if you asked me for odds I'd say evens, but in our line of work it doesn't pay to be an optimist, does it? Best to assume the worst and then work back from there: if we don't plan for it then we're not really doing our job, are we?'

Basil grunted in agreement and pointed his knife at the bowl of potato Lyonnaise, indicating Barney should help himself.

'You do realise of course, Basil, that if – God forbid – we go to war then you'll rather be our front line here, won't you?'

The other man nodded, a resigned look on his face. 'Indeed – ask for some mustard, if you wish, Barney, I can't abide the stuff but it's not against the rules. I was hoping to retire, you know, but I can't see that happening for a while. I've been told that we'll need to beef up the station here once we start to exchange fire, so to speak. Looks like London want me to do it on the same budget though. I have been told we'll get reinforcements from

Berlin: apparently, I can have my pick of the station there. Do you know them?'

'I keep my distance from them but Foley's a good sort, but I doubt they'd send him here. One chap I've had dealings with who I rate highly is Noel Moore – do you know him? He works with Foley in the Passport Control Office. I'd suggest putting in a request for him when the time is right. I do have a favour to ask from you though, Basil.'

'Go on.'

'I have a potential agent in Berlin, someone I've been keeping my eye on. I think they could be first class but they're on a very long fuse, personally I don't think they'll sign up until we're at war. In that case I need to find a way of letting them contact us and I thought you could help – maybe running a totally reliable address they could send a message to?'

Basil paused as he tried to dislodge some meat from between his teeth. 'Sorry about that, yes, of course. Come to the embassy at ten tomorrow morning. It's on Thunstrasse, on the other side of the River Aar. You can take a taxi, but if you fancy a walk, cross over on Kirchenfeldbrücke, my favourite bridge in the whole of Switzerland. Everyone there knows what I do, of course, but do remember to play along with the charade that I'm a commercial attaché, eh? My father's family would be outraged to think I was in trade!'

–

After his visit to the embassy on the Thursday, Barney Allen travelled to Zurich, where he remained until the following Tuesday. He was hoping to make contact with a senior official from the German Finance Ministry whom Werner had tipped him off about: the man was based temporarily at Germany's consulate in Zurich where he 'moved currency around', as Werner put it. Werner had heard – through a friend of someone who knew him – that this man was known to have reservations about the regime and was about to be posted back to Berlin, which he wasn't happy about. It was all rather vague, but Barney had learnt this was so often how contacts were made: following up on a rumour, moving cautiously – taking the temperature, Piers called it. If it was true and the man did indeed 'have reservations about the regime' then it would still be a long step from that to spying for the British, but that was how it started.

But Zurich didn't go well: on the Friday Barney tracked down where the man lived, delivered a note there leaving a telephone number for him to call to discuss 'matters of mutual interest', but to no avail. He watched his house over the weekend but never saw the man and on the Monday, telephoned him at work and said they had mutual friends in Berlin, but the man put the telephone down and took no more calls after that. Barney watched the consulate but it was a busy building and he couldn't be sure what the man looked like. All in all he felt he'd not handled matters as well as he could have done and left Zurich with his tail between his legs.

The journey to Berlin took up all of Tuesday. They crossed the border into Germany at Friedrichshafen, which was as straightforward as Basil had assured him it would be – *Not quite the same if you try and get out of Germany though!*

He arrived at Anhalter Bahnhof as it got dark and used the underpass from the station, under Askanischen Platz, directly into the Excelsior Hotel. The hotel was not as luxurious as the Kaiserhof or the Adlon but it was large and given the atmosphere in Berlin he calculated its anonymity could be an advantage.

He rang Werner in the morning from a telephone box round the corner from the hotel. Werner didn't sound as pleased to hear from Barney as he normally did: there was a noticeable edge to his voice.

'Are you alone?'

'Of course I am, you know I never have anyone back here. I didn't realise you were in Berlin.'

'I only arrived last night. I did say I was coming.'

'You said in May.'

'It is May.'

A pause as if Werner was checking what month it was. 'Yes, but… you didn't say exactly when.'

'I never do actually, but enough of this friendly chit-chat, we need to meet today… Hello, are you there?'

'Yes, I was thinking – where are you staying?'

'The Excelsior.'

'Very well… I'll tell you what, on Obentraut Strasse there's a shop selling gentlemen's hats: wait in the doorway of the office block next door. I'll meet you there in an hour.'

Werner was half an hour late and Barney was furious. A foreigner – anyone in fact – standing in a doorway in Berlin for that length of time could arouse suspicion. He'd got through five cigarettes as he waited. Eventually a dirty black Volkswagen drove past, sounded its horn and then parked just up the road. Werner leaned out of the driver's window and waved.

'I didn't know you'd got a car?'

'I haven't.'

'So what is this, Werner, a horse and cart?'

'It's not my car, Barnaby, I pay a man in the apartment below me to let me use it from time to time. I thought we'd drive out to Grunewald Forest: it's quiet there. We can talk.'

'Can't we talk in the city, Werner?'

'We can, Barnaby, but things are getting so much worse, that's one of the things I wanted to discuss with you. In the past few weeks, the situation has deteriorated considerably. There are more police on the streets and there seem to be Gestapo everywhere. I've heard of so many people being arrested, mostly for crimes that didn't exist even months ago. My neighbour – the one who lends me this car – he told me he was in a food shop last week and a woman in the queue made a casual remark about how expensive everything was these days – not even blaming the regime – and another man in the shop pulled out his Gestapo badge and took her away. Last week I was stopped on the train to Dresden and they started to question me for no reason and only just seemed satisfied when they saw I'm a Party member.'

'You should have told me, Werner.'

'I'm telling you now! I just feel it's as if… I don't know how to put it, it's as if the city's closing in on me. Everything I do seems to be a risk, so I thought it would be a good idea to come out here. I used to come here before… you know.'

'What about now, won't we look suspicious?'

'Less suspicious than in the city.'

They parked the Volkswagen and walked in silence into the forest. Werner obviously knew the area well, they turned off the main path and headed through the dense trees until they came to a narrower path. The canopy of the trees was now so high it was noticeably darker.

'We met in Cologne at the end of February, didn't we, Barnaby?'

'That's right.'

'And we discussed Tadashi Kimura and Arno Marcus then, didn't we?'

'And the SS friend of yours—'

'I don't want to talk about him at the moment.'

'I'd quite like to.'

'I need to talk about the others first. You said you wanted something from Kimura to check he's genuine and then we could get Arno out of Germany and to England.'

'Indeed.'

'Well he did give me some documents, Barnaby, and I passed them on to you and I've heard nothing since. You told me how Japan was a priority, any intelligence we could get on them would be invaluable and I got you a document from their embassy, but there's been no response. They're getting very impatient; it's been over two months now. Surely you see the urgency of this? We have the opportunity to have a well-placed source inside the Japanese embassy and I don't know what's going on. Even when – if – you do give me the go-ahead to get Arno out of Berlin it is still going to take time to arrange. I've already told you; this place gets more dangerous by the day and I—'

'I'd keep your voice down, Werner, there's really no need to shout.'

'No one can hear us here: we're in the middle of a bloody forest!'

'It took a month for anything from Mr Kimura to arrive in London, in fact I think it was early April, so we've only had it for one month.'

'I told you, he had to find the right documents and then the right time to copy them. It was never going to be quick.'

'I accept that, but of course once the documents arrived in London they had to be translated and then analysed: taking a view as to whether they're genuine or whether they're sophisticated fakes and we're being taken for a ride – that's a very difficult call, Werner. The Japanese are very practised in the art of disinformation. The main document was to do with a co-operation agreement between the Kriegsmarine and the Imperial Japanese Navy. It was an exceedingly complex document and we needed our Royal Navy chaps to have a look at it and well... the long and the short of it is that it was only while I was in Zurich that I heard everyone agrees it is genuine – and jolly useful, which is putting it mildly. One's sense that having a better awareness of Japan's intentions was a priority has been vindicated, I believe. There is a general agreement that this document does indicate that Japan does indeed have hostile intentions, so the view inside the Service is that we want whatever we can get from Kimura. You can get a move on now and get Arno on his way. You said it'll cost a lot?'

'There are obviously bound to be costs, Barnaby.'

The Englishman stopped and handed an envelope to Werner. 'There's five hundred Reichsmarks in here. Now what about this SS friend of yours: when did you last see him?'

'I've not seen him since the night I copied those documents.'

'Why not?'

'I was waiting to see what you said and, in any case, he's not really my type – he came into the bed wearing his SS uniform, for Christ's sake, Barnaby.'

'I'm not sure I want to know that kind of detail actually, Werner. The view in London is that this material is also first class, he's an excellent source and needs to be looked after. The von Brauchitsch document was very useful but the Army chaps were more excited with the lists of names, ranks and military units. That's bloody useful for them, so more of the same, please. You're going to need to resume your friendship with Untersturmführer Harald Fuchs.'

Werner nodded in a resigned manner and Barney said he was doing an excellent job what with the diplomat and the SS chap and he reckoned he deserved a good meal as a thank-you. Werner said it would be safer to meet for lunch the following day as Sundays tended to be busy and the atmosphere in the city felt less tense. He knew a place that had recently opened on Kaiser-Franz-Josef-Platz.

The restaurant was ideal and Werner was considerably more relaxed than he'd been the previous day. They discussed how it would now be best for him to distance himself from Holborn College and concentrate on his family business. Barney would write a letter severing Werner's relationship with the College, pointing out Werner's increasingly hostile attitude to Britain. They also talked about what would happen in the event of war between the two countries and agreed Werner would remain in Berlin but be inactive for the first couple of months, just in case…

When they left the restaurant, they strolled into Französische Strasse. Barney said he was going back to the hotel and would remain in Berlin for a few more days but wouldn't contact Werner on this trip unless it was urgent. Werner agreed: he said that sounded safer and he now had plenty to get on with anyway. They stopped by the cathedral: Werner said he was going to head back to his apartment and the two men shook hands and slapped each other on the shoulder and Barney watched as Werner headed south with that familiar spring in his step.

He felt relieved: Werner had clearly needed to vent his worries and Barney realised he'd probably not made enough allowance for the pressure he worked under. He was pleased Werner seemed to be back to normal and he was also pleased with how well things were going in Berlin. Piers was also delighted: he'd told Barney how he liked to think of a properly functioning network of spies as being like a wolf pack.

'I thought the idea was for these agents to be independent of each other – to be unaware of each other's existence?'

'Up to a point, Barney, but there'll be a time when you need them to act together – no animal does that more effectively than a pack of wolves, whatever danger they face.'

Barney was thinking of his pack of wolves, roaming the streets of Berlin. It was quite busy and Barney wasn't taking much notice of what was around him. Had he done so, as he'd been trained to do, then life would have turned out very differently.

Chapter 16

Berlin
May 1939

Barney Allen woke around eight o'clock on the morning of Monday, 8 May having slept better than he'd done for some time. Ever since he'd met Sophia von Naundorf in August 1936, he'd been hoping to recruit her as an agent. If asked to give odds on turning the disillusioned and unhappy wife of a senior SS officer into a British agent he'd have said 33/1 at least: a long shot but worth a try.

When he'd first met Sophia, he'd asked if they could keep in touch and she'd replied it would be nice to hear from him but only call during the day and never at weekends.

He'd waited until March the following year to call when he was in Berlin: she said she was busy and maybe he could call another time, which he did that November, but this time she sounded nervous and said this wasn't a good time so he waited until the middle of 1938. She paused when he said who it was, as if thinking about what to do. She was happy he'd called, she said, but now wasn't... perhaps in a few months? The last time he'd called was in January when she reacted in a similar manner, though this time he thought he detected a degree of hesitancy in her voice.

But this time it was a very different matter. He'd waited until the Thursday morning to telephone her.

'Good morning – I do hope I'm not disturbing you, it's Edward Campion. We last—'

'Edward – how nice to hear from you! Are you in Berlin?'

Barney Allen said he was and he'd brought some wonderful English weather with him and they both laughed. He wondered if perhaps she'd like to meet for coffee?

'Not before the weekend, please, it won't be convenient then. Perhaps Monday? Maybe if you call me around this time and we can arrange where to meet.'

Barney had planned to tell Werner about Sophia when they'd met for lunch on the Sunday. If she showed any sign of being prepared to work for the British then he wanted Werner to run her. It would be good for them to meet while Barney was still in Berlin. He wanted to make the introductions himself and he suspected Werner and Sophia would get on well. But first he needed to be sure about Sophia.

He left the hotel and walked along Saarland Strasse until he found a telephone box. She sounded pleased to hear from him. 'We could meet for lunch, Edward: do you know Wertheim's?'

'No, but I'm sure I could—'

'It's an enormous department store on Leipziger Platz. Use the entrance on Vossstrasse and go... may I ask, Edward, are you married?'

'Well, yes, I—'

'Good, then go to the perfume department on the fourth floor and buy something nice for your wife: make sure they gift wrap it. Then go up one floor where there's a very busy restaurant, people tend to share tables there. I'll be waiting for you.'

He returned to the Excelsior for breakfast and then went to his room to have a bath, which gave him time to think. He thought of Piers and his comparison of a network of spies to a pack of wolves.

'When the time's right, Barney, you'll know when to pull them together – when to form the pack.'

He reckoned that time was fast approaching. He didn't know how many more trips he'd be able to make to Berlin – the political situation was deteriorating so fast. Only a few weeks previously the prime minister had told Parliament that in the event of any action threatening Polish independence the British and French governments would lend Poland 'all support in their power'. For Barney Allen that seemed to be charting a steady course towards war.

Jack Miller was returning to Berlin that night from Essen. They were due to meet the following day and Barney felt the time was right to tell him about Werner and Sophia. The pack of spies was forming and he allowed himself to feel excited.

He left the hotel early for his meeting with Sophia, stopping at a telephone box to call Werner, which was a necessarily drawn-out affair. He'd send the code and meet at today's rendezvous point, three o'clock by a tabac on Behrenstrasse where hopefully he'd be able to tell Werner about Sophia and Jack too.

He allowed the phone to ring twice before replacing the receiver, waited thirty seconds and rang again: three more rings. Satisfied the message had got through he headed off for Vossstrasse.

—

Sophia von Naundorf was as Barney Allen remembered her though if anything the past three years had made her more beautiful. Her once pale skin now had a healthier pallor and her large dark eyes looked even more remarkable. She wore an elegant beret and her smart coat had a fur trim with a cameo brooch on the collar.

She moved a plate and glass to allow Barney to sit down, silently indicating the place was free. The restaurant was as busy as she'd described, so noisy it was unlikely anyone would overhear let alone notice them.

'I'm sorry we've not been able to meet before but... circumstances, you understand. Life with Karl-Heinrich is very demanding. It was difficult when we met during the Olympics, but now...' She toyed with her potato salad and shook her head.

'Karl-Heinrich's now a Standartenführer, which is what I think you'd call a colonel. He commands a *Standarte* of five hundred men based in Breslau near the Polish border, which means he only returns to Berlin for a long weekend once or twice a month: he left early this morning. All I hear when he's back is how the Jews and the Bolsheviks run the world... and the banks... and how they want another war, which is ironic of course because he clearly wants another war, he says he can't wait to start fighting. It's as if there's a competition in the SS to see which officer can be more Nazi than the other. Sometimes when he's drunk too much he tells me more about what he's up to in Breslau than I think he means to. Have you heard of the *Selbstschutz*, Edward?'

He shook his head and she pushed her plate to one side, some of her potato salad and cold meat remaining uneaten.

'As far as I understand the *Selbstschutz* are militias of ethnic Germans in Poland. They're Nazis and I think their role is to help the Reich's plans for Poland. So, if we go to war with Poland and invade it the *Selbstschutz* will be there to help them.'

'Like a third column?'

'Exactly. From what Karl-Heinrich tells me his *Standarte* is responsible for the *Selbstschutz* in much of the western part of Poland. They give them military training and the *Selbstschutz* also have the task of providing intelligence, like local lists of Jews and socialists and trade unionists. He says that when – not if, but when – the Reich takes over Poland then I won't believe what will happen to all these people, especially the Jews.

'The Nazis use the word *Untermenschen* to describe what they see as inferior people, non-Aryans, especially Jews and Slavs. If you have the misfortune to read any of Hitler's...' She paused to lower her voice and Barney leaned forward. 'Any of his nonsense, then you'll see he's obsessed with the idea of *Untermenschen* and what he'll do to them.

'One of Karl-Heinrich's areas of responsibility is the Polish city of Łódź, he tells me he has a very large *Selbstschutz* unit there. This weekend he was going on and on about their plans for Łódź: they're even planning to rename the city Litzmannstadt. Apparently, the city has a population of around seven hundred thousand and a third are Jews and he says they don't know what to do with them. The city's a major textile production centre and should they put them to work for the Reich or re-settle them or… I can't stand it, Edward, and the worst part is that I have no one to speak to. We ought to order a coffee and cake otherwise it may look odd.'

They sipped their coffee in silence for a while.

'I did have my friend Esther – did I ever mention the Goldmanns to you, Edward? They lived in an apartment below us, Dr Goldmann was a doctor at the Charité. The daughter, Esther, became my best friend and confidante. Karl-Heinrich made their lives a misery. He got the Gestapo to raid their apartment and helped ensure the father lost his job as soon as Jewish doctors were banned from working. I think Karl-Heinrich inadvertently did them a favour: he was so awful to them they left last year and as far as I know they're now in Belgium. Had they waited until now… it's very hard for Jews to get out. So that is my life, I'm married to a Nazi and have to go along with it though sometimes wonder if I really do have to, I…'

Her voice tailed off and she looked past Barney, her big black eyes now moist with sadness. She wondered whether to mention about helping Kurt to escape from Berlin but decided against it.

'There may be a way you could help, Sophia.'

The eyes turned to him.

'There are people I know… in London… people who would be grateful to receive whatever information you have about… military and political matters, about the kind of things you hear from your husband.'

She didn't look shocked as he'd expected her to, if anything she now looked more relaxed as she cut her cake and ate some while managing to keep her dark red lipstick untouched.

'I could find a way of ensuring there's no danger to you, Sophia… there'd be someone I totally trust here in Berlin who'd—'

'These people you talk about, Edward, the people you say would be grateful to receive the information... are you one of them?'

Barney shrugged.

'I do hope so... though I'm not sure this is the right time, but there will be a time when I feel I have to help you.'

'It may be, Sophia – if there's war between our countries – then it will be too dangerous for me to contact you and vice versa. In a moment I'm going to pass a piece of paper to you: it's an address in Interlaken in Switzerland of someone called Annemarie who you're to pretend was a penfriend of yours many years ago. When you feel in a position to help us, write to her saying you've decided to get in touch after all these years because you were wondering how she is. Don't say anything negative, obviously. In fact, go out of your way to say how wonderful Karl-Heinrich is and how much you approve of what is happening in Germany: assume your letter will be read. We'll then know you want to help us and you'll receive a reply from this Annemarie. Soon after you'll be contacted by someone saying they're Friedrich – a cousin of Annemarie. You'll be able to absolutely trust them.'

–

Barney Allen left the restaurant first and walked through Wertheim's with the intention of leaving through the main entrance on Leipziger Platz. The meeting with Sophia, he decided, had gone very well: far better than he'd hoped. She was, after all, an intelligent woman and he doubted she could have misunderstood his approach to her. It hadn't exactly been an ambiguous one.

...people I know... in London... people who would be grateful to receive whatever information you have about... military and political matters, about the kind of things you hear from your husband...

And she'd clearly understood it, checking if he happened to be one of these people. But then he began to wonder whether it had gone too well.

He paused by a display of men's wallets on the ground floor, allowing himself an opportunity to have a good look around him, to be as sure as he could that he wasn't being followed while at the same time trying to decipher her reaction.

She appeared genuine enough and he had checked her out when they'd first met in 1936, when Noel Moore had ascertained her story about being friendly with her Jewish neighbour was true. And yet... and yet... his experience of her in 1936 was that she was somewhat timid, cowed by her husband – and still in her twenties. There was nothing about her to suggest she was eager to be a British agent but despite this she'd responded to his telephone call with quite a sophisticated plan for how they should meet up. Wertheim's was a clever place to meet – and its cafeteria was ideal – busy, noisy, and their encounter looked like a spontaneous one, two strangers sharing a table. The idea about perfume for his wife – gift wrapped – was a neat touch, though he had no intention of giving it to his wife who thought he was in Scotland on business and who in any case would be suspicious as to why he'd bought her perfume.

He imagined Piers Devereux would tell him not to worry too much.

When recruiting agents we have to rely on our instincts far more than you'd imagine, Barney... there's a limit as to how far one can check out a story... if someone isn't genuine they may well have gone to extraordinary lengths to fool us. If someone tells you their mother's maiden name is Wolstencraft and gives an address in Somerset and tells you who the neighbour was when they were a child... well, if that all checks out – and invariably it does – then it's too easy for us to think therefore they're fine and to be trusted.

An assistant asked Barney if he was interested in the wallet he was looking at and Barney was so absorbed in his thoughts he began to say 'pardon' in English before checking himself. He smiled and moved on until he found a bench behind the lifts and decided to wait there for a final check on whether he'd been followed.

He would rely on his instinct, which was to trust Sophia. She had all the makings of an excellent agent. Her readiness to betray her husband, her country, was, he decided, born out of a sense of injustice. Her cleverness at arranging their meeting – while surprising – should be seen as a good thing: she was a natural as a secret agent, someone who Piers would describe as 'intuitive', which he was forever saying was what he was looking for.

The information Sophia had given about her husband being based in Breslau and what they were up to with the German militia in Poland and the plans for Łódź… that alone was invaluable. He'd write up the report as soon as he returned to London and the MI6 and Foreign Office analysts would be able to verify it. If nothing else it was further evidence of Germany's hostile intent towards Poland.

–

He left the store and headed to the rendezvous with Werner on Behrenstrasse. He was annoyed rather than worried when the German didn't show up: Werner's attitude on this visit certainly left much to be desired and while he was prepared to make allowances for the pressure the man was clearly under, he wondered whether he ought not give him a bit of a talking to when they met. Not quite reading the Riot Act but something pretty stern nonetheless.

The fall-back was to call between four thirty and five that afternoon. Barney made the call from a telephone box in Anhalter station. The protocol for an afternoon call was three rings, terminate the call and one minute later four rings. But on just the second ring someone answered the phone. 'Hello… who's that?' It was a male voice, far deeper and rougher than Werner's, and in the background, Barney could hear a noise like something heavy being moved.

It was one of those moments of profound shock when even in the noisiest of places – and Anhalter station certainly came into that category – a chilling silence seemed to fill the void. He felt a ringing in his ear and his throat tighten as he slowly replaced the receiver: Werner was clearly in trouble; he'd never answer a call so early in case it was a coded message and whoever answered the phone was not Werner – or a friend. Barney looked around and watched as two policemen walked past and he worried he'd made a mistake calling from the station: the background noise gave too much away.

He allowed himself a few precious seconds to remain in the call box and regain his composure and come up with some kind of plan. Werner was clearly in trouble and there was nothing Barney could do about it, other than ensure he left Berlin before the spotlight trained on him.

He hurried out of the station and back to the hotel via the tunnel under Askanischen Platz. In his room he wrote a letter to Jack, apparently from his plumber saying he regretted he was unable to visit tomorrow due to a family problem: Jack would know something was up and he was to lay low for a week.

He rang the hotel reception: he'd received some bad news, unfortunately, and had to leave Berlin. If they could prepare his bill, he'd be very grateful – and he understood there was a night train to Amsterdam, perhaps they could ask the concierge to book him onto that?

First class, please.

He collected the ticket at reception and asked what time he was due to arrive in Amsterdam, speaking loudly enough for the security officer on the next desk to hear.

He headed back into Anhalter station but once there – and certain he'd not been followed – left through another exit and crossed the city to Lehrter station, where he travelled second class to Hannover.

If anyone had picked up his trail in Berlin, he hoped they were following the wrong scent to Amsterdam.

Once in Hannover he realised he needed to keep moving. He caught the last train out of Hannover up to Hamburg, where he knew he'd be safe overnight.

The following morning, he caught the first train of the day to Lübeck. It was only when he was on the ferry to Copenhagen that he could relax, if that was the right word for it. As he watched the German coast fade from view he wondered about Werner: had he managed to escape, or was he in the hands of the Gestapo?

Either way, he wondered if he'd been too hasty leaving Berlin. Poor Werner.

Chapter 17

Maureen Holland was even more bitter than usual. For as long as she could remember she'd been resentful of those around her – their looks, their wealth, their careers… friendships, health… their happiness.

She'd never forgotten when she was fifteen overhearing her father describe her as the runt of the litter, and on the rare occasions she dared complain to her mother about how life was treating her, she was told there was nothing she could do about being plain: she'd have to make do with the hand she'd been dealt.

Her twenties were spent in a series of tedious jobs. At twenty-eight she was engaged to a man fifteen years her senior who took advantage of her in a most distressing manner before breaking off the engagement.

When she was thirty, she treated herself to a coach holiday to Germany and was fascinated with the country. It was 1927 and the country was in a state of turmoil but she nonetheless fell in love with the place. She enjoyed the atmosphere, the sense of order, the culture and even the food: she felt she belonged there.

When she returned to England, she enrolled in German night classes and after a while reached a reasonable level of competence in the language, reinforced by annual visits to Germany when she could afford them.

She also became interested in politics. Her father had always told her politics should only be of concern to people who under-stood it, which certainly didn't include her. But she admired the political direction in which Germany was moving and found herself wishing that were the case in England.

Around this time – it would have been 1932 – she developed a hatred of Jews, who she saw as responsible for so much ill fortune in the world (they'd started and financed the Great War after all). This hatred had a personal dimension too. She'd found a job as a clerk at an insurance firm in the City where some knowledge of German was a requirement. It was the best job she'd ever had – quite well paid, in a smart, modern office and with good prospects.

But then a new girl arrived, a German Jew with excellent English. One day Maureen's boss took her aside and said because her German wasn't as good as the new girl's English they were letting her go and he was sure she'd understand and would find a new job soon enough and he'd happily give her a good reference.

The following year she joined the British Union of Fascists and returned to night school, improved her German and moved to Berlin in 1937. She found a job as a teaching assistant and for a while life was pleasant enough, even if she didn't feel quite as fulfilled as she'd hoped. German men treated her no better than English men had done, if anything they were worse – physically very aggressive.

In early 1939 she found a job at German radio, which was setting up an English language service at its brand-new studios in Westend. She was disappointed when the job turned out to be more menial than she'd been led to believe and for a few weeks found herself working for a very smart woman producer – a native of Berlin but fluent in English and countless other languages. One day Maureen had been complaining about her workload and a headache and her lodgings and the woman took her aside.

You always seem resentful and ready to moan about life and how you're feeling. Let me tell you, there's no point in moaning all the time, no one cares – you need to take a grip on yourself and make something of your life.

She'd been shocked someone could speak to her like that, but then she thought about it and thought maybe the woman had a point. She recognised she did have a tendency to feel sorry for herself and maybe other people noticed that, so she decided to follow the woman's advice and do something that she'd been thinking about. The Gestapo had an office within the building on Masurenallee and one lunchtime she summoned up the nerve to visit it. She explained she was a British citizen but a committed supporter of Nazi Germany. She'd like to offer her services in whatever capacity the Reich thought fit.

She didn't imagine anything would come of it – who'd be interested in her after all – but to her surprise just one week later she was called back to the Gestapo office where a man who introduced himself as Karl Henniger took her into a private room and explained he was from section 4E of the Gestapo, which dealt with counter-intelligence and they were especially interested in British espionage operations in Berlin and they wanted to send her to London for her to offer her services to British Intelligence.

'If they take you on then we'll be able to find out about what they're up to here!'

She was taken away for a week to be briefed on what to do in London and sure enough within a short time of her arrival there she was meeting with British Intelligence, who seemed to be very keen on recruiting her. They asked her to return to Berlin and to the radio station where they had an agent working. They gave her an envelope to pass on to him.

She was surprised – which was putting it mildly – that the British agent turned out to be Ken Ridley, a man she disliked intensely. He was a drunk with no evident interest in hygiene, lazy and loud and rarely missed an opportunity to treat women appallingly. He seemed to regard himself as more Nazi than the Nazis, even calling himself Fritz, and he was the last person she'd expect to be a British spy, but when she thought about it, she realised that was the whole point – someone so ridiculous the Germans wouldn't suspect him.

She passed the information on to Karl on her return to Berlin. She imagined the Gestapo would watch him to see what other British agents he was in contact with while she'd start operating as a double agent herself. When Karl told her Ridley had been arrested, she was surprised that it had happened quite so soon but assumed they knew what they were doing. She was even more shocked when she found out that Ridley had been executed by the Gestapo just a few days after his arrest: she'd assumed there'd be an investigation and a trial and...

And this was why she was now so bitter. The Gestapo no longer had an interest in her because the British would know what she'd done. She'd been discarded by them and the thought of what would happen to her if she returned to England kept her awake at night.

Both Britain and Germany had used her. Life could not feel more hopeless.

–

On the first Sunday of May, Maureen Holland took the tram from outside her lodging house in Neukölln up to Mitte. It was a pleasant day and while she didn't exactly feel full of the joys of spring it was sunny and she planned to stop by the Reichstag and then walk down the Unter den Linden and find a cheap place to eat and then maybe explore the area near the cathedral, which she didn't know so well, and then return in time to do her laundry.

She was delighted to come across a small military parade on Königs Platz, which she watched with her chest bursting with pride. All around her was a sense of power and authority: the ubiquitous black and green uniforms seemed, perversely, to brighten the city. The red swastika banners draping from the buildings made Berlin feel like the centre of the world, such a wonderful contrast to London. After treating herself to lunch at a Bavarian cafe she walked through Kaiser-Franz-Josef-Platz towards the cathedral.

And that was when she saw him.

Ahead of her two men were talking, one older and taller than the other. They seemed to be friends as they slapped each other on the shoulder and shook hands warmly. As she got closer, she realised the older man was the one who'd interviewed her twice in London the previous month, the man who introduced himself as Mr Walton and told her about Ridley.

The man who'd tricked her.

She moved across the road to get a better view of Mr Walton. She'd told Karl that it was difficult to describe him but she'd know him if she saw him again. Now she had no doubt whatsoever.

The two men shook hands once more and moved off in different directions. The man calling himself Walton moved down Französische Strasse while the other man headed south past the cathedral. She knew she had to follow Mr Walton, but he quickly disappeared from view into a crowd of people.

But the other man was still in sight and she followed him. He caught a tram on Jerusalemer Strasse and she stayed with him as he left the tram on Tauentzienstrasse where he entered an apartment building. She waited across the road, watching the building for an hour and deciding this must be where he lived. She checked at the entrance and there were only eight apartments in the block.

That ought to be enough for Karl.

–

Before he'd transferred to the Gestapo Karl Henniger had been a police officer in nearby Potsdam. He was continuing a family tradition: his maternal grandfather had been a police officer, as had two of his uncles. And he always remembered his grandfather's advice: *trust your instincts.*

As advice went it didn't seem especially profound – more a case of stating the obvious – but as his career moved on and especially once he transferred to the Gestapo the more he realised that the process of policing often got in the way of what he instinctively knew was the right thing to do. His bosses tended to be too cautious, too occupied with paperwork and cutting corners.

Trust your instincts.

The Englishman Ken Ridley was a good example of this. His instinct told him something wasn't right about the case, but his boss wasn't having any of it: he was delighted they'd caught a British spy and insisted that once he'd confessed there was no reason to delay his execution.

But Karl Henniger knew that the Englishman had held out for so long under torture and only confessed out of desperation, when he'd do anything to stop it. Henniger had no problem with torture *per se*, but he did think it sometimes got in the way of the truth. He couldn't reconcile the fact that Ridley had confessed to being a British spy yet they found no physical evidence that he was. They'd turned his rooms in Pankow upside down, pulled up the floorboards and examined every scrap of paper. They checked his desk at the radio station and interviewed everyone who knew him but there was nothing. Despite the confession – and his execution – Ridley came across as a drunk, someone it was hard to take seriously.

The nagging doubts about Ridley's guilt and whether Maureen Holland had been tricked by the British remained.

One afternoon at the end of April Henniger decided there was nothing to be lost in calling in on the house in Pankow where Ridley had lived. The landlady was an odd sort, dressed for winter and smelling of fried potatoes and muttering to herself as she shuffled round the lodging house.

'What about the rest of his possessions – all these clothes? I can't let the room until it's all gone.'

The Gestapo man said they'd finished with everything so she could get rid of them. Her eyes lit up when he suggested she sell them.

'And the floorboards and the panels you pulled off the walls – what about them?'

'They were put back as we found them.'

'Not very well, sir.'

He asked her if she really wanted to make an official complaint against the Gestapo and she said of course not, in fact nothing could be further from her mind and if there was anything she could do to help… talking of which, was Herr Henniger interested in a man asking her about Herr Ridley?

'I beg your pardon?'

She told him about the short man possibly in his thirties who came to look round maybe a week after Herr Ridley died and he seemed very interested when she showed him this room and wanted to know the name of the man who was a British spy and—

'You told him he was a British spy?'

'I didn't know I wasn't meant to, sir. He seemed very interested. And there was something about him, sir... German certainly, was nicely dressed and well-mannered and – with respect to my other tenants – not the kind of man I would be expecting to be renting a room here.'

Henniger questioned her closely: no, he didn't give her his name, no, she couldn't describe him other than what she'd already told him.

'But I'd know him again if I saw him, sir!'

Now it was a Monday morning and Maureen Holland had asked to see him and was insisting that the previous day she'd seen the British man who'd recruited her in London – the one called Mr Walton – on Französische Strasse.

'You're certain?'

'Absolutely certain: I said I'd know him if I saw him and it was definitely him.'

'So you followed him?'

'I lost him in the crowd, sir.'

She was sitting on the other side of his desk looking a bit too smug for someone who'd apparently seen a British spy in the centre of Berlin and then lost them. He shook his head and muttered something about that not being good enough and maybe it was her imagination and really...

'But I did follow the other man.'

'Which other man?'

'I told you, Mr Walton was talking to another man – they were near the cathedral. When I couldn't spot Mr Walton, I decided to follow the other man. I managed to follow him on the tram and then on foot to an apartment building on Tauentzienstrasse.'

'Can you describe him?'

'He was quite short, well dressed – but I'd definitely know him if I saw him again.'

—

Maureen Holland had that opportunity just a few hours later.

Two of the apartments on Tauentzienstrasse were occupied by single women and three by couples where the man was either older or taller than the man described by Maureen Holland. It was late in the morning when the other three men were hauled in to the Gestapo headquarters on Prinz-Albrecht-Strasse where they were taken to separate cells and left alone.

Werner felt sick when the cell door slammed shut. He felt his heart pounding hard. He was as certain as he could be they'd find nothing incriminating in his apartment. He always contacted Barnaby either by telephone or letter, always in code and always with ample precautions. He never telephoned from the same place and likewise with post boxes. He'd memorised all the telephone numbers and addresses. He'd even removed the metal boxes in which he kept the camera, money and some documents from under the floorboards. He'd discovered he could access the roof space his block shared with the house next door and was able to secrete the boxes in their eaves.

When the cell door opened he joined his two neighbours in the corridor and they were marched up a flight of stairs and into a large room where five other men were waiting. All eight of them were given a numbered card to hold in front of them and then made to stand in line with bright lights shining at them.

He became aware of two figures walking in front of them. It was hard to make them out but one was certainly a woman. There was a pause and the door closed and then opened and two more figures walked in front of them.

'Number two, come with me. The rest of you can go.'

It was only when the other seven moved away from the line that Werner realised he was standing alone. He looked down at his number.

Two.

–

It had almost been civilised at first.

The Gestapo officer introduced himself as Karl Henniger and told the guards to undo Werner's handcuffs and then leave them alone. He was quietly spoken and seemed almost apologetic. He was sure that Herr Lustenberger understood that these things had to be investigated. *Would you like some water? Please help yourself.*

There was a pause as Henniger looked at his notes and Werner wondered quite what he meant by 'these things'.

'Yesterday a woman saw a man she recognised as a British Intelligence officer on Französische Strasse. This man was talking with another man and she decided to follow that man, which she did to an apartment block on Tauentzienstrasse. This matter was reported to me this morning. The woman was the first person to view the identity parade, which you have just taken part in, and she had no hesitation in identifying you.'

Werner thought about responding but remembered the advice he'd been given on his training in England. *Don't say anything for as long as possible: wait until they've revealed everything they know.*

'The second person to attend the identity parade was the landlady of a lodging house on Forcheimer Strasse in Pankow. She identified you as the person who'd been there a few weeks previously enquiring about a British spy who'd lived there and who I had the pleasure of arresting. She was certain that you are the man who came to the house. Is that so, Herr Lustenberger?'

Werner said he hadn't been to Pankow for many years.

'And meeting the man in Französische Strasse?'

Stick to your story: be consistent.

He shook his head. 'I only went as far as the Kurfürstendamm yesterday.' He thought about Barnaby and wondered what he'd do when he didn't turn up outside the tabac on Behrenstrasse. Maybe he'd realise he was in danger and do something about it, though for the life of him he couldn't imagine what Barnaby could do.

Don't say any more than is absolutely necessary.

'But these denials, Herr Lustenberger, they don't explain why two women – who've never met each other, I ought to add – both identified you on the identity parade. I've done many of these parades and I can tell you that neither of them was hesitant in any way.'

Behave as an innocent man would in those circumstances: be outraged at being falsely accused.

Werner was taking some heart from the fact that this was all they seemed to have on him. 'I'm sure this is all a misunderstanding and I know you have a job to do but I can assure you this is a matter of mistaken identity.'

'You worked for the British, Herr Lustenberger.'

'For a college, not for their intelligence service... and the bastards sacked me.'

He stopped himself. *Don't come across as being clever.*

'This interrogation will continue in due course. I can assure you that the longer it goes on the more intense it will become and if necessary, I'll bring in colleagues who are specialists at obtaining information that people are reluctant to give. In the meantime, I'll give you time to think. Let me leave you with this one thought...'

The Gestapo man stood up and leaned over the table as if about to speak in confidence. 'An early confession and a full disclosure of information invariably leads to a prisoner's life being spared. Many people in your position regret mistakes they have made and choose to co-operate with us, which is always appreciated. You may wish to keep that in mind.'

–

Untersturmführer Harald Fuchs was in the courtyard at Prinz-Albrecht-Strasse when his world began to disintegrate. He was standing with a couple of colleagues admiring a new staff car and without a care in the world. He watched as a convoy of Gestapo cars screeched to a halt at the entrance to their part of the building.

Three men were dragged from the cars and marched to the door. For a few seconds they were facing him and one of them was, unquestionably, the man he knew as Josef but whose real name was Werner and who knew him as Rudi. He was now a prisoner of the Gestapo.

He felt himself go numb and sway and the voices around him became muffled and his throat tightened. One of his colleagues asked if he was all right and he said something about feeling a bit sick and perhaps if he went inside and sat down and had a cigarette.

After a while he told his colleagues he needed to go to Registry and may be a while. Once there he found a quiet spot behind a high rack of shelving and sat down, closed his eyes and thought carefully as he smoked his way through a packet of cigarettes even though the idiot in charge of Registry didn't approve of smoking there.

If Lustenberger was a prisoner of the Gestapo it was only a matter of time before Harald's name came up... he had no idea why the man had been arrested, but he couldn't afford to take the risk that he would say nothing or even be released. If he said anything about his relationship with Harald then he'd be finished. He'd be drummed out of the SS and end up in one of those camps.

If I get away with this, I'll never look at another man again!

That evening he waited until all of his colleagues had left the office and his floor was more or less deserted and then moved through the offices until he found what he was looking for. He then waited until midnight when he knew no one would be around.

He rang the Gestapo custody office and told the duty sergeant it was Sturmbannführer Müller and please could he confirm if any prisoners by the name of Werner – he wasn't sure of the surname – were being held overnight.

He knew the sergeant would have felt intimidated by a call from an SS major but Harald Fuchs had made sure he came across as very measured, to the obvious relief of the custody sergeant who said yes, there was a prisoner by the name of Werner Lustenberger in custody, that's L -U-S... and Fuchs laughed and said not to worry he knew how to spell it and the custody sergeant laughed too and said yes of course the Sturmbannführer could come down and see the prisoner and, yes, of course he understood this was routine and there was no need for bothersome paperwork.

'It would be simpler all round if I met one of your men outside the cell, there's really no need for you to come down.'

He dressed in the Sturmbannführer uniform he'd found – he reckoned a rank any higher may arouse suspicion given his age – and went straight to the cell where a guard was waiting outside. He told the guard to give him the keys, he wasn't to worry, he'd return them. 'You can go now.'

The first thing Josef said as he entered the cell was 'Rudi!' He looked at him in astonishment. The man was sitting on the edge of a narrow bed and Rudi went to sit next to him.

'What is this all about Joe?'

'Nothing.' He was shaking violently and his eyes were red. His breath smelt of fear. 'I mean, it's obviously not nothing... otherwise I wouldn't be here. It's a misunderstanding, Rudi, a case of mistaken identity!'

'Who do they think you are?'

'Would you believe it, a British spy – it's ridiculous!'

Harald Fuchs world disintegrated a little further. 'You've not mentioned anything about me, have you?'

'No, Rudi, I mean not yet—'

'What the hell do you mean not *yet*?'

'I thought I could say you're a friend so you can vouch for me – just a friend, no more than that – obviously. What with you and my *Mitgliedskarte*... you'll vouch for me, Rudi, won't you... are you even listening?'

Rudi was lost in another world, one where he was being tortured and then dragged naked through the streets of Lübeck and forced to marry Else in front of everyone he knew while still naked and... Christ, his parents, they'd...

'Rudi!'

'Yes, sorry, I am listening, Joe, keep your voice down. I'll get you out of here, don't worry.'

'Really?' He looked pitifully grateful and threw his arms round the young SS officer. Fuchs knew it was his opportunity to act. He pulled Josef close to him, the smell of the man's sweat almost overpowering. He moved his hands to Josef's head and ruffled his hair in as affectionate a manner as he could manage and then moved his hand to his cheek, stroking it gently before placing it across his mouth. He used his weight to force the man down and his hands to cover his mouth and nose. He was surprised how long it took Josef to realise what was happening, by which time it was too late. He was surprised at how quickly Josef suffocated. He'd expected it to take longer.

He sat with the limp and lifeless body for a while, gently stroking his head as if helping him to sleep before covering it with the coarse blanket, pulling it up to cover most of his face. Untersturmführer Harald Fuchs was remarkably composed as he closed the cell door and stopped outside the guard's office to throw the keys on his desk and tell him prisoner Lustenberger was now asleep and he should leave him be. Back in the SS offices he took off the Sturmbannführer's uniform and put his own back on. He didn't want to risk being seen leaving the building so late or someone noticing him arriving home well past one so he found a quiet inner office where he could rest for a few hours and then be at his desk when his colleagues arrived in the morning.

–

Karl Henniger arrived early the following morning, looking forward to the interrogation of Werner Lustenberger. Having the two women identify him so readily was a real coup. It was only a matter of time before he confessed and this time Henniger ensured he'd find out everything about who he was working for. And overnight there'd been more good news: the specialist search team had found a metal box hidden in the eaves of the roof of the building next door to where Lustenberger lived. It contained a Minox Riga camera and other paperwork.

Karl Henniger was on the verge of breaking a British spy ring. Surely promotion was now inevitable.

Then the telephone rang.

–

At first it appeared Werner Lustenberger had died in his sleep, which was of course a disaster but could be put down to sheer bad luck. It was only early in the afternoon that the autopsy report came in, showing he'd been suffocated. After that all hell broke loose. The custody officer and the guard who'd been on duty that night were brought in and slowly the tale of the mysterious Sturmbannführer emerged. The custody sergeant explained he'd not actually seen him but he had definitely called on an internal SS line and the guard said yes it was definitely a Sturmbannführer but it was dimly lit in the corridor and he didn't get a very good view.

No, he wouldn't know him if he saw him again.

Chapter 18

Berlin
August 1939

If you don't get out there now it may be too late.

It was what everyone was telling Barney Allen. Piers Devereux was part of a now increasingly influential group at 54 Broadway convinced war was imminent. The MI6 director Sir Hugh Sinclair was slightly more cautious but no less pessimistic. The Foreign Office was all over the place as usual: it was hard to make out what they really thought though the consensus at Broadway was that they were counting too much on forming an alliance with the Soviet Union and they'd left this far too late.

But most of all it was also what his network in Germany was telling him, especially Jack Miller. It wasn't that Jack was panicking – he wasn't the type – but there was a nervous tone to his communications.

I need to know what's going to happen if... you know... When are you coming over? If you're planning to come over you'd better make it sooner rather than later... do you have a date yet? Maybe I should come to London...

It was that last message that determined it for Barney Allen. He couldn't risk Jack Miller coming to London: he doubted Jack would get back into Germany and he needed Jack in Berlin.

Over the past few months much of Barney's network of spies, sources and contacts had withered away. For a start there was the group run by Werner. Since his arrest and death Barney had decided to avoid contact with any of Werner's sub-agents, even though it appeared he'd died without giving anything away. They were cast adrift like the rear carriage from a moving train.

Then there were Jack's sub-agents: by now, many of them had fled Germany or were refusing to have anything to do with him any more and Barney couldn't really blame them. He knew they were lucky none had been arrested and betrayed Jack. He put that down to their taking care in recruiting people and his skill at managing to keep in contact with them while still operating on the cell principle, whereby they were as isolated as possible from other agents in the network.

Barney Allen arrived in Berlin on a Tuesday morning in the middle of August on the night train from Paris. It was just over three months since he'd been in the city when he'd fled from it on another night train, this one to Amsterdam.

He didn't think anyone suspected him of being connected with Werner Lustenberger but couldn't be certain, and nor could he be sure if his hurried departure from Berlin hadn't aroused suspicion. So Edward Campion became an accountant called Brian McKenzie, a Canadian citizen from Toronto, in Berlin because he'd been on business in Paris and his office had asked him while he was in Europe – they thought Europe was like a small country – to go to Berlin to chase a debt owed to one of their clients by a company called Kohn and Sons. In case anyone checked, Kohn and Sons was a Jewish-owned company, which the owners had closed down two years previously rather than being forced to give it away. Barney had to admit Broadway came up with some bloody good cover stories.

Brian McKenzie was booked into a small hotel just off Pariser Strasse, the kind of place the Gestapo paid less attention to than the larger hotels. It was also a short walk from Jack's apartment on Sächsische Strasse, where they met a few hours after his arrival.

'You don't have a Canadian accent.'

'Hopefully the Germans won't realise that and with some luck I won't bump into too many Canadians.'

'You don't look like a Brian either.'

Barney shrugged and looked round Jack's apartment. It was a comfortable place, bright and airy with a nice parquet floor, but a complete mess with piles of papers everywhere, along with three typewriters, a dozen empty bottles and a half a dozen soon-to-be-empty ones. The kitchen had at least a week's worth of washing up on display. If the Gestapo ever raided the place, they wouldn't know where to start. They were sitting facing each other in armchairs and Barney noticed a silk scarf draped over the back of Jack's chair. The scarf was dark green with a floral motif in bright colours. Barney nodded towards it.

'Is that yours, Jack?'

The American turned round and smiled as he rubbed the silk between his fingers. He shook his head.

'Have you had a woman here?'

'Plural.'

'I beg your pardon?'

'Women rather than woman. You don't need to worry though, Brian, none of them are Nazis. That's just the kind of thing a Brian would worry about.'

'It's too dangerous having a woman here.'

'Helps my cover story though, don't you think? Young American abroad… money, drink, women… Less suspicious than living a monastic life. I'm interested in sport, women and drink – not politics, remember? I'm careful who I bring back, you don't need to worry.'

'I'm pleased to hear you vet them, that's a relief.'

Jack held up the silk scarf. 'This belonged to a Polish Jewish girl, the most beautiful woman I've met in Berlin. She was something interesting in the fashion industry here but fled with her family to Paris a year ago. She was back last month to collect some things.'

'Foolish of her to return.'

'She'd managed to get French papers. Have you ever noticed how a woman's scent remains on a silk scarf for ever?'

Barney looked carefully at Jack: despite the carefree, almost louche manner his face was more lined and he seemed fidgety, bouncing a foot up and down in an annoying manner and chewing his fingernails. He hadn't stopped smoking since Barney had arrived.

'How come you never told me about this Werner Lustenberger?'

'I did, Jack.'

'After he was arrested, when you asked me to find out what had happened to him.'

'I was going to tell you. He was arrested on the Monday, wasn't he, and we were due to meet on the Tuesday. I was planning to tell you about him then and vice versa and I was going to get you to work as a team. You were going to be my pack of wolves, Jack: now you're a lone wolf. So, what did you find out?'

'I've told you what I know: at the end of June his apartment was advertised for rent. I wasn't going to risk going in to enquire, they were bound to be checking on that. But then there were the death notices for him in the *Völkischer Beobachter* and *Der Angriff* – they must have wanted to make sure people knew he was dead.'

'There's an important contact Werner was looking after. Now I need you to take them over. Listen carefully.'

It took Barney an hour to carefully explain everything to Jack Miller, the American listening carefully, and when Barney finished Jack sat back and ran the silk scarf under his nose.

'I can see why you want to keep this one going.'

'You'll get on with it, Jack?'

The American nodded.

'I think I'll be here for at least a week. It will take me that long to find out that Kohn and Sons has closed down and there's no way my clients in Canada can get their money back.'

'There is something else, before you go. My commissions have dried up: British newspapers don't seem very interested in sports stories from Germany these days and as for the American ones – I've more or less run out of travel stories, to be honest. I'm not too sure about this but if I'm going to maintain my credibility here, I think I'm going to need to immerse myself in the foreign press corps – up to now I've avoided them. Otherwise, the authorities will start wondering what I'm up to. I need to register as a news correspondent at the Propaganda Ministry and start attending their briefings. There's an Italian restaurant where the English-speaking reporters hang out – I need to join them. If I start writing news features can you make sure they get published?'

'I'll sort that out – but nothing too controversial, Jack, I—'

'For Christ's sake – anything and everything in the damn country is controversial.'

'It sounds like a good idea: why the hesitation?'

'Because the foreign correspondents here – especially the American ones – tend to fall into one of two camps: there are those who are frankly too credulous about the regime, they tend to believe and write too readily what they're told. Then there are those who are less credulous and far more critical – proper journalists in other words – but they tend not to last too long before they have their accreditation withdrawn and they're thrown out—'

'We can't be having that.'

'I know.'

'So what's the problem, Jack? You'll just have to join the former camp and get on with it, as unpleasant as it may feel. In the meantime, you'd better get on with that contact I was telling you about.'

–

Jack Miller became a British agent at the end of 1937, since when he'd reminded himself every day that however many precautions he took and however careful he was, it was impossible to eliminate danger.

He knew whenever he turned up to meet a contact there was a real possibility he'd been betrayed and the Gestapo would be waiting for him. What surprised him was how when he was back at his apartment at the end of a successful meeting he'd sit in his armchair and reflect on how exhilarating the experience had been. At first, he assumed there was something wrong with him – what normal person flirts with death like that? – but then realised if he didn't feel that way he wouldn't have lasted as long as he had.

But this mission was testing his resolve to its absolute limit. The day after the Englishman gave him his instructions, he went on a dry run, feeling more exposed than usual because it wasn't as if he was on his way to cover a sporting event or writing a travel piece.

He took the U-Bahn to Tiergarten and headed north. He knew a nice restaurant in Moabit and if stopped he'd say he was heading there, explaining it was such a pleasant evening he'd decided to go this way. He entered Brücken Allee from the south and walked along until he came to the apartment block, pausing opposite it to light a cigarette and take a closer look. He couldn't spot anything obviously suspicious: no one lurking in the shadows, no twitching curtains, no car parked outside the building with the driver pretending to doze. He moved on: he knew these days the Gestapo were more subtle, less obvious. He left Brücken Allee through its north side and caught the U-Bahn back from Bellevue.

The following evening, he walked all the way to Brücken Allee and went down the side of the apartment block where some large rubbish bins gave him a place to hide. He'd imagined it would be a long wait but he'd only been there for ten minutes when he heard footsteps and peered out through the bins. It was a Japanese man walking towards the door. Jack moved towards him as the man carefully unlocked the door and looked round in a confused manner and held the door open for Jack to follow him.

The man did glance round as Jack followed him up the stairs: Jack smiled and wished him 'good evening' and doffed his trilby and the man nodded. He glanced round again as they passed the third floor and then stopped on the stairs, clearly unsure whether to say anything. Jack stepped towards him.

'I'm a friend of Werner and I need to speak with you – in your apartment.'

Tadashi Kimura looked shocked at first and then angry and said that wasn't possible and Jack said it had to be, it was urgent: they could hardly discuss matters here on the stairs, could they – what about the neighbours?

Moments later they were inside the apartment. Kimura remained standing for a while and then closed the curtains, finally indicating Jack should sit.

'Can you sit down too please, Tadashi? You're making me nervous.'

'I don't know who you are.'

Jack resisted the temptation to say he wasn't sure either and wondered whether it would be rude to take out his cigarettes. 'I told you, I'm a friend of Werner.'

'I don't know anyone called Werner. I'm not sure who you are or what this is about and I—'

'You met Werner at a club for homosexuals in February and you brought him to this apartment where you introduced him to Arno and… please let me finish… and you asked for his help in getting Arno out of Berlin and to England and Werner said he'd help but in return he'd want secret information from the Japanese embassy which the British would be interested in and you handed that over to Werner towards the end of March.'

He paused, unsure whether the Japanese diplomat had taken all that in. Tadashi said nothing and remained motionless as he watched Jack as if looking for some clue.

'Where is Arno?'

Still no reaction. Tadashi continued to study Jack through the spiral of smoke as he removed his jacket, loosened his tie and leaned forward.

'How do you know Werner?'

You'll have to tell him, Jack, there's no point in keeping anything from him… he's too important.

'We were colleagues: we're in the same line of work.'

'You're not German?'

'I'm an American.'

The first sign of a reaction, slightly raised eyebrows.

'You said you were a colleague of Werner: has anything happened to him?'

'When did you last see him, Tadashi?'

'You tell me.'

'I know you saw him at the end of March when you handed the documents over and I believe he next came to see you towards the end of April to assure you everything was in order and soon he'd be able to help Arno escape.'

The Japanese diplomat nodded. 'He told me it wouldn't be too long and I said it had taken too long already but he said they had to be very careful. Since then, I've heard nothing. I have no idea where he is – he lied to us and tricked me into giving him the—'

'He's dead, Tadashi.'

'Who?'

'Werner: he was arrested by the Gestapo on 6 May. He was about to arrange Arno's escape. We assume he was killed by the Gestapo, probably soon after his arrest, we—'

'How can you be so certain?' Tadashi looked nervous, wringing his hands before getting up and pacing the room.

'Because as far as we know none of his contacts or sources have been arrested or questioned. If they'd tortured him, he'd have told them something, but we don't think that happened. No one's approached you, have they?'

'No.'

'There we are then… it's just over three months since his arrest. If the Gestapo knew anything about you you'd have heard by now so we can now resume our relationship. As we promised, we'll get Arno out of Berlin and once you know he's safe in England you can supply us with more intelligence. London are very keen to know more about Japan's intentions in case there is a war between Britain and Germany.'

Tadashi stopped pacing the room and sat down again, he was shaking his head and continued to do so and when he finally spoke it was with a bitter smile on his face.

'The only flaw in that plan is that I have no idea where Arno is.'

Chapter 19

They'd waited until the middle of June before doing anything and even then, there was precious little they could do.

At first, they were annoyed, Arno more so than Tadashi who had some sense of how these things worked and how slow government departments and agencies could be. He told Arno he still instinctively trusted Werner and he was sure that when he eventually showed up there'd be a satisfactory explanation.

But Arno grew increasingly nervous and irritable. He no longer bothered with his medical textbooks or studied English, telling Tadashi there was no point: why would he bother if he wasn't going to England? He'd be slumped on the sofa in his dressing gown when Tadashi left for work and would still be like that when he returned. He'd say very little but at some stage in the evening he'd snap and there'd be a whispered argument during which Arno would berate the older man for being so stupid.

In the middle of June, the tension with Arno reached such an intolerable level that Tadashi promised to do something. One evening he travelled down to Schöneberg and to the club on Reppich Strasse where he'd first met Werner in February. The club had been closed down, though he knew that wouldn't satisfy Arno, so Tadashi told him he'd spoken to a barman there who knew Werner and said he thought he was out of town for a few weeks because his mother was ill.

'Where is his mother ill?'

'I have no idea. But it shows we have no reason to worry.'

But Arno was unshakeable in the belief he did had every reason to worry and this was underlined a month later, on a Saturday evening in July, when Tadashi agreed Arno could go out for a walk. He'd not left the apartment for weeks and Tadashi felt a walk might calm him down.

They took every precaution – waiting until a time when dusk was about to give up the struggle with night and darkness would drop onto the city. Tadashi went to the ground floor, checked all was clear and propped open the side door and waited in the doorway so he could watch both the stairs and the pathway. He coughed – three times – and on this signal that all was clear Arno came down the stairs in his stockinged feet and holding his shoes in an effort to minimise any noise.

As he passed the door to the apartment on the second floor it flew open and Frau Sauer was standing there, her arms folded high on her chest as if preparing to scold a naughty child.

'Who,' she demanded, 'are you? And what the hell are you doing here – why are you in your socks and carrying your shoes: you must be a burglar!'

Arno replied in his most deferential manner: nothing could be further from the truth – he was simply delivering a letter and had removed his shoes because on this floor they made a noise and at this time of night—

'I don't believe you! Who removes their shoes like that? And why is the door open down there, it's meant to be closed at all times. I've seen you before, haven't I – with that foreign man on the fourth floor?'

Arno shrugged and muttered something about being very sorry and it wouldn't happen again. Frau Sauer unfolded her arms and started to move back inside her flat when Tadashi appeared from downstairs.

'You don't need to worry – this gentleman is with me, there's no problem, I can assure you.'

She looked far from assured as Tadashi took Arno's elbow and guided him back up the stairs.

'And what happened then?' Jack noticed that Tadashi's composure had broken, he seemed to be on the verge of tears.

'Fortunately, nothing happened with Frau Sauer, she's a busy-body rather than a Nazi informer. I took her a very expensive box of Swiss chocolates and apologised and said the man was my German tutor and neither of us had mentioned it at the time because I'm embarrassed about my German. I don't know whether she believed me but nothing came of it. It was too much for Arno though: he was convinced someone was going to inform the Gestapo and they'd raid the apartment and arrest him and… I tried to reassure him but he wasn't having any of it. He told me if he was caught in my apartment I'd be in trouble too even though I'm a diplomat… I thought I'd managed to calm him down but later that week – it was a Wednesday, 19 July – I came home from work to find him gone. There was a note saying it was for the best and not to try and look for him and to take care, that was it…'

Tadashi's voiced trailed off. He looked devastated. 'I cannot tell you how… bereft I am. My world feels as if it has come to an end. I blame myself. Maybe I should never have approached Werner for help.'

'You have no idea where he is?'

'None whatsoever. I wouldn't know where to start looking and even if I did it would only make matters worse, I'm hardly inconspicuous.'

'What can I do to help?'

'Find Arno and get him out of this wretched country and to England. Once he's there and I know he's safe you have my solemn word I'll give you the pick of intelligence from the embassy.'

–

Barney Allen – Brian McKenzie – had no idea how Noel Moore found him.

It was the Friday morning, the day after Jack had been to see Tadashi Kimura – they were due to catch up that afternoon – and Brian McKenzie was on the pointless trail of Kohn and Sons and as he suspected not getting anywhere, which suited him fine. As long as it helped verify his cover story.

He was on Dorotheen Strasse having just left the Reich Ministry for the Interior where an earnest and severely asthmatic young man – first name Adolf – in the Office for Jewish Affairs was trying to explain the situation to Mr McKenzie from Canada.

The meeting had got off to an awkward start when he remarked that Adolf was probably a useful name to have in career terms and the young Adolf looked mortified as he nervously glanced around the room to check no one had heard that. He explained that although a small sum of money had been found in the Kohn and Sons bank account it was now the property of the Reich and Mr McKenzie could fill in a form if he wished but he doubted a Canadian company would be very high up the list of beneficiaries.

Mr McKenzie asked for this in writing and Adolf told him to return on Monday and it would be waiting for him – *there is a small fee, you understand.*

It wasn't quite lunchtime but he was hungry and not due to meet Jack until he'd finished at the Propaganda Ministry so he was looking for somewhere to eat when a man appeared alongside him and said very *sotto voce* to keep on walking and then take the next left and they could wander up to the Spree and walk along its banks and have a nice chat.

'Have you heard the news?' Noel Moore was less relaxed than when they'd last met, more nervous – but then that seemed to be the case with most people in Berlin. The whole city appeared to be on edge.

'Not for a day or so, I did look at yesterday's *Der Angriff.*'

'Don't bother. This is news that won't be in any newspapers, not yet at any rate: there are rumours that the Nazis and the Soviets are about to announce some kind of treaty or alliance.'

'What? That's impossible surely—'

'We don't know quite what it is but it's likely to be a non-aggression pact of sorts. Apparently, Moscow station have picked that up and one or two of our sources are saying the same. They've already got a commercial agreement in place and evidently the talks in Moscow between us and the French and the Soviets are going badly. All hell's broken loose at the embassy and at our place too. Have you ever met the ambassador?'

'You mean Henderson? No, I can't say I have: Piers can't stand him though.'

'Not surprised – he's been one of the most ardent appeasers of Hitler and now look at all the good that's done him, landed Britain right in it. Christ… the fools… we're making plans to get out, you know. We're sending out what we can by diplomatic bag and burning the rest – it's like a version of hell in our office, I can tell you. It's bloody August and we have all the fires raging away, it's unbearable, an actual inferno. They're even making plans for where to send us – Frank's going to Oslo and I've just been told I'm off to Bern.'

'With Basil – yes, I know.'

'How?'

'I recommended you, Noel. Basil's a good sort but getting on a bit. He could do with you there and Switzerland's going to be a very important place for us assuming they can remain neutral. I'll be needing some favours from you. What about your networks here?'

'We're dismantling them as we speak – Frank's dishing out exit visas left, right and centre. Our networks have shrunk considerably in recent weeks but the message to those remaining is to go to ground and forget about us but the truth is folk don't really need telling that, that was what they were planning to do. I'm not prying, but do I take it you have people in Berlin still running agents?'

Barney Allen nodded. Half a dozen SS officers were walking towards them and the two Englishmen stepped either side to allow them through, nodding politely as they did so.

'Frank's planning to run a few who'll remain here from Oslo, not too sure how he's going to manage that. There is one though…'

Noel Moore hesitated, seemingly unsure whether to continue. 'Around two years ago – it would have been early summer 1937 because it wasn't long after Henderson became ambassador – I came across this chap. Are you a golfer, by any chance?'

'Well, the odd round, you know, but horses are more my thing: in my experience they're more obedient than golf balls.'

'There's a very decent golf club here in Berlin, the Wannsee Golf and Country Club and I used to play there most weekends up to a year ago when it all became unbearable: difficult to concentrate on a putt when there's a bloody swastika flag above the hole. They'd even started putting little Nazi eagles on the golf balls. That summer I met this very agreeable German chap: I was due to play with a chap from the French embassy but he didn't turn up and this man – who I knew by sight – his partner had cried off too so we played a round together. We both played off the same handicap and were very well matched and not just in terms of golf, but also in how we got on: conversation was easy and the silences weren't awkward. I told him I was a minor official in the consular section of the British embassy and he told me he worked in one of the ministries and that was that. We arranged to play another round a fortnight later and then a week or so after that and by the August we were really rather pally. We're a similar age, both divorced and without children, so that was something else in common and we arranged to have dinner at the club one evening and that's when he told me he works at the Air Ministry and he's a Luftwaffe officer. Let's go down there, it's a bit quieter.'

They turned away from the river and into a quiet lane.

'Turns out Ernst is an Oberstleutnant, equivalent to a wing commander in the RAF, so pretty senior. But he didn't say what he did and to be honest I didn't push it because at that stage there was no indication at all that he'd want to work for us and I didn't want to blow my own cover by asking him. He'd mentioned he wasn't a Nazi Party member but he never said anything against the

Nazis: he came across as very loyal, rather the Prussian officer-type if you know what I mean.

'By the autumn we'd taken to having dinner every few weeks and one evening he asked me about my divorce: it was a bit out of the blue, took me aback, to be frank – you know… was it mutual thing, any regrets – could have been awkward but in fact it was rather helpful to get it off my chest – lots of regrets as it happens. Then Ernst told me his story, which is really rather pitiful.

'He's from Leipzig and met his wife there and by all accounts it was a very happy marriage, but in 1935 – after those anti-Jewish laws came out – it turned out that her father's mother had been Jewish, which his wife had no idea about. It didn't stop her being a German citizen but she was concerned it would affect her career as she was a schoolteacher, so for some convoluted reason, she insisted on divorcing him because she didn't want his career to be damaged either. As far as I understand it, the plan was that once they were divorced, they'd sort out her paperwork and one thing and another and they could re-marry, but it all went dreadfully wrong and she ended up killing herself in a bedsit in Frankfurt.'

'That's dreadful, Noel, appalling.'

'I could tell you literally hundreds of stories like this, it's far too common, I'm afraid. Ernst told me that this all happened just before he moved to Berlin so no one is aware of this, just that he's divorced.'

'How dreadful. Is that what made you approach him?'

'I was thinking about it, but before I could make the first move, he asked if I know anyone at the British embassy who may be interested in information that may prevent a war, words to that effect. As per the rule book I played it very straight, said that wasn't my area but I could ask around to see if anyone knew anyone – you know the score, and then did nothing, waited for him to bring up the subject again. When he did so I asked him why he was doing this and he said it was his way of getting his own back after what happened to his wife. He'd thought of leaving Germany but had nowhere to go, doesn't speak another language et cetera, no money… whereas if he stayed here he'd have a job and access to all kinds of information. He told me his job was to do with the development of a new fighter aircraft, which was then in its very early stages.

'I told him I'd see what I could do and of course reported the matter to Frank and he told me that Henderson was being bloody awkward. By now we're well into 1938 and the embassy was toeing the Foreign Office line that we're to do nothing that would damage our relationship with Germany and certainly nothing that could undermine our mutual desire to defeat Bolshevism, though I'm not sure how that will play if it's true that Germany and the Soviet Union are to become best friends. Frank described Henderson as an arch proponent of the Foreign Office view that espionage is a distasteful business and they'd take an especially dim view of a senior Luftwaffe officer becoming a British spy—'

'I find that somewhat hard to believe…'

'It's true, I'm afraid: he did ask Broadway for their approval and they said to check with Henderson so Frank raised it with him in rather vague terms… senior German officer, based at one of their ministries… nothing to give them a clue as to who he was, and they said absolutely not.

'I was prepared to go ahead nonetheless and I think Frank was too but then… Ernst – his surname's Scholz, by the way – began to have second thoughts and, to be frank, I don't think our dilly-dallying helped. He said he'd decided he could only justify supplying intelligence in the event of war breaking out. I didn't think I was on awfully strong grounds to argue, though I did point out that sometimes intelligence can help avert a war. So that's the situation, Barney: potentially the best bloody spy I'd have ever recruited except I'll be out of Berlin. He'll need someone to handle him in person. That's why I asked if you had someone in Berlin – someone good I could hand him over to before I bugger off to Switzerland.'

'I think I do have just the person, Noel.'

'You are being serious, aren't you?'

'Whyever not, Jack?'

It was the Tuesday afternoon, 22 August, and they were in Jack's apartment, with little sign of the American's normally care-free attitude. He looked stunned.

'I'll tell you whyever not… last week after I saw the Japanese diplomat you told me that finding this Arno guy and getting him out of Germany and to England was my number one priority and after that running the diplomat would be my new number one priority. Now you're telling me that tomorrow morning I'm going to be introduced to a Luftwaffe officer and if there's a war I'm going to run him too and he'll also be my number one priority. And that's not forgetting all my other agents I have to travel round the country to see. You'll forgive me for appearing confused – and overworked.'

'I'm afraid that's what happens, Jack.'

'I need some help.'

'I'm working on that.'

'What the hell does that mean?'

'It means that I have an excellent potential agent but I'm waiting to hear from them… the time's not right at the moment.'

'Jesus… meanwhile I look after everything on my own. You've heard they're bringing in rations?'

'I saw something in—'

Jack went over to the table and came back with a sheet of paper, which he read from. 'Seven hundred grams of meat a week; one eighth of a pound of coffee; one hundred and ten grams of marmalade – I can't stand the stuff; two hundred and eighty grams of sugar. Apparently, bread is going to be rationed too but no one's sure how much. There is some good news though…'

'Go on.'

'I'm told that foreign correspondents in Berlin will be in the same category as heavy labourers and we'll get double rations.'

'Well, that's something.'

'Yes, two hundred and twenty grams of marmalade.'

'Is that official then?'

'As I'm now a fully signed up foreign correspondent I've started hanging around the Propaganda Ministry for their daily briefings, which is tedious but could turn out to be useful, and I met a couple of American correspondents who invited me to join them at an Italian restaurant where they have a *Stammtisch* – have you heard of that?'

'A table of some sort?'

'It's a corner table reserved for them – they just turn up late in the evening and the owner lets them stay as long as they want, I'm not surprised, given the amount they drink. I think it's going to be a useful place to pick up gossip. That's where I heard about the possibility of us getting double rations.'

'Anyone there who could be of use, Jack?'

The American shrugged. 'Not seen enough of them sober. You never know though: I'll keep my eyes open. How much longer are you in Berlin?'

'As long as I'm able to be, Jack: if the Nazis announce their pact with the Soviet Union then I'd say it's just a matter of days before we sign something with Poland and once that happens I think Berlin will be a less than hospitable place for an Englishman. I aim to be in Belgium or France by the end of the week.'

'You're Canadian – remember?'

'Even so – I don't fancy sitting in a Gestapo cell answering a general knowledge quiz about Canada to prove my credentials.'

'The Mackenzie.'

'I beg your pardon?'

'The Mackenzie's the longest river in Canada, if the Gestapo ask you.'

'Thank you, Jack, that's terribly helpful. Noel Moore will introduce you to the Luftwaffe officer tomorrow and after that you'll make your own arrangements. And of course, once war starts, you'll only be able to write for your American newspapers so…'

'We've been through this, yes, I know.'

'That chap in New York – Ted Morris – he's been terribly helpful, very committed to helping us.'

'I think you'll find most Jews are.'

'Indeed. And you have the code sheets somewhere safe? You will find it takes longer to formulate a message that way, but once he sees your copy is preceded by a coded message, he'll pass it on to our man in New York. You'll soon get used to it.'

'You must have been through this a dozen times at least.'

'Practice makes perfect. Now, just one more thing… you need to know how to get something like photographs to us or communicate with us in a real emergency. Come closer.'

1940

Chapter 20

Kielce, Poland
January 1940

Oberführer Karl-Heinrich von Naundorf was beginning to realise that war was a funny business. Not funny as in hilarious, although it certainly had its amusing moments. But more funny as in unusual.

One of the unusual aspects to war – which he'd not expected – was the pace of it: short bursts of intense activity followed by long periods when very little happened.

That was certainly the case with von Naundorf's SS battalion. They'd been heavily involved in a brief spell of at times quite bitter fighting during the invasion of Poland in September 1939, though in truth the conquest of the country hadn't exactly been a battle between equals. The following few weeks had seen more intense activity as they rounded up local officials, prominent Jews, socialists, communists and Polish nationalists, as well as officers from the Polish army.

He'd allowed his unit to have plenty of fun with their prisoners – until at a meeting of the divisional command it was pointed out that one of the main purposes of taking prisoners was to put them in prison, preferably while they were still alive.

After that he exercised more discipline with his battalion and in the middle of December they were posted to Kielce, a city one hundred miles south of Warsaw, which was becoming full of Jews who'd been expelled from their homes in the surrounding towns and villages. As a result, the Jews now made up around a third of the city's population of about eighty thousand, a fact that angered the local Polish population who didn't seem to like the Jews any more than the Germans did.

Von Naundorf's unit was there to help guard the Jews and keep an eye on the locals. They became part of the 4th SS Police Regiment and this led to a growing sense of disquiet among his men. They were soldiers, they insisted: fighters, certainly not policemen. There was also a tension between Karl-Heinrich von Naundorf and Oberführer Fritz Katzmann who was based in Kielce but was in charge of policing for the whole of the Radom district. Von Naundorf the lawyer felt that even though both men were of the same rank, he was superior to Katzmann, a man who'd been a mere carpenter before joining the Nazi Party rescued him from obscurity, as it had done with so many others.

Von Naundorf did his best to ensure there was plenty to keep his men occupied. There were the beginnings of some resistance in the area that took up some of their time and he did his best to ensure there were plenty of actions against the Jews.

In this respect von Naundorf had an ally at their headquarters on the corner of Paderewskiego and Solna Streets. Franz Wittek was something of an enigmatic character, sometimes referred to as the Scarlet Pimpernel. No one was quite sure who he was, where he was from or indeed where he was and what he was doing at any particular time.

In fact von Naundorf had first met Wittek when he was running the *Selbstschutz* operation in Breslau before the war. Wittek was originally a Croat who'd spent many years in Germany and was now able to pass himself off as a Pole. He was also a committed Nazi and a clever, ruthless man. In Kielce he'd set up an effective network of informers and was loathed by the local population.

Von Naundorf did all he could to encourage Wittek and most important of all ensure that he was given the best tip-offs first. It hadn't quite been like that on the last Friday in January though. Wittek had discovered that a group of young Jews – all members of the Jewish Socialist Bund – were hiding in a house on Pocieszka, just behind Targowa. But somehow Wittek had managed to tell Katzmann about this first and von Naundorf was furious.

He burst into Katzmann's office and demanded to know what was going on. Katzmann said not to worry: everything was under control and he'd 'got his eyes on them'.

'Katzmann what the hell's the point of keeping your eyes on them? What are you waiting for – you want them to start taking shots at our boys?'

'I'm sick and tired of you always criticising, Naundorf. You deal with it.' Katzmann had a habit of dropping the 'von' in an attempt to bring his fellow officer down to his level.

So Oberführer Karl-Heinrich von Naundorf did deal with it. He treated it as a proper operation, surrounding the area and then leading his men into the house on Pocieszka. There were around a dozen Bundists in the house: all in their late teens or early twenties, a mixture of men and women. They looked shocked but one of the men asked von Naundorf if they had a warrant, so von Naundorf hit him across the face with his Luger.

The search of the house revealed nothing and the group was lined up outside the house waiting to be marched to the Gestapo headquarters on Paderewskiego. It was then that one of the women – more a girl, really – said they were ready to go along with them and although his troops laughed, von Naundorf thought that was odd. It was as if they were eager to get away from the house, so he ordered another search and told his men that this time they need to be thorough, like opening the odd door.

It didn't take them long: they found a trap door under a sheet of tarpaulin in the cellar and under it a tiny cellar – with half a dozen petrified young children aged around five or six hidden in it.

All hell broke loose when they dragged the children into the street to join the older ones, some of whom even tried to bargain with the officers, pleading with them to take the adults but spare the children.

They marched the prisoners along for a while, the children crying and the adults trying to calm them down and assuring them all would be fine and von Naundorf noticed one of his storm troopers looked pale and upset and briefly put a comforting hand on the shoulder of a young boy. He made a mental note to have him transferred east that night. That would teach him.

Then one of his junior officers, an Obersturmführer from Dresden called Gerd, had a smart idea, one that appealed to von Naundorf. It would serve the dual purpose of keeping his men amused and getting a problem off their hands. They came to the River Silnica and Gerd ordered his men to line the children up on the riverbank. He waited until the children realised what was about to happen before pushing them into the freezing water. Each of them only thrashed around very briefly before drowning. When it was all over – it had only taken a minute or two – the men noticed a group of local Poles had lined up on the bank of the Silnica and were cheering.

Von Naundorf didn't know whether to be appalled that they'd done something the Poles approved of or pleased they appreciated it. War was a funny business.

It all became rather messy after that. A lorry was meant to meet them to take the other prisoners back to Paderewskiego but it didn't turn up so he decided they'd march there, but hadn't reckoned on it taking as long as it did and then it started to pour with rain, so by the time they got back there he was soaking wet and had had enough.

As a consequence, he wasn't in the mood for dealing with Oberführer Katzmann who was insisting that as von Naundorf was responsible for arresting the group he was also responsible for processing them and when von Naundorf replied there was really no need for that Katzmann said there really was, unless he had a problem with orders that came from the Führer himself and von Naundorf said not to be so ridiculous, the Führer had more important things to worry about than fingerprinting and photographing Jewish prisoners – and it all descended into a shouting match, which became quite unedifying.

Von Naundorf stormed out of Katzmann's office and ordered Gerd to assemble the prisoners in the yard and line them up against the wall.

They realised what was happening, of course. They were all defiant, pushing and pulling and swearing at the Germans in Yiddish or Polish, but they knew what their fate was and as the last of them was put against the wall they fell quiet and stared at the Germans in a dignified manner and von Naundorf noticed that unsettled one or two of his men so he told them to get a move on and then the prisoners began to sing, quietly but in a remarkably harmonious way, so much so they sounded like a choir.

The song didn't last long, of course, before it was broken by the machine-gun fire.

Try as he might, Oberführer Karl-Heinrich von Naundorf couldn't get that song out of his head. That was the night that his nightmares began.

War was a funny business.

Chapter 21

Berlin
February 1940

Life was difficult in so many ways for Jack Miller that he sometimes wondered quite how he coped.

Of course, life was unquestionably difficult for any civilian in
Berlin, having to survive on ever-diminishing food rations and
meagre clothing coupons. At least as a foreign correspondent
he was entitled to increased rations, but life was still hard. The
winter had been particularly gruesome: no coal for homes and
they weren't allowed to use gas for hot water, which was only
available on Sundays. He was dreading the next winter.

There was also an atmosphere in the city that was hard to
ignore. When the war began the previous September the majority
of the population were shocked. They'd not expected war, having
been assured the British and the French would bow to the might
of Germany. As a result, a pall of gloom had descended over the
capital. Much of the civilian population appeared to be distressed.
One of the ways in which the reality of war showed itself was the
death notices in the newspapers. The approved form of death
notice was to say a soldier had 'died for the Führer'. It didn't take
long for this phrase to disappear from many of the death notices.

Since the previous August – just before the start of the war
– he'd made an effort to be an 'official' foreign correspondent.
Although this had undoubted advantages, it was also time-
consuming. He attended the Propaganda Ministry daily briefings
as often as possible, always making a point of being sociable with

the other foreign correspondents and seeking out Boehmer, the man in charge of foreign press at the ministry who it was advisable to keep on the right side of. At least twice a week he'd go over to the Reich Foreign Ministry on Unterwasserstrasse where matters were altogether more sombre and foreign correspondents treated with more suspicion. The daily briefings were carried out in a large conference room in the basement: on the days they were allowed to attend, the foreign reporters had to sit in the rows behind the German journalists.

But it was important to be there and just as he cultivated Dr Boehmer at Propaganda, he also did his best to maintain good relations with Dr Aschmann, the head of the press office at the Foreign Ministry, and with Dr Zallatt, a nervous-looking man whose job it was to look after the American press pack. He knew it was important to get to know the right people and stay on the right side of them and for that reason he also made frequent trips to Westend to maintain his relations with the Reich Sports Office and to bump into the Reichssportführer.

He envied the foreign correspondents whose job seemed to revolve around attending the daily briefings, going on the occasional escorted press trip and then writing up their copy before heading to their regular Italian restaurant and a late night around their *Stammtisch*.

Jack Miller also had all his sporting events to cover and on top of this, being a British agent in Berlin was more than a full-time job, yet the journalism – the 'day job' as Barney called it – was a vital front to allow him to do his espionage, the 'night shift', as described by Barney. He felt over-worked and exhausted. Most nights he fell asleep in his armchair and occasionally at his desk. He felt he'd aged ten years and it had been months since he'd brought a woman back to his apartment.

Increasingly he felt overwhelmed by the sheer volume of work along with the omnipresent threat of being caught and the fear that came with that. Sometimes he allowed himself the indulgence of wondering why on earth he was doing this, why he'd agreed to become a British agent. But when he thought about it he realised he'd not so much agreed to become a British agent but rather he'd discovered he'd already been recruited as one and the decision he'd had to make then was whether to stop – and it was far harder to stop than to start.

He got into the habit of going for a walk through to the nearby Preussenpark, which was just a short stroll from his apartment and which tended to be particularly quiet in the middle of the morning or early afternoon and it felt safe to lose himself in his thoughts, and it was here he debated with himself what would happen if he stopped, if he decided to leave Germany and return to the United States and write a brief but perfectly civil letter to Barney – he'd have to send it care of the British embassy in Washington but he was sure it would find its way to him. He'd explain that he'd felt he'd done as much as could be reasonably expected of him – he liked that phrase, it felt very 'British' – and he'd felt it would be a good time to leave, before he became a liability, and he was sure Barney would understand and he'd wish him all the best and he thought about adding a postscript that Barney had his word that he would never write about his experiences working for the British, but then thought that could be a hostage to fortune as he'd been thinking of writing a novel about an American journalist spying for the British. In Germany. He'd wait until the war was over, of course, and he'd assure readers that it was entirely fictional.

But then something would cause him to snap out of such daydreams and make him realise why he was prepared to continue taking the enormous risk of spying for the British. It could be rumours of an atrocity – there were enough of those – or the publication of yet more appalling restrictions on liberty or something he'd see as he went about life in Berlin.

Earlier that month had been a good example. He been for a walk in Preussenpark in what were for him the ideal conditions: a light but persistent drizzle, which meant he was alone in the park and with his thoughts. He reached a vague conclusion that he'd give Berlin a few more months – perhaps May, maybe June – and then he could leave with his head held high, though not so high as to draw attention to himself.

He left the park on Brandenburgische Strasse, hoping to find a bakery with some bread in it. As he passed to the corner of Sauerland Strasse he saw a commotion – lots of police and shouting – and the journalist in him knew turning into the road and walking by was less likely to draw attention to himself than standing and watching.

As he walked down the street, he saw the cause of the commotion. Gestapo officers were dragging a family out of a basement and towards a police van parked in the street. Jack Miller slowed down a little, just enough to spot the terrified father and the weeping mother and the three young children following in their wake. The yellow stars on their coats told him all he needed to know. At that moment a Gestapo officer looked quizzically over at him.

Jack turned into the entrance of an insurance building where he waited a few minutes for someone to give him a form for insuring the contents of his apartment.

By the time he left, the street was empty and he knew he would carry on as a British agent for as long as it took.

He'd made his decision.

And there was some hope. Just before he'd left Berlin Barney Allen had hinted there'd be another agent to work with him and whenever he asked when that help would be forthcoming the reply would be the same as Barney Allen had always given: *the time's not right at the moment*.

He'd come to doubt the time was ever going to be right.

–

It had been a couple of weeks before the start of the war – August 1939 – when Jack had been to see Tadashi Kimura to tell him about Werner's death – and when the Japanese diplomat informed him about Arno's disappearance.

Kimura had been very clear: he'd only help the British if Jack found Arno and got him from Berlin to England. Jack knew getting Arno out of Berlin and then out of Germany and to England would be quite the most perilous thing he'd ever attempted. But he couldn't even begin to think about that until he found Arno and he had no idea of where to start.

In March he'd risked another trip to see Tadashi Kimura. He waited across the road and when he appeared in Brücken Allee just before six Jack followed him into the apartment, the diplomat acknowledging him with a brief nod of the head and a gesture indicating he should climb the stairs before him.

'Have you found Arno?'

'No, not yet I'm—'

'I said you were to only come back when you've found him. Until then I won't co-operate. It's too dangerous for you to be here.'

'I want to know if you've thought of anything that could help me find him? I need something to work on.'

Kimura shook his head and said he often stayed awake all night going over and over in his mind whether there was something Arno may have said that would be a clue. He walked over to the window, which looked out over Brücken Allee.

'You see this black vase? I always keep it here. If I ever think of anything or have any news, I'll move it from the window. Then you know to come and see me. Otherwise, I only ever want to see you again when you have news on Arno.'

—

Ernst Scholz – Oberstleutnant Ernst Scholz – was proving to be as elusive.

It had started promisingly enough that August when Barney had brought another Englishman to Jack's apartment on Sächsische Strasse, a man he introduced as Noel. Noel explained at great length – far too great a length actually – about this very agreeable Luftwaffe officer he'd become awfully pally with and how this officer's wife had turned out to have a Jewish grandparent and as a result they'd got divorced while they tried to sort it all out and it had all gone terribly wrong and she'd killed herself and of course he was bereft and as a consequence had determined to help the British but only if there was a war.

He'd delivered this in what sounded like one long sentence and paused to catch his breath.

'Which there will be, of course.'

'Will be what?'

'A war: which means yours truly will have to leave Germany, though I can assure you I won't need much asking. But that does rather leave poor Ernst finally willing to hand intelligence over to us but with no one to hand it to. Which is where you come in.'

'And we trust him?'

'Yes: I've known him for two years now and if he was going to do the dirty on me, he'd have done so by now. Everything he's told me turns out to be true, we were even able to confirm that his wife's paternal grandmother was Jewish – that took some digging, I can tell you. You're a sports journalist, I hear, Jack?'

The American nodded.

'Golf by any chance?'

'Not really, I don't have the patience.'

'Well Ernst lives for his golf. A little enthusiasm for it would be helpful.'

–

Noel Moore introduced Jack to Oberstleutnant Ernst Scholz the following evening. Scholz lived in a grand apartment block on Düsseldorfer Strasse, close to the junction with Brandenburgische Strasse. He suggested they meet in the cellar. *It's just used for storage and people rarely go down there. I'll leave it unlocked and wait for you.*

Scholz was waiting in a far corner of the cellar, standing back in the shadows of the low-ceilinged and poorly lit space. He stepped out of the shadows to shake the hands of the two visitors and then back into them.

'If anyone comes down just go to the crate there, pretend to be looking for something. You won't look out of place; it's a big block and people keep to themselves.'

Noel introduced Jack and said Jack was to be trusted just as much as him, in fact possibly more so because he was American – and then had to explain to the bemused German that was a joke.

'And you work for the same people as, Noel?'

Jack nodded.

'Good. And Noel's told you the arrangement – that I'm only prepared to help once war starts?'

'He mentioned that, yes. But we need to agree a way you can let me know when you're ready to start.'

'I was thinking about that too. Here – take my key for the cellar and this other key – the smaller one – is for my storage locker, just here. I've had another set made.'

He gestured behind him to a cage covered in steel mesh. It was about seven-foot high and full of boxes and old pieces of carpet.

'You see that box on the floor with old cans of paint in it? I'll cover it with some carpet. Come in here on a weekday – I rarely see anyone down here then – and even if you see someone, they'll ignore you. Maybe if you make a point of coming in here once a week or so. When I'm ready for us to meet I'll leave a message for you in an old envelope underneath one of the cans of paint. The message will simply give a place and time where we should meet. So I know you've seen the message and will be there, take the carpet off the box and replace it with that piece of tarpaulin. You understand all that?'

'I do.'

'Very professional, Ernst: sounds like you've done this type of thing before.'

The Luftwaffe officer moved forward, away from the shadows. Even in the dim light he looked nervous, beads of perspiration forming on his forehead. 'I've had plenty of time to think about it, Noel.'

Once the war started Jack Miller did visit the cellar underneath the Luftwaffe officer's apartment block once a week. Düsseldorfer Strasse was located between where Jack lived on Sächsische Strasse and Kurfürstendamm, making it perfectly feasible for him to be in that area.

But he knew he needed a credible reason for being in the cellar so devised a story about how a friend had rented an apartment there for a short while in 1937 and now lived in Vienna and had asked Jack to check if a suitcase he'd left behind was still in the cellar by any chance – and if anyone asked, he'd say he found the cellar door unlocked.

He varied the days and times of his visits to Düsseldorfer Strasse but no letter appeared in the box of old paint cans. In early December he had a close shave when he used the key to enter the cellar only to find the door was unlocked and a man in his fifties asked him if he could help.

Jack replied with the story about the friend and the suitcase.

'What is your friend called – I may know him?'

'Hans.'

'And his surname?'

Jack said he was terribly sorry but Hans was more of an acquaintance than a friend and he'd momentarily forgotten his surname but as he lived nearby – which he immediately regretted saying, such a basic error – he asked him to pop by.

'How come you had a key – I heard it in the lock?'

He wasn't sure how to respond and at that moment the man started to walk towards him to get a better look in the dim light. Jack said he was sorry and hurried away, the man calling after him demanding to know his name.

He didn't return to Düsseldorfer Strasse until the middle of January, angry with himself for being so ill prepared before. He took some consolation from the fact he'd not given his name and the man wouldn't have had a good look at him.

It was a bitterly cold Tuesday morning when he next went, the snow compacted into ice making the pavements treacherous and the sky so grey that even though it was approaching noon it felt like the end of the afternoon.

There was now a light on above the steps down to the cellar, which he couldn't recall having seen before. Something else was different too, a large sign attached to the door: *luftschutzkeller* – air raid shelter. This time the door was locked.

The cellar seemed different. The lighting was much better and along one wall was a large pile of mattresses and a pile of blankets. There was also a metal crate with a red cross on it.

He waited a minute to be sure no one else was there and hurried over to Scholz's storage locker. He opened the steel mesh door and moved the carpet from on top of the box of old paint. There was a used envelope under the largest can. A slip of paper showed the details of when and where they should meet. He folded the envelope into his pocket and shut the door, only to open it again when he remembered he had to cover the box with the tarpaulin as a sign he'd received the message.

–

The Kaiser Wilhelm Memorial Church – known to everyone in Berlin as the *Gedächtniskirche* – was on Auguste-Viktoria-Platz, close to where Budapester Strasse opened onto it. It was where Oberstleutnant Ernst Scholz wanted to meet Jack:

Gedächtniskirche, Thursday, one thirty.

Auguste-Viktoria-Platz wasn't too far from Jack's own apartment so he took the long route there, approaching the square from Ranke Strasse, the opposite direction he'd be expected to come from. The large church dominated the square, with four small spires on each corner leading to a high one above the building. He walked round the square, carefully taking in any side doors or other parts of the church where someone could lay in wait. Looking out for men in uniform was a pointless task given that half the men one came across were wearing one kind of uniform, but he watched to see where they were going and where they were looking. He wandered up and down the smaller streets spanning off the square but couldn't see anything suspicious.

He entered the church at exactly one thirty. He'd spotted two elderly ladies shuffle uncertainly across the ice and approach the church on its north side before ringing a bell above a side door. He hurried over and was able to follow them in.

The church was even larger inside than he'd imagined: almost like a cathedral but without the ornate designs and general sense of grandeur. This church felt cavernous, poorly lit and with a musty smell of damp and sawdust. A service was underway with the sparse congregation spread out across the benches. He avoided looking around too obviously, but as far as he could tell Ernst Scholz wasn't there.

He found a place on a bench towards the back of the church and picked up a prayer book, flicking through it until he came to what he hoped was the right page, and listened as the man taking the service from a pulpit far in the distance appeared to be shouting about victory.

If it was a sermon then it was lasting even longer than the ones Jack Miller remembered from his childhood in Philadelphia. He wrapped his coat tightly round himself and thrust his hands deep into the pockets. It felt even colder inside the church than outside, the air still, apart from the clouds of breath rising from the worshippers.

The sermon came to an end – the preacher speaking so softly now even the people in the front row bent forward to catch what he was saying. When the congregation stood up in prayer Jack Miller became aware of someone moving into the bench behind him, just to his right. As a prayer started among the worshippers the man leaned forward.

'I thought you'd given up on me!'

Jack Miller turned round to check who it was and mutter 'sorry' to Ernst Scholz.

'I've left messages for you for three weeks now. I was getting concerned something may have happened to you. Is everything in order?'

Jack said it was and asked Scholz how things were with him.

'Everything is in order too. I have some information for you to pass on to your friends. In fact, I have compiled a detailed report including photographs and technical drawings. Will you be able to get that to the people who need to see it?'

Jack said that wouldn't be a problem. 'Is this really the best place for us to talk?'

'It's as good or as bad as anywhere else but you'll need to listen carefully. The service ends in a couple of minutes so I'll have to be quick. Everything you need to know is in my report, but very briefly, this all goes back to the autumn of 1937 when I was seconded as a Luftwaffe liaison officer to work on a top-secret project at the Ministry of Aviation. It's called Project Shrike and—'

'Shrike?'

'It's a bird. The Ministry of Aviation was concerned that in the event of a war the Luftwaffe would be relying too much on the Messerschmitt 109 as its principal fighter aircraft. The aim of Project Shrike is to develop an alternative fighter aircraft for the 109. The aircraft is being developed by Focke-Wulf and it's known as the Focke-Wulf 190. A designer was appointed – a man called Kurt Tank.

'We are still at the development stage – we're on version five of the prototype at the moment and it's improving all the time. Even so, it's likely to be at least another year before the aircraft is operational. The service is ending now… let me tell you how to get the document.'

—

Ernst Scholz had told Jack to remain seated and allow ten minutes for him to get away. A few other people also stayed, some reading from the prayer book, others just sitting on their own, looking around and giving the impression they had nothing else to do.

Jack Miller pretended to read from the prayer book and after fifteen minutes stood up and headed to the side of the church.

The door next to the bookcase – it leads down to the crypt. When you get to the bottom of the stairs turn right and go through the swing doors. You'll see a corridor on your left: at the end of that is a door.

When he opened the door it was as Scholz had described, a storeroom with chairs stacked against one wall and boxes covering the floor and surrounding a small desk behind which sat a thin young man wearing a work coat who looked up at Jack as he entered and asked if he could help.

'I was looking for the toilet – someone told me it was here; I must have misunderstood them.'

'Don't worry,' said the man as he stood up and moved to the front of the desk. 'That happens all the time, I keep telling them they need to put up proper signs but do you know what they tell me?'

'That there's a war on?'

'How did you know?'

Because Ernst Scholz told me to say it. 'Because that's the excuse everyone uses these days!'

The younger man smiled and then indicated to Jack that he should close the door. He beckoned him over. 'This is the envelope, here.' He reached into one of the boxes on the floor and took out a large, thick envelope and handed Jack a black cloth bag with the words *Kaiser Wilhelm Gedächtniskirche* in white lettering. Jack removed his scarf and wrapped the package in it and then took two prayer books to place on top.

All he had to do now was find a way of getting this package to London.

Chapter 22

New York and Hamburg
April 1940

Ted Morris wasn't surprised, at least not at first. The telephone call from his old friend Herschel Applebaum – he'd always called him Hersh – had come in the middle of 1939 and suggested they meet for lunch, something they did from time to time.

He and Hersh had grown up together in Brooklyn and still kept in touch. Hersh had done particularly well for himself: he'd become a successful district attorney and now ran his own law firm on Wall Street and while Ted Morris had only moved as far as Flatbush, Hersh now lived in a very smart apartment on the Upper West Side. He was also involved with the Democrats and there was even talk of him running for Congress: Hersh Applebaum now wore tailored suits made from Italian cloth – and had changed his name to Henry Adams.

They met in the club-like dining room of a very good restaurant a few blocks from Ted Morris's office on West 43rd Street. It was dimly lit and smelled of leather and wealth.

'It's good to see you, Ted. Take a seat.'

'A seat of this quality I am tempted to take it. It's good to see you too, Hersh.'

'It's Henry now, Ted, you know that.'

'Yeah – and I'm Ted Roosevelt. Come on, Hersh, you can be Henry to your clients and colleagues but to me you'll always be Hersh. Who do they imagine you are anyway, the great-grandson of John Quincy Adams?'

The other man laughed politely and said they should order. The menu Ted Morris had been given showed no prices. It was his kind of menu.

They asked after each other's families and Ted said he'd been to a mutual friend's grandson's *bar mitzvah* and Hersh asked him to keep his voice down. *Do me a favour, Ted, not here.*

When the waiter next appeared, Henry told him to leave them alone for a few minutes and dropped his voice and told Ted he had something very important to say and would appreciate it if he heard him out.

'So, no wisecracks, all right? One of my firm's clients is the British Consulate here in New York. If there are ever any particularly sensitive matters, we look after them.'

'What kind of sensitive matters?'

'The kind they don't want to see in newspapers like yours, Ted. Matters that they want to be handled in a discreet manner, matters they know we can sort out without anything coming back to the British government. This is all confidential, you understand, Ted?'

'Now you tell me?'

'I'm being serious, Ted – listen. I take personal charge of these cases and we have a very good relationship. Last month they asked me to meet one of their officials, a man calling himself Royd.'

'What kind of a name is Royd?'

'An English one – look, I'm going to come straight to the point, Ted, and I'm going to insist you hear me out. You have a reporter called Jack Miller, is that correct?'

'Miller used to be a staffer on the *Philadelphia Bulletin* then I sent him out to Berlin to cover the Olympics three years ago and he stayed. He's now a freelancer and the deal is he gives me first refusal on articles: I rarely have any trouble placing them.'

'Is he good?'

'Very, writes like an angel – what's he been up to, Hersh?'

'Do you get on with him?'

'As well as I get on with anyone, yeah… come on, Hersh…'

'Royd works for British Intelligence – and so does Jack Miller.'

'He told you that?'

The lawyer nodded. Ted Morris downed a glass of very expensive red wine in one go and then studied his childhood friend's face. *Was this meant to be good or bad?*

'And what, you want me to stop using him?'

'On the contrary: the British want you to continue using him, very much so, in fact. They're very convinced there'll soon be a war involving Britain and Germany and that will mean Miller will no longer be able to send articles to British newspapers, who are major clients of his. It's vital he maintains his cover as a working journalist. A war will also mean communication between him and London will be most difficult. Royd wants to be sure that in the event of war not only would you continue to use him, but that you'd take more articles and also… and I appreciate this is especially sensitive, Ted… act as a conduit between Miller and Royd.'

The restaurant was quiet apart from the clink sounds of ice on crystal. Conversations were conducted at low volume and an expensive carpet muffled the footsteps.

'You mean he sends messages to me and I pass them on to this Royd?'

'Exactly. And the articles – they'll want you to start commissioning more sports pieces, especially ones on soccer, and that will mean you asking Miller to go to certain places in Germany to cover matches.'

'What about if I have a problem with all this, Hersh?'

'A problem with what exactly, Ted?'

'Miller's a journalist: a journalist should be independent; his only masters should be the truth and facts. Being an espionage agent compromises a journalist's integrity.'

Henry Adams looked at Ted Morris with a smile on his face.

'Really, Ted, you think that? Come on – you should be proud of Miller rather than lecturing me on journalism ethics. You know as well as I do what the Nazis are up to. Hitler made a speech in the Reichstag just a few weeks ago when he said if Jewish financiers succeed in starting another world war then the result will be "the annihilation of the Jewish race in Europe". Those were his exact words, Ted, "the annihilation of the Jewish race in Europe". So, which fucking side do you want Jack Miller to be on?'

Hersh Applebaum had raised his voice and struck the table and one or two of the other diners turned round.

'I didn't say I have a problem with this, Hersh, I asked what *if* I have a problem with it.'

'So, do you? You want Jack Miller to be on our side, Ted? Come on, I still have family in Europe, what the hell are they going to do?'

'Change their name to Adams?'

'Please don't joke, Ted, this is deadly serious. Come on – will you help?'

Ted Morris didn't reply at first, drumming his fingers on the immaculate table cloth before finally turning his gaze to his companion. 'Of course I will, Hersh: how could I not? What will I need to do?'

'You'll get to meet Royd but as far as I gather some of the articles Miller sends you will be preceded by messages in code and you're to pass those on and then the British will also want you to send messages to him and also send him to places, as I said – "I want you to go to Munich" – that kind of thing, Ted. But as I say, Royd will explain.'

'Who'd have thought it, eh? Hersh Applebaum, secret agent!'

'And so are you now, Ted Morris!'

Chapter 23

Hamburg
April 1940

Jack Miller could never quite make out Hamburg. Someone had once explained the city's history to him: its origins as a member of the Hanseatic League meant it had long been an independent city state and some of that spirit carried over, even in 1940. The city traditionally had a radical edge to it; leaning to the left in the way that Berlin leant towards liberalism and Munich very much the opposite. Of course, what remained of that had been forced deep underground, but there was definitely an atmosphere to the city that marked it out from Berlin. Hamburg could not be more different from the capital: the swagger that came from it being a major port was always there.

Not only was it the Reich's second largest city but it was also the country's largest port, with an important naval dockyard and shipbuilding facilities. Early on in the war it was evident to Jack Miller that the RAF had its sights on Hamburg. It was an obvious target – and an easier one to reach from the RAF's English bases than Berlin, and not as far inland as the Ruhr towns, so a safer place to attack.

But the RAF needed to know what to aim for, especially as they carried out their bombing raids at night. As one message to Jack made clear, they could have countless aerial reconnaissance flights over a target but they were meaningless without people on the ground spotting things that a camera on a plane tens of thousands of feet in the air couldn't make out.

And then there was *fussball* – football, as the British insisted on calling it, but soccer to his American readers and as they were the only ones he now had, soccer it was. Even before the end of 1939 Jack Miller was being sent to the city on a regular basis – and he always had a perfectly legitimate reason for being there. As well as being Germany's premier port, Hamburg was arguably its premier soccer city. With the country's soccer competition organised into sixteen main Gauligen, Hamburg was part of Gauliga Nordmark and at various times no less than nine teams from the city played in Gauliga Nordmark. In so far as jokes were permitted in the German press a constant one was that the league should be re-named Gauliga Hamburg. The most important teams were Hamburger SV, Victoria Hamburg and St Pauli.

Hamburger had won the Nordmark in the three years leading up to 1940 and seemed destined to be champions in 1940 too. Victoria was pushing them in second place and St Pauli was struggling.

Jack loved the compactness of the city and the fact he'd come to know his way around it and felt more at ease than in Berlin. It was a short walk from the station to his hotel, the rather grand Vier Jahreszeiten on the shore of the Binnenalster, the smaller of the two man-made lakes formed from the River Alste in the centre of the city. London carped on about the cost of the hotel but he told them that ought to be the least of their worries – and in any case, he had a good operational reason for staying there.

The hotel was well placed for Hamburger who played at the Sportplatz on Rothenbaumchaussee in the district of Rotherbaum, not far from the larger of the lakes, the Aussenalster. Victoria's ground – Stadion Hoheluft – was a bit further north, in Eppendorf in the north of the city.

But St Pauli was his favourite club. Their ground – the Heiligengeistfeld – was in the heart of St Pauli, just north of the Reeperbahn, still an anarchic area with a distinct feel to it: not as grey, not quite as many swastikas on display. A visit to the Heiligengeistfeld gave him an excuse to visit the Reeperbahn and once he was in that area he was close to the port and docks, which spread out on both banks of the Elbe.

He had two good contacts in Hamburg, one who knew full well whom she was supplying information to, the other who'd have been horrified had he the slightest inkling.

Magda was a chambermaid at the Vier Jahreszeiten, giving him a perfect excuse for staying there. He'd run an agent in the city until early 1939, a communist docker called Klaus who'd managed to keep his politics secret and was willing to supply information about the port. He was especially useful because he was an expert at installing cranes and as a result was sometimes sent to Kiel, the major German navy base to the north of Hamburg. The intelligence he came up with was good – sometimes excellent – though his reports tended to be peppered with lengthy discourses on Marxism. Klaus seemed convinced that the revolution would start on the banks of the Elbe. Until February 1939 that was, when he announced he was leaving.

'Where are you going?'

'I'm leaving Germany.'

'The Soviet Union?'

'I've told you, I'm not that kind of communist: if I was I'd have been supplying them with information, wouldn't I? I'm a proper Marxist: I follow the direction of comrade Trotsky and there's a group in Brussels I'm going to join. My mother was half Dutch so I speak the language. I've got a leaving gift for you though.'

Magda was the leaving gift. She was a neighbour of Klaus who shared his political views: a committed Marxist with a hatred of the Soviet Union and enough common sense to have kept all that hidden. No one would have guessed that the shy chambermaid had any interest in politics. He always booked a room on the third floor overlooking the Binnenalster, one of the dozen rooms Magda was responsible for cleaning, which made communication between them quite simple.

He'd ask her to check out various locations in the city, note the times of goods trains, especially those using the smaller stations around the docks. She'd come up with information about the mood in the city, anything she could pick up on troop movements, food prices, what was happening to the city's Jewish population, what was going on at Neuengamme in the north of Hamburg where the SS had built one of its feared prison camps.

The contact who didn't know he was a contact was Jürgen, a local freelance journalist who covered St Pauli and who Jack paid for information on the club. Jürgen could not have been a more disagreeable character: a short, grossly overweight man with awful body odour, highly opinionated and with a misplaced sense of his own intelligence. He was a Nazi Party member with a seething hatred of Jews and a conviction he'd somehow been hard done by, blaming the people the Nazis targeted for his misfortune.

But he was a mine of information on St Pauli and whenever he visited Hamburg Jack would contact Jürgen and take him out for a meal. The German would talk non-stop – a mouthful of food was no impediment to conversation – and Jack would listen and make the occasional note and at the end of the evening slip Jürgen some money. *I have no idea what I'd do without you, Jürgen, you're marvellous!*

But Jürgen was worth every painful minute Jack had to spend listening to his nonsense. This was because Jürgen saw himself as some kind of personality in the St Pauli area of the city, especially around the Reeperbahn and the even seedier side streets that ran off it and in the docks on the north bank of the Elbe and the port on its south bank. Jürgen did seem to know everyone and everyone appeared to know him. Of course, what Jürgen interpreted as respect and even friendship towards him was more a sense of fear, mixed with a recognition that if played the right way Jürgen could be of some use. He was a good source of tickets for matches at the Heiligengeistfeld and sometimes even for games at the Sportplatz or Stadion Hoheluft.

And then there were the women. Jürgen was evidently some kind of part-time pimp, bringing young girls from the villages of Lower Saxony to the city. He'd boast to Jack that all the girls were handpicked and tested by him and then sold on to the brothels around the Reeperbahn. *I train them myself, Jack – each one of them!*

All these activities seemed to give Jürgen the run of the port area and Jack would always be more than happy to accompany him.

Come, Jack, we'll cross the river to Steinwerder, they're finishing a new warship there… There's a cafe we can visit in Waltershof: you can see the oil installations there – what a magnificent sight, Jack. How can we lose the war? There's a new restaurant in Altona we could try – if you're feeling rich: it's close to the waterfront. Are you sure you don't want to use that brothel I was telling you about? I've supplied all the girls – two of them are fifteen! You wouldn't need to pay.

The intelligence he gathered on the tours of the port was invaluable. The trip to Hamburg at the beginning of May was a case in point.

Urgent – urgent – urgent, was how the message from London had started, encoded in a telegram from Ted Morris. *Vital you confirm locations of oil installations in and around Waltershof and further up river. Please identify possible target Brunsbüttel.*

Brunsbüttel was ridiculous: it was almost at the point where the Elbe joined the North Sea and had already been bombed in the first month of the war. He'd been there once and he wasn't going to risk a return trip.

But Waltershof was Jürgen's hunting ground. Within four days of getting the message, Jack was back in Hamburg, timing his visit with Victoria playing at home to Polizei Lübeck, which was not a team to mess around with – a joke Jack found hard to resist in match reports.

He arrived two days before the game. Magda promised to take a day trip to Brunsbüttel but wouldn't be able to visit for at least a week. She told Jack what she could about oil installations along the Elbe, but that didn't amount to a lot.

Jürgen was delighted to see his very good friend Jack all the way from the United States of America, the country which was so wisely not meddling in European affairs and a man who appreciated good football and good food and good girls, especially the young ones?

'That cafe you took me to earlier in the year, Jürgen: the one that you said served the best seafood in Hamburg?'

'I don't remember.'

'You took the owner some Victoria tickets?'

'Ah – that one! In Waltershof, yes… the food is no longer so good, supplies you know…'

'Shame, I'd love to visit it again – the fresh herring was wonderful. Do you fancy lunch there tomorrow?'

'Why not, though the herring's not so fresh these days. I'll take him some tickets for the Lübeck game. We may get a free lunch then.'

The food was poor – it had been the first time Jürgen took him there – but the view was magnificent: the large oil tanks, the complicated spider's web of piping leading from one tank to another and then over the road before running along the ground to the quayside… the anti-aircraft batteries positioned on each corner and behind the refinery area a large lorry park covered with camouflage netting, a dozen tankers parked under it. They'd gone for a walk after lunch from the cafe towards the Elbe, past the refinery. Jürgen was smoking, which made Jack nervous but he needed to concentrate on working out how far the lorry park was from the refinery, how the pipes over the road could be identified, the distance from the building they led into to the quayside—

'Stop!'

Two men in uniform emerged from inside the refinery, Jack recognised them as the *Hafensicherungstruppen* – the harbour police, a branch of the SS. He remembered Jürgen complaining to him once about the *Hafensicherungstruppen*: 'the bastards are too straight, you can't bribe them!'

One of the officers was older and shorter than the other and looked unconcerned. The other one was that dangerous breed, an enthusiastic policeman.

Where are you going… what the hell are you doing here… this is a restricted area, you know… let me see your identity cards…

Jürgen – who never failed to misread a situation – announced that this was ridiculous, that they had every right to be here. 'I am a Nazi Party member – here, look at my *Mitgliedskarte*!' He thrust the card under the officer's nose in an aggressive manner and moved close to him. Jack spotted the man put his hand to his nose and step back.

'Very good, and are you here on Party business?'

'We were having lunch and decided to go for a walk and you have no right to stop us, especially me being a Party member. Tell me, are you a Party member? I want your name! And my friend here is an American journalist!'

This was the worst thing Jürgen could have told them. He should have been conciliatory from the start – *so sorry, officer, we weren't thinking, of course we'll leave now*. Instead, the officer now seemed interested in Jack.

'Card, please.'

Jack presented all the paperwork: his identity card, his residence permit, his permit allowing him to travel to and from Hamburg, his press card from the Propaganda Ministry and his even more impressive credentials from the *Nationalsozialistischer Reichsbund für Leibesübungen* – the Ministry of Sport.

'I'm here to cover the match between Victoria and Polizei Lübeck.'

'Where?'

'I beg your pardon?'

'Where is the match?'

'Stadion Hoheluft.'

'And where is that?'

'Eppendorf.'

The officer looked round, gazing into the distance, north, south, east and west, shielding his eyes from the sun so as to see better. 'I can't see the ground round here, can you, Jens?'

The older policeman said no he couldn't.

'So why are you here?'

Jack spoke politely and apologetically. *My colleague, Jürgen, is a sports journalist in the city and we always meet before a game and we visited the seafood cafe for lunch and then went for a stroll and of course we didn't realise this was a prohibited area and we apologise for being here. I can assure you had we known we shouldn't be here we wouldn't...*

He stopped talking, not sure he'd convinced the younger officer.

'You're a foreigner.'

'American: we're a neutral country. I have no interest in politics or anything like that. I cover sport.'

'You'll need to come with me. Both of you.'

Jürgen started to say something, but Jack put out an arm to stop him. 'That would mean I'll miss the match.'

The older officer glanced at his watch and strolled forward. 'Otto, we need to finish the patrol and then it's our break. They've given an explanation and that one has a *Mitgliedskarte*. Just take their details and we can put it in our daily report. It will be fine.'

Otto looked annoyed but did as he was told, though not without an air of resentment. He wrote all their details in his notebook and assured them it would all be in their report at the end of the day.

Jack Miller returned to Berlin the following day. He stayed up late to encode his message about the oil installations along the Elbe, putting in as much detail as he could remember. He decided not to mention the encounter with the *Hafensicherungstruppen*, though the thought of what they may have written in their report kept him awake for most of that night.

–

The reports in *Der Angriff* were vague and he had to read between the lines, much as he did when decoding the messages from London.

How could 'failed enemy action over Hamburg', for example, be reconciled with a reference to 'minor damage' in the same report? Presumably saying 'fuel supplies on the Elbe have now been resumed' meant they had been interrupted... and if 'many

237

enemy aircraft were shot down' how come earlier in the report it said 'less than five RAF planes took part in the raid'?

Jack's view was that the raid on the night of 17 and 18 May must have been a success and maybe he should go back to Hamburg to see what had happened but the message was to wait. *Not yet.*

He found out why at the end of the month: two more raids, on the nights of 27 and 28 and 30 and 31.

Now go to Hamburg… tell us what you find… try and take photographs…

–

It was another week before he could travel to Hamburg, by which time Hamburger SV had won the Gauliga Nordmark. The trip was to write a feature on the team's success.

He decided not to contact Jürgen this time. Magda was very helpful as they stood in the bathroom of the hotel room, the taps running as she whispered in his ear her account of the raids.

'Three separate raids, Herr Miller… You have the dates, I presume?'

He nodded.

'I can tell you, Herr Miller, they've quite shaken everyone in the city. Of course, people are too wary of saying they're frightened, but they don't need to, I can see it in their eyes. People are unnerved. The first raid, the one on the night of the seventeenth and eighteenth was the heaviest but funnily enough that wasn't the one that unnerved people the most. The third one – the last raid – that was the worst, not so much because of the amount of damage but because it came just two days after the second raid and people started to think they were never going to end. I even heard someone say this in the queue at the butcher's – can you imagine that?'

Jack said he couldn't, but while this was very useful what he really needed was information on what damage the raids had done. Magda shrugged and said that was difficult because the police kept people well away from the bomb damage, especially around the port.

'One of my neighbours said her uncle told her one of the refineries on the other side of the Elbe was hit – Waltershof, I think she said. What I can tell you, Herr Miller, is that the second raid was further up the river, but the third one – the third one was so loud, the fires were still burning the following afternoon. Is that helpful?'

Jack said it was helpful but perhaps next time there was an air raid – she appeared to shudder when he said that – could she make a point of getting even more specific information on what had been hit by bombs?

Magda said of course, she'd make a point of that.

'You know, Herr Miller, even though the raids were terrifying, I was elated by them – I felt that if this is happening all over Germany, the Nazis will be defeated. I felt like going into the street and cheering the British planes!'

–

Jack headed down to the port after that. He couldn't tell much from the north bank of the Elbe so crossed over and walked through the port to Waltershof and to the refinery he'd visited before.

It had clearly been badly hit. Two of the large oil tanks were now a blackened wreck, the lorry park behind it was a graveyard for the skeletons of at least a dozen tankers and the complex network of pipes was now a tangled mess.

It was noisy in the area: workers were repairing one tank and a group of slave labourers were hauling away pieces of metal. It was notable that the damage was still serious. He looked for somewhere to take a photograph as surreptitiously as possible and spotted a building on the other side of the road which had a deep covered entrance. It looked perfect.

'You, stop!'

To his utter horror he recognised the *Hafensicherungstruppen* officer called Otto, the one who was going to write about him in his report.

'I recognise you, don't I?'

'I was just…' He stopped, unsure of what to say, regretting his unforgiveable mistake of not having a plausible cover story.

'Just what?'

'Just seeing what had happened. Last time I was here this looked so magnificent and now… I spotted it from the Reeperbahn and… this is terrible!' He shook his head and handed his papers to the policeman, feeling the shape of his Minox Riga in his inside pocket as he took them out. If they searched him he was done for.

Otto studied the papers and then put them in his own pocket.

Jack didn't need telling this was a bad sign.

'You're in trouble, Mister Jack Miller from America: come with me!'

Chapter 24

Berlin and Hamburg
April 1940

In Berlin in 1940 any kind of appointment felt more like a summons, bound to strike fear in the heart of its recipient. This could apply to something as innocuous as an appointment with a bank manager or even one's tailor.

Everyone seemed to have heard a version of the latter story, though never first hand. It involved a client receiving a call from his tailor to say he'd just taken delivery of a small consignment of the finest Italian cloth (in one unlikely version it was Harris Tweed), enough to make just five suits and if he could present himself by noon then he could be measured for one of those suits. When the hapless client arrived at the tailor's the Gestapo would be waiting for him and he'd never be heard of again.

Jack Miller had no doubt this was an apocryphal tale but it did rather sum up the sense of constant fear pervading life in Berlin, a variation of waiting for a knock at the door. It had taken Jack the best part of one evening and a good deal of brandy to calm his next-door neighbour who'd received such a summons from his bank manager. The man sat there white faced, his hands gripping the side of the armchair, insisting he'd done nothing wrong.

'In which case you have absolutely nothing to worry about, Heinz!'

'You don't understand, Jack' – Heinz pronounced 'Jack' as in the French 'Jacques' – 'I'm a loyal citizen but everyone can make a mistake...'

'What mistake could you have made, Heinz?'

'I don't know, that's the problem.'

In the event there was no problem and Jack had told Heinz he really shouldn't get so worked up, but soon after he was the recipient of a summons and he experienced the same sense of dread of having done something wrong and he was about to be exposed. The fact that the summons was to attend the headquarters of the *Nationalsozialistischer Reichsbund für Leibesübungen* – the Reich Sports Office – made no difference. He'd been there many times before but this time it was no ordinary summons. This time it was to meet the man with the grand title of Reichssportführer and an even grander name to go with it: Hans von Tschammer und Osten. The telephone call told him the Reichssportführer would see him at ten the morning after next. He woke at five on the day of the meeting and worked his way through a packet of cigarettes and allowed himself a shot of brandy in his coffee before setting off ridiculously early, so much so he got off the U-Bahn at Heerstrasse and took the long walk up Westend Allee to the Reichssportfeld where the Reich Sports Office was based.

'I cannot work you out, Herr Miller.'

Von Tschammer said nothing for a while after that but looked at Jack Miller as if he was still trying to work him out, tilting his head one way and then the other as though the different angles may give him a clue. His demeanour while not exactly hostile couldn't be described as friendly either.

'I'm afraid there's not a lot to work out, sir: I'm a rather boring type.'

'On the contrary, Herr Miller: here you are, an American journalist in Berlin, but unlike so many of the other Americans and other journalists from so-called neutral countries you don't cause problems for us. You don't meddle in areas you are not meant to; you are not openly hostile to the regime and you don't try and trick our censors by inserting your own opinions into your articles.'

There was a pause. Jack Miller was waiting for a 'but', still trying to out what von Tschammer wanted. It wasn't the first time he'd met the Reichssportführer but it was the first time he'd been on his own with him. Von Tschammer was in his early fifties, with an aristocratic bearing and an assured manner. He'd been running German sport since 1933. Every aspect of it.

'And not only that, Herr Miller: you write articles which actually present a positive picture of everyday life in the Reich. You appreciate how important sport is in Germany, how seriously the Führer himself sees the role of sport in building a stronger and healthier nation.'

Jack Miller settled back in his chair and concentrated on looking impassive. This was turning into the usual nonsense on the master race.

'In some respects, Herr Miller, you are too good to be true: an American writing about sport in Germany, being published in newspapers across the United States... indeed I am occasionally asked if because of this there may be something... suspicious about you.'

Von Tschammer raised his eyebrows, suggesting he was awaiting a response from his guest.

'But then I tell them your articles are clearly not propaganda: you display a passion for sport and especially for football.'

'Thank you, Herr von Tschammer.' Miller was unsure whether he had to add the 'und Osten'. He ought to have checked.

'Maybe you are wondering why I've asked you to come and see me?'

Jack Miller shook his head as if to convey that the thought hadn't even crossed his mind.

'Do you know how many sports I control through the Reich Sports Office, Herr Miller?'

'Quite a lot, I'd have thought.'

'More than thirty, Herr Miller! Can you believe that?'

Jack Miller shook his head in amazement.

'Go on, Herr Miller – name a sport – any sport!'

'Football?'

'Apart from football, that's too obvious. A smaller one.'

'Canoeing?'

'Very good: department twelve here is responsible for canoeing. Another one?'

'Well… golf?' He didn't know if he was meant to try and catch von Tschammer out.

'Department twenty-one. You weren't expecting that, were you? The point I am making is that we cover every single aspect of every sport in the Reich here. I appreciate how you write about our sports. I would like to make a request though…'

Jack Miller leaned forward.

'The Propaganda Ministry take the view that presenting a broader picture of German life helps show the Reich in a more positive light in your country at a time when relations between Germany and the United States are not always easy. They would like you to cover some more of our sports: we will facilitate this, but of course will not interfere with what you write. And in return, Herr Miller, you can be assured of my own personal help, should you ever need it.'

He leaned across the desk and handed Jack Miller a visiting card and told him his private number was on it, should he ever require assistance.

—

Of all the thoughts that went through Jack Miller's head that afternoon in Hamburg the one he clung on to most tightly was that the idea of German efficiency and organisation under the Nazis was clearly something of a myth.

Since his arrest near the ruined oil refinery at Waltershof it had been a catalogue of basic errors: once his papers had been confiscated he assumed he'd be searched. But Otto seemed more concerned about where he should take his prisoner. During the walk to the *Hafensicherungstruppen* police station in nearby Stein-werder Jack recalled the advice given in his training.

If you have time to think, work out what your weakest points are and work back from there.

It wasn't bad advice. Most of the advice the British had given him when he'd come to England for his training seemed to be obvious but they'd presented in a clear way, which made it easy to remember when you needed to.

Like now.

He knew that when they searched his hotel room they'd find nothing and his papers were all in order. His weakest point – apart from having been found in an area recently bombed by the RAF – was the camera. The tiny Minox Riga weighed less than five ounces and was just three inches long and an inch wide. It fitted perfectly into the clever pouch, which had been sown into his inside jacket pocket, but even so it wouldn't be too hard to find. He could only pray he'd have an opportunity to get rid of it.

The duty officer at the station in Steinwerder seemed unimpressed with Otto's account.

'What was he doing?'

'Nothing – he was just there.'

'So you arrested a man for being in the street?'

'It was near where the bastards bombed the refinery.'

'Was he with anyone?'

'No – but I'd seen him there before.'

'This isn't a matter for us. Take him to the police at David-wache in Reeperbahn and they can handle it. Then come back and resume your patrol.'

The police station in Reeperbahn didn't want to know either. *What the hell is this to do with us? Send him to Neuer Wall.*

He knew that Neuer Wall was the headquarters of the Hamburg police, close to the Binnenalster and his hotel. At least he wasn't being handed over to the Gestapo. Not yet.

He arrived at Neuer Wall as one shift was ending and another taking over. *Put him in a cell for the time being.*

By the time Jack's eyes adjusted to the dim light in the cell he realised the rank smell came from a grate in the floor in one corner. It was what passed as a toilet, with an open sewer running below it. He quickly removed the camera from his jacket and did his best to break it up into as many small pieces as possible before dropping them through the grating, relieved to hear the tiny splashes as they reached their target.

Five minutes later he was taken to an interview room where he thoroughly searched before being given a glass of water and a plate of cheese and bread. The cheese was surprisingly good: maybe Ted Morris would take seven fifty words on German prison food.

Half an hour later an officer entered the room. Please could Herr Miller explain exactly what he was doing in Waltershof and how come he was in an area that just a few weeks before he'd been told was a restricted area?

He replied with the story about going to the cafe for lunch and having a stroll beforehand and he'd not recognised the area and—

'You're staying at the Vier Jahreszeiten, aren't you?'

'Yes, I always—'

'The best hotel in Hamburg and yet you go all the way into the docks for lunch at a very ordinary cafe – I could name a hundred better ones for you – and go for a stroll, which so happens to be in an area that the British bombed in the past few weeks?'

Jack Miller told him he had absolutely no idea about the bombings, in fact he was appalled to hear about them and if he'd known then of course he wouldn't have gone anywhere near there because if the truth be told he was a bit of a coward and the last thing he'd do was go somewhere they'd bombed because they could always come back again.

'The British always bomb at night. They're cowards.'

Jack said he'd never visit that area again and in fact he'd never cross the Elbe again and he could see why it all looked odd but he really must believe that—

'I don't believe you.'

There will be a point in an interrogation when you sense it moving against you. You may consider at this point becoming angry because an innocent person – as you must present yourself to be – will be angry at what they see as an injustice and an inconvenience.

'This is outrageous! I'm a respectable American journalist trying to earn a decent living covering sport in your country and I made a simple mistake for which I've apologised and you treat me like this – like I'm a spy! Is this how you wish to treat someone whose work was commended only a few weeks ago by one of the most senior officials in the Reich?'

The officer shifted slightly uneasily and asked what he meant.

'I presume you have heard of Hans von Tschammer und Osten, the Reichssportführer no less?'

The policeman nodded.

'Well, I have to tell you that Hans' – he paused to allow the officer to appreciate that he was on first name terms with such an important man – 'is a personal friend of mine. In fact, if you'd be so good as to find my wallet, I'll show you!'

The officer looked at Hans von Tschammer und Osten's visiting card, holding it carefully by his fingertips.

'His private number is there: perhaps you'd care to call him and explain why you're stopping me going about my lawful work?'

–

He was out of the police station and back in the hotel within half an hour. They offered to drive him, but he said he preferred to walk. In fact, they asked if there was anything they could do for him but Jack Miller decided not to press his luck. The policeman changed his tune as soon as he'd been presented with the card and called von Tschammer.

All a misunderstanding, please understand that I had to ask a few questions… of course you are free to leave…

He'd got away with it and was rather pleased with himself but that sense of satisfaction didn't last long as he walked the long way round the Binnenalster back to hotel.

It was too close, he realised. Maybe he should think again about leaving Germany. He'd been careless and then he'd been lucky.

Nobody's luck lasts for ever.

Chapter 25

Switzerland and London
May 1940

Harald Mettler was the kind of person others didn't take too much notice of. They tended to underestimate this obedient and mild-mannered young Swiss German from Fribourg who'd moved to Bern when he was eighteen and three years later had found a job as a very junior clerk at the Federal Political Department, which was the name the Swiss gave to their foreign ministry.

As time went on Harald Mettler began to be recognised as being particularly competent and able – discreet and trustworthy, and while reserved by nature, he was capable of being quite personable. Without ever actually applying for promotion he began to move up the organisation, though there was never any question of him becoming a diplomat.

He'd been at the ministry for nearly ten years – so he was thirty years old – when he met the Englishman.

In the spring of 1936 Harald Mettler had spent a week's holiday in Germany. He wasn't an especially political person but was appalled at what he saw – and heard – in Germany. People seemed to assume he shared their views and accordingly were open with him about what they hoped the Nazis would do with all the undesirables, as they put it, in their country. Everything he experienced on that horrendous holiday left him in no doubt how dangerous the Nazis were.

Soon after returning to Switzerland he read in the *Tribune de Genève* of an anti-fascist meeting in Geneva the following weekend and he travelled to it. He returned a month later for another meeting but left doubting he'd return because the meeting seemed more to do with left-wing organisations arguing amongst themselves than with doing anything about the Nazis.

On the train back to Bern he fell into conversation with a very pleasant older man, smartly dressed and speaking very good German though with an accent he couldn't place. The man asked what he did and he saw no reason to lie to a stranger so he told him and the man said he had dealings with the Federal Political Department and Harald asked him how come?

'I work for the British embassy.'

'On Thunstrasse?'

'You know it?'

'I sometimes have to deliver important documents there. My name is Harald Mettler: may I ask yours?'

'Basil,' the man replied, 'Basil Remington-Barber.'

–

They met frequently after that. Towards the end of 1936 Basil admitted he knew full well Harald had been attending anti-fascist meetings in Geneva and Harald begged him not to tell anyone and Basil said he wouldn't dream of it and then raised the subject of Harald working for the British. It was much more subtle than that, something which emerged over a series of meetings, and Basil said by working for the British that didn't mean against the Swiss – far from it. It would be a way of combatting the Nazis – he'd be doing his bit: it would be an act of patriotism.

Basil encouraged him to apply for a posting abroad and to put Berlin down as his first preference and then be patient, it could take months.

It was early in 1938 when he heard he was to be posted to the Swiss embassy in Berlin. He'd start in April as a senior clerk in the consular department on Corneliusstrasse and would share an apartment nearby on Luther Strasse with two other embassy clerks.

Before he left Bern the Englishman gave him a series of very thorough briefings of what he expected of him in Berlin. 'Every morning you'll pass a news kiosk on Budapester Strasse. Every morning you will stop there to buy a newspaper. The man at the kiosk is someone you can trust: he's a war veteran with one arm, called Reinhard. If you are ever in trouble, tell him you've run out of matches and are desperate – so don't buy matches there in ordinary circumstances. Sometimes Reinhard may have instructions or a package for you. If so, he'll tell you he has the magazine you requested: the magazine will contain instructions. You say part of your duties will be as a courier, is that right?

'Apparently a courier carries the diplomatic bag from Berlin to Bern every Monday, Wednesday and Friday. The courier returns with a diplomatic bag the following day, apart from the Friday, when you return on the Monday. We get to do the round trip once a fortnight.'

–

Berlin worked out very well for Harald Mettler. He enjoyed the work, though it did feel increasingly desperate as people clamoured for visas into Switzerland, especially Jews. Berlin was horrific in many ways, but unquestionably more interesting than Bern. Every morning he bought a newspaper or cigarettes from the kiosk on Budapester Strasse. If he was the only customer and no one was within earshot Reinhard would mutter something encouraging as he chewed on a cigarette, something like 'victory' or 'the bastards'. Occasionally he'd hand Harald a magazine and inside he'd find instructions.

His biggest challenge came in February 1940 when he stopped at the kiosk and noticed Reinhard make a gesture that he should wait until the customer he was serving had left. He stepped forward and asked for some cigarettes but Reinhard spoke over him.

'Do you have space in that bag?'

He nodded.

'I'm to ask you if your bag gets searched when you enter your embassy – or leave it?'

'Never.'

'And it stays with you all the time?'

'I'll make sure it does.'

'Good. Here are the magazines you ordered. It's quite bulky, put it straight in your bag. Good luck.'

He had to wait until he was back in his room that evening before he dared open the package inside the magazines. The main item was a large, stiff, thick envelope bound by tape. There was a smaller envelope and inside it a message.

Bring this to me in Bern on your next trip.

He'd only just returned from a bag trip, as they called them, so would have to wait another fortnight. But he had an idea. His flatmate Erich was due to do the trip the following Monday and Harald's next trip was going to be the most popular one, a Friday. *Would Erich mind swapping? No, there's no catch, but I need to collect some new spectacles and I'd rather not wait any longer – yes, Erich, you'll owe me a drink!*

He arrived at the Swiss embassy on Corneliusstrasse at five o'clock on the Monday morning and collected the diplomatic bag from the duty officer. In the taxi on the way to Tempelhof he unlocked the bag and placed the package among the documents. He was at the airport in good time for the seven o'clock Swissair flight to Zurich and after brief stops in Leipzig and Stuttgart landed at Zurich just before a quarter past eleven.

That gave him two hours for his connecting flight to Bern, enough time to find a telephone box and call a Bern number. The flight to the Swiss capital was just forty minutes. By four o'clock he was outside the small terminal building and had spotted the car.

A black Citroën Traction Avant, the driver's called Jean and will be looking out for you.

A few blocks from their destination the driver pulled into a side street and then turned into a courtyard. The rear door opened and Basil Remington-Barber climbed in.

'Well done, Harald: any problems?'

'None at all: here you are.'

The Englishman took the package and held it as if it were a valuable piece of art. 'You'd better get back to work, Harald, and I'd better get this to London, eh?'

—

'It took how long to get to London, Barney?'

'Rather too long, I'm afraid, Piers. I say any chance of slowing down a bit? You walk so fast.'

'That's because you spend too much time on bloody horses: they make you lazy. What on earth was Basil playing at?'

'I'm not altogether sure, Piers: seemed he got it in his head that putting it in the regular diplomatic bag from Bern was too risky, though I've no idea why. Then he took his instructions that it was to be handed to me personally and to no one else rather too literally. He was going to bring it himself through France then got cold feet in case the Germans invaded France while he was travelling through it…'

'Christ Almighty, they weren't even in Belgium then!'

'I know, Piers, I know… eventually I said bring the bloody thing here through France pronto or I'll come and get it myself and that seemed to do the trick. Arrived a bit later than I'd have liked but at least it's here and one thing I will say about Basil is that he was able to organise getting the package out of Berlin. Jack took it to Basil's go-between and he passed it on to Basil's courier chap.'

'Do we know who he is?'

'No.'

'Of course. Sorry we're not meeting at our place but as you know the director didn't want those RAF types sniffing round Broadway. The room in the War Office is very secure though. Do you know Frank Hamilton?'

'I don't believe so.'

'Air vice-marshal, runs the RAF Intelligence Branch – he'll bring a couple of his chaps with him, the ones who've spent the last couple of months studying the file. Hopefully they'll have formed a reasonably coherent view as to its veracity. Here we are, need to show our passes.'

'Just a reminder, Piers – no one else will know of Scholz's identity, will they?'

'Absolutely not: as far as everyone else other than us is concerned he's Karl, a source inside one of the ministries.'

–

It was a convivial start to the meeting, as was the way in Whitehall. A lengthy round of friendly introductions, one or two connections established, inevitable references to shared schooldays. And then it was down to business. Piers took the lead.

'Thanks to Barney's first-class work a source we've been cultivating in Berlin for quite some time has finally come up with something for us to get our teeth into. Karl is a source inside a ministry in Berlin and according to him in the autumn of 1937 the German Ministry of Aviation started Project Shrike with the aim of exploring the possibility of developing an alternative fighter plane to the Messerschmitt 109. The project is now at an advanced prototype stage. That's the essence of it. He supplied our agent with a very detailed report, including photographs and designs. You have all been given copies of this report. The purpose of this meeting is two-fold: firstly, for you to give your opinion on the veracity of this report, and secondly, if appropriate, discuss what to do about it. Frank?'

Air Vice-Marshal Frank Hamilton nodded and stubbed out his cigarette. 'Thank you, Piers, and of course you, Barney: jolly well done for getting hold of this and getting it out of Germany. Glad to hear none of our planes bombed it en route!'

A polite ripple of laughter went round the table as the air vice-marshal opened a file in front of him.

'If I may summarise, then. The report does indeed show that the aim of Project Shrike is to develop an alternative to the Messerschmitt 109, which I have to say is extremely sensible: it is never ideal to rely on just one type of aircraft – we of course have both the Spitfire and the Hurricane as our principal single-seater fighter aircraft and Fighter Command feel the two aircraft complement each other: always a mistake to put all of one's eggs in the same basket and if I were them I'd worry in case it was discovered that the Messerschmitt had a fatal flaw that meant it had to be grounded.

'The principal designer of this new aircraft is Kurt Tank – I don't think tank has the same meaning in German, in case you were wondering. Tank works for Focke-Wulfe and is particularly well known for designing the Focke-Wulfe FW200, better known as the Condor. It was originally a civilian passenger aircraft and has since been adapted for military use. If you'll excuse my language, it is a bloody good aircraft, and Tank is a bloody good aircraft designer. The development stage for the Condor was just one year, which is remarkable, and in 1938 – a year after it went into service – it flew non-stop from Berlin to New York, which is even more remarkable.'

'If Tank is the man in charge of the design, then we do need to take this most seriously. The report also acknowledges that the Messerschmitt 109 is best suited to optimum flying and take-off or landing conditions. In other words, it could struggle when conditions aren't necessarily in its favour. So they're going down a very sensible route. As far as we can tell, they're still very much at the development stage – it would appear they're on version five of the prototype at the moment. As far as we can gather it's likely to be at least another year before the aircraft is operational.

'Nonetheless… we are intrigued by the design. Perhaps, Cromwell, if you'd take us through it, in layman's terms if possible, please, for the benefit of our friends here? Cromwell's one of our chaps who actually understands how planes get in the air and stay there!'

There was more polite laughter as Cromwell coughed and nervously shuffled his papers. He was a short man in civilian dress but with the RAF handlebar moustache.

'The 190 would appear to incorporate some very radical new technology. Kurt Tank's design is for a far more robust single-seater fighter than the Messerschmitt 109 – there's a reference within the document to Tank describing the 190 as a cavalry horse rather than a racehorse like the 109, which makes a good deal of sense. For example, I don't believe the Messerschmitt copes terribly well with uneven airstrips. I come now to a very complex area, one that we've taken a good deal of time to analyse: we believe the 190 has a number of very interesting and potentially extremely clever new features, including the wing design and landing gear. The 190 will also carry much heavier armament than the Messerschmitt.

'Finally – and this is awfully complex so I'll summarise it as plainly as I can: Tank's design uses a radial engine, which in layman's terms means its cylinders – in this case fourteen of them – are mounted in a circular manner around the crankshaft. It's a radical technology to use in the manner they're proposing but our view is that it could well work.'

'So should we take the 190 seriously, Cromwell?'

'In a word: yes. It's not difficult to design a plane to get up in the air, stay there for a while and then land in one piece, but we have to consider how much of a threat is it to us once it's up there. Our conclusion – on the basis of what my colleagues and I have seen from this report – is that it could pose a considerable threat and thus needs to be taken most seriously. The lengths they've gone to, the detail here… the drawings… there's no question this is genuine. Remember, I'm summarising weeks of our poring over all this – we've even tested some aspects of the design in our specialist workshops.'

There was silence in the room, broken only by someone tapping their pencil on the table.

'And Project Shrike – could that be a clue to anything?'

'It's a bird, Frank.'

'Yes, but could it point to anything about the plane?'

'I very much doubt it,' said Piers Devereux. 'The purpose of code names is not to give too much away. I suggest we don't spend too much time on ornithology. Frank, you've been looking at the locations relevant to the 190?'

'May I ask Tim to lead on this? Wing Commander Carter here is our expert in this area.'

The young officer stood up and moved to a wall of maps at one end of the room. 'Bit of a geography lesson: from what we've read in Karl's report and from our own intelligence – including aerial reconnaissance – we believe the plane is being developed here... at the Luftwaffe's Erprobungsstelle test facility in Rechlin, which is just north of Berlin, as you can see, sixty miles north-west of it, to be precise. There are also indications in the report, again backed up by our own intelligence, that the plane is being built at these two Focke-Wulf factories: the Flugzeugwerke here in Oschersleben, twenty-five miles south-west of Magdeburg and their own factory some one hundred and thirty miles north of it here, in Bremen.'

'So do you propose we bomb them – wouldn't that make sense?' It was the first time Barney Allen had spoken.

'Yes and no,' said Frank Hamilton. 'There's a school of thought – one to which I have to say I subscribe – that we should hold our fire, rather like a sniper waiting until their target comes closer. As the 190 is a year or so away from flying in combat we should let them carry on putting all their efforts into developing it and building it. It will be more devastating for them if we hit their factories at a later stage of development.'

'May I make another point, sir?' It was the young wing commander. 'We still need better intelligence on the sites at Oschersleben and Bremen – there's inevitably a limit to the quality of what we can see from the air. Ideally before any bombing mission we'd require ground-level intelligence: photographs, drawings and the like.'

'Is that something you can help with, Piers?'

'Barney?'

'Perhaps we can discuss this later, Piers.'

–

'What did you make of that, Barney?' They were back at Broadway.

'Encouraging in that the RAF have no doubt about the veracity of Project Shrike. It would mean Scholz is genuine, which has always been Noel Moore's view.'

'Can we get your American to check out these two sites?'

'Bremen ought to be easier than the other place, which I understand is quite small, not somewhere he'd have a good reason to go.'

'Needs a German to go there.'

'Which is what I was thinking too, Piers.'

'No news on the SS officer's wife?'

'Which is also what I was thinking.'

Chapter 26

Berlin and Switzerland
October 1940

Berlin, Monday, 7 October, 1940

My dearest Annemarie!

I pray that this letter reaches you: I hope you'll remember me, Sophia Schaeffer from the gymnasium in Wedding in Berlin − your penfriend from eighteen years ago!

This weekend I was sorting out some storage boxes and came across my diary from 1922 and at the back of the diary, I found letters from you and I spent a very nostalgic hour reading them. They brought back such happy memories: although our friendship was conducted by post I did feel that I could trust you and I sense from your letters that you felt the same.

It would be delightful if we could resume our correspondence − I have so much to tell you! I am married to a wonderful man: Karl-Heinrich is a senior officer in our armed forces and bravely serving the German Reich. These are historic and momentous times for Germany and I feel very privileged to be living through them. I am unshaken in my belief that the Führer has the true interests of not only Germany but also all of Europe at heart. If you were able to visit Germany you would be astonished at how marvellous life is here.

I will anxiously await a reply from you: I do hope to hear that your life has turned out as well as I was always sure would be the case.

Your very good friend
Sophia

—

Interlaken, Thursday, 11 October, 1940

Dear Sophia

What a wonderful and unexpected surprise − I was so delighted to hear from you and to read your news. Karl-Heinrich sounds like a splendid man though you must worry about him, being a soldier. How brave he must be! You don't mention children: please do tell me if you have any. I am married to Hans who is an electrician and we have a boy and a girl, Hans and Maria, aged ten and twelve.

I'm sorry this is not a longer letter but I wanted to reply to you immediately to reassure you that you did indeed find me. When you reply I will write with more news, though my life in Switzerland is not nearly as interesting as yours in Germany.

Your friend, always
Annemarie

—

'When did these arrive, Barney?'

'Noel Moore put them in yesterday's diplomatic bag. It's terrific news − just goes to show, eh? I first made contact with her in August 1936 − it's taken more than four years.'

'And the address in Interlaken… there won't be any problems if the Germans knock on doors there, so to speak?'

'Basil's taken care of everything, we don't need to worry.'

'And sorry to go on a bit, Barney, but looks like it's been opened?'

'Our understanding is that all letters posted from Germany to other countries are opened and checked by the censor. That would be why this one has clearly been resealed and has a tick in blue crayon on the envelope.'

'And the reply from Annemarie…?'

'Well, obviously that's just a copy of the one that should be with Sophia by now. You do realise how important this is, don't you? She's the wife of a senior SS officer: having her on our books will be an enormous achievement. Hopefully she'll be a big help for Jack Miller too, I do worry he's got too much on his plate at times.'

'What are your plans for her, Barney?'

'Jack's drawn a complete blank looking for Arno Marcus. Until we find him the Japanese diplomat won't play ball. I thought she may be the ideal person to help find him.'

'Christ knows we could do with him coming up with the goods – Japan's an absolute priority at the moment. Don't forget, Barney, we're on our own in this bloody war, apart from the Commonwealth, of course. We've been taking on the might of the German army for over a year now and there's a real concern in Whitehall that we may not be able to keep this up for much longer. Dunkirk knocked the stuffing out of us and the Battle of Britain's taken its toll, even if it now looks as if we're seeing off the Luftwaffe. But they'll be back and there are chaps I speak to high up in the Army and the RAF – and not the doom-monger types, I have to tell you – who wonder how much longer we can keep this up on our own. The Germans don't seem to be short of their own allies – the Italians and assorted other Europeans – and if the Japanese join them then we're in trouble.'

Piers Devereux paused, lost for a moment in his thoughts. 'But the Japanese joining the war could be a blessing in disguise.'

'Meaning…?'

'Meaning they see their enemy as the United States: they undoubtedly have hostile intents against them. If they join the war then they'll draw the US into it too – and that means we'll at last have a powerful ally. So when Sir Hugh heard last year that we had a possible contact inside the Japanese embassy he knew just how important that could be and dropped a hint about it to one or two people he trusts in the Foreign Office, which I wouldn't have done, but then I'm not director of the Service and so not under the pressure he is in Whitehall. He's always having to come up with results – they have no patience – so he does need to throw them some tit-bits every so often to keep them quiet. I'm now forever being asked "when are we going to get something from this Japanese cha?". Do they have wolves in Japan, do you know, Barney?'

'I haven't the faintest idea, Piers: they've been extinct here for a few hundred years but as for Japan, I don't know. Why do you ask?'

'I recall reading something about wolves being considered lucky in Japan: they're regarded as protectors. They even have shrines to them. Could be a good omen for us.'

'In what way?'

'When our pack of wolves start to circle the Japanese embassy, when they find their prey. The Foreign Office is convinced the Japanese are up to something as far as the United States is concerned and now of course Winston's taking an interest in the matter, which is all we need: Sir Hugh says he sometimes calls him at one in the morning. Could we not go down the blackmail line with him – I mean Kimura of course, not the prime minister?'

Barney shook his head. 'I think that would be very much a last resort: let's not get too far ahead of ourselves. The most preferable course of action remains finding Arno and bringing him over here – the priority now is to get Jack to make contact with Sophia.'

The two men stood up and Piers Devereux followed Barney Allen to the door of his office. 'One thought though, Barney: you first met her four years ago and the war started just over a year ago – do you have any idea what made her decide to contact us now?'

–

Since she'd met the Englishman called Edward Campion in Wertheim's the previous May not a day had passed when she hadn't replayed the conversation they'd had over and over in her mind.

There are people I know… in London… people who would be grateful to receive whatever information you have about… military and political matters, about the kind of things you hear from your husband.

The moment he'd uttered those words she'd known her immediate reaction would dictate the course of her life. She could have looked offended and even annoyed and told him he'd completely misunderstood her and indeed had abused their friendship. She could have got up without making a scene – one didn't do that in Wertheim's – and left, insisting he never contacted her again.

But instead, she'd felt very calm and even relieved that her suspicions about Edward Campion were correct. She'd asked him whether he happened to be one of the people he'd just mentioned and it was clear that he was. She replied that she wasn't sure this was the right time but assured him there would be a time when she'd feel she had to help. Edward had passed her a piece of paper and explained how to send a message to him.

And for seventeen months she wondered when would be the right time and worried whether – when that time came – she'd have the courage to go through with it. She was never in any doubt that she'd be committing treason and she was fully aware of the consequences.

But when the moment came it was surprisingly easy. One evening in October she'd heard the maid scream and it turned out she'd spotted a mouse, which they chased into Karl-Heinrich's study – he was in Poland – and it disappeared through a gap in the floorboards under the desk and when she looked further, she found she could lift the floorboards, under which a package was hidden.

The following day, when the maid was out, she retrieved the package. Among its contents was a diary of Karl-Heinrich's, full of the most terrible accounts of what he and his men were up to in Poland. One account was especially horrific: of how in January 1940, he and his men had raided a house in Kielce to arrest a group of young Jews. Karl-Heinrich had ordered an even more thorough search of the house and they discovered half a dozen Jewish children, aged five or six. They were marching the whole group back to SS headquarters when they stopped by the banks of the River Silnica and pushed all the children into it, one by one. He even wrote how some local Poles had watched and cheered.

Life had become increasingly intolerable with Karl-Heinrich but until then she'd done nothing about it. He was rarely in Berlin and these absences enabled her to cope. But reading his diary was the last straw. She could no longer pretend to herself that she didn't know what was going on or wasn't involved in it. Now she realised that just being aware meant she was involved.

She'd replaced the package under the floorboards and resolved to do two things. She'd copy out every word from the diary, a task that would take her many weeks. But first, she'd write to Annemarie in Interlaken.

–

Sophia liked Wilmersdorfer Strasse. Somehow the road seemed more colourful: the flower shops which were such a rare sight in Berlin now, one clothes shop aimed at younger women with dresses in the window that seemed to be very Parisian in design – something apparently disapproved of; the shops selling second-hand jewellery and silverware, which she knew had been purchased cheaply from Jews desperate for cash.

In the morning she'd walk there from their apartment on Potsdamer Strasse, starting at Richard Wagner Platz and then heading south down Wilmersdorfer Strasse. The walk could take a good hour until she reached Bismarckstrasse, at which point she would stop in a small cafe for an early lunch. It was an expensive and dimly lit place so she could be assured she'd be left alone.

It was 24 October, a Thursday, and Karl-Heinrich would be returning home that evening for a long weekend. The thought filled her with dread: recently he seemed to be more irritable than usual and was drinking far too much. He hardly talked and seemed content to ignore her.

She ordered a glass of *Eiswein* to calm herself down and a Scandinavian sandwich with smoked salmon. It was ridiculously expensive, of course, but she reminded herself she was the wife of an SS general and should behave accordingly.

She always sat in an area that was in effect the corridor from the kitchen to the front of the cafe. It had just two tables, both with just one chair. A pleasant-looking man came to sit at the other table, his back to her though he had nodded briefly as he sat down. Sophia liked to look at people and imagine their story: she reckoned this man was in his early thirties, rather attractive, in need of a haircut and in a suit that could do with being properly dry-cleaned. She liked the fact he looked so un-military, but reckoned he was neither formal or stuffy enough to be a civil servant, so maybe something in the arts – film, maybe – or what was left of them; no wedding ring as far as she could tell and he smoked as he ate and— He turned round, a very pleasant smile. *May I borrow your ashtray?*

The accent: she was normally good on accents, but his was hard to place… maybe Czech, or Polish?

She pushed the ashtray towards him and he turned his chair round and offered her a cigarette and she shook her head and pointed to her Scandinavian sandwich and he turned his chair round even further and she noticed he really was very attractive. He appeared not to have shaved that day and the top collar of his shirt was undone and his tie slightly loose. *Would she like a coffee?*

'Do you mean real coffee?'

'Of course.'

'Have you seen the price of real coffee here?'

He gestured as if to indicate that was really no problem and when the waitress passed, he ordered two coffees, please. *The best you have!*

She was surprised at how forward and informal he was – definitely not a Berliner – slightly presumptuous but at the same time rather charming and she could still not work out his accent.

'My name is Friedrich. I'm a cousin of Annemarie from Interlaken.'

She must have looked shocked and he paused and gave her a pleasant smile. 'Don't look shocked, please. I've been watching you since you received the letter from Annemarie: you're a woman of routine, which is helpful. You don't need to say much but don't look so worried. Do drink the coffee. A cigarette will help to stop your hands shaking.'

He spoke very quietly: she wasn't to ask him any questions – that was for another time – but he was a colleague of Edward Campion. 'He mentioned someone would contact you, didn't he?'

She nodded. *I could find a way of ensuring there's no danger to you, Sophia... there'd be someone I totally trust here in Berlin...*

'We'll be working very closely together, I hope. Edward wants me to pass on his very best wishes to you.'

She smiled and asked for hers to be returned to him.

'He asks if you are still willing to help – we know sending the letter to Interlaken indicates that you are, but we just need to be sure you're still keen to help us.'

She smiled again and then realised it was a question so without hesitating she said yes of course she was and wondered whether to mention anything about her husband's diary but then thought perhaps now was not the time.

'And are you safe – no one could possibly suspect you of anything?'

No.

'By which I mean you haven't indulged in any activities against the Reich?'

She shook her head.

'Or made remarks against it, even passing ones to people you may trust?'

'I'm an SS general's wife and I behave like one. And there's no one I trust.'

'That's for the best: you should trust no one – except me now.'

–

'I don't think Sophia von Naundorf is a plant, in fact I'm pretty certain of it. Had she been they'd have arrested me by now. When I met her first and the dinner at her apartment… she struck me as absolutely sincere.' It was one of their last conversations before Barney Allen left Berlin the previous August and he'd just revealed her existence to Jack Miller. 'Nevertheless, if she ever does make contact you'll need to give her one test, Jack, set a trap for her and if she falls for it then you'd better be ready to get away from Berlin sharpish. Until then don't tell her anything about yourself.'

When they met in the cafe Jack Miller – Fredrich as far Sophia was concerned – told her they'd meet on the following Tuesday.

'There's a bookshop round the corner from here on Kauffmann Strasse, near the corner of Kaiser Friedrich Strasse.'

'I know it.'

'Enter the bookshop between eleven and eleven fifteen that morning and look around. You'll see me looking around too. If I am holding a volume of Goethe then you know all is well. Allow me to leave the shop first and then meet me here.'

'And if you're not there?'

'Wait fifteen minutes, buy a book and then return home.'

Jack Miller had chosen the bookshop on Kauffmann Strasse carefully. It had no rear entrance or back office. He'd been in it a number of times – up until 1937 it had sold English books too – and the only way in and out was through the front door. The owner worked from a cluttered desk behind the counter. It meant no one could conceal themselves in the shop or enter it unseen.

The other advantage of the shop was that it was overlooked by a large office block that housed a number of small companies. Jack Miller had checked the building out carefully and had found a vantage point on the second floor with perfect views of the exterior and the interior of the bookshop and the full length of Kauffmann Strasse. He'd be able to wait by the window, leafing through papers as if preparing for a meeting and watching the shop and the street.

Sophia arrived at the bookshop at five past eleven that Tuesday morning. She walked more slowly than he'd have liked and glanced behind her once or twice, which was something he'd have to talk to her about. She entered the shop and he waited. Kauffmann Strasse was quiet, no cars parked near it, no men in the giveaway civilian dress of the Gestapo walking by, no pedestrians spending too long looking in the shop window. At one stage he allowed himself a brief glimpse out of the window to see if he could spot anything on Kaiser Friedrich Strasse but nothing seemed out of the ordinary.

He was as certain as he could be that had she alerted the Gestapo there'd have been some sign of them, if not waiting inside the shop then in the street eager to catch their prey. But all appeared to be normal: the street wasn't even unnaturally quiet, as it could be in these situations.

He spotted her at the counter paying for a book and at eleven twenty she left the shop, stopping to look up and down the street as if hoping to see him. She turned left and headed west back towards her apartment. Jack waited until she was out of view and once he was satisfied no one had followed her, hurried out of the office block and in her direction.

'An interesting book, I hope?'

He'd caught up with her on Schloss Strasse and although he'd avoided running – one didn't run in Berlin if one could help it – he was still out of breath. She appeared pleased to see him. He looked round and all was clear.

'I apologise for not being in the bookshop, but I'm here now. Perhaps if we walk?'

'You swim at the *stadtbad* on Krumme Strasse, don't you?'

'How did you know that?'

'And you also belong to the member's club there, I have recently joined it too.'

'I've never seen you there.'

'Men and women swim on different days.'

'Apart from Saturdays.'

'And your private locker in the club area is one hundred and forty-six, correct?'

'This is like one of those shows where you're called on to stage and a mind reader apparently knows everything about you.'

'My locker is number eighty-seven, it's two rows above yours. We can leave messages for each other by slipping them through the air vents on the front of the locker. No one else ever opens the lockers so this ought to be a safe way of communicating. At each meeting we'll agree a location for the next meeting, along with a fall-back location. Do you understand?'

'It's a lot to take in.'

'It is, but it soon becomes normal, the way you behave. Don't look worried, that's a giveaway. Try to act as normal as possible. Don't walk too slowly, don't walk too fast. Always have a story: if I'm meeting you at a location have a place close to it that you're on your way to.'

They'd stopped and were now facing each other on the grass area in the middle of Schloss Strasse. She was smiling and tilted her head in a demure manner, as if somehow indicating she'd be fine.

Jack Miller's message that night to Barney Allen was that Sophia von Naundorf had passed the test: he trusted her.

1941

Chapter 27

Berlin

January 1941

'You really have no clues about him, Jack – a name he could be using, an address... anything?'

Jack shook his head. Long before he'd asked Sophia to find Arno Marcus, he'd felt it was a hopeless task and from her reaction she felt the same. He promised he'd go back to see Tadashi Kimura: maybe something had occurred to him since their last, difficult meeting.

He returned to the Japanese diplomat's apartment on Brücken Allee on a Sunday morning towards the end of November. The apartment block was silent as he walked down the side path and he listened carefully at the door before pressing the bell for Kimura's apartment. The diplomat said nothing as he let him in and they hurried upstairs.

'You have news on Arno?'

'I hope to – soon, Tadashi. I've come to tell you I now have someone working with me who I think is very well connected and I'm hoping they'll be in a better position than I am to find him.'

'So you have no news.'

'Not yet, but I have this person who—'

'What kind of person?'

'I can't tell you that, you must realise... but I think they may be less conspicuous than me.'

'You mean a German?'

Jack Miller nodded. Tadashi gazed up at the ceiling, still looking at it as he spoke.

'Sometimes I'm convinced Arno must be dead – either caught by the Germans or just dead somewhere. Other times I believe he's alive and still in Berlin. I have no idea what to do. My fear is I'll be sent back to Japan or posted elsewhere and then Arno tries to contact me.'

'You remember I urged you to think of anything that could help us find Arno – is there anything you've thought of since then, something that may have slipped your mind before?'

Tadashi Kimura leaned back in the sofa and let out a long sigh.

'Arno was a very careful and private person.' He paused and for a moment Jack thought that was as much as he was going to say. 'When I first met him at the club in Pankow and brought him back here I assumed…' He paused and leaned over to the coffee table to pick up a packet of cigarettes. 'I assumed I was the first man he'd been with, I thought maybe he'd only gone to that club out of sheer desperation, as a way of finding a man who'd help him in return for… you understand?'

Jack nodded.

'We spoke very little about our personal lives: in fact, it was a few months before I told him about my wife in Japan. It came up one evening when we'd drunk a bottle of wine and were having a more involved conversation than we usually had and I asked him if he'd ever had a girlfriend and he told me he had but had then become very attached to one of his professors. He said nothing after that, he gave the very clear impression he'd said more than he intended to, which was usually the case with Arno.'

'He didn't give a name?'

'No, I'd certainly have remembered that – however… recently I was sorting out Arno's medical textbooks, which I'd been keeping under my bed. I'd decided to put them in boxes and store them in a wardrobe. As I was packing them, I noticed one of the books was on eye surgery and I recalled how insistent Arno had been I get this book for him, even if I had to buy it brand new. He'd told me that when he qualified this is what he'd like to do, eye surgery. I once asked him why and he said one of his professors specialised in it and was a very charismatic man who'd had a big influence on him. I noticed the book was written by a Doctor Ludwig Vogt, a professor at Charité Medical School in Berlin.'

'Where Arno was a student.'

'Indeed: I'd not made the connection before and of course maybe there is no connection, but we're reduced to scraps, aren't we – could this Ludwig Vogt be the professor he was talking about, the one he said he was attached to? The book was published in Berlin in 1935 so it's perfectly feasible.'

'You should have told me about it before, Tadashi.'

'This was only last week and even now I wonder if I'm clutching at straws. The person you mentioned, the one you say is working with you, do you think they could do something with this information?'

–

'And you say the pain is behind your eye, Frau von Naundorf?'

'Yes, Doctor Vogt.'

'And which eye may I ask again?'

'Sometimes the left, sometimes the right.'

The doctor frowned as he continued his examination of Sophia's eyes. He was being very proper but Sophia nonetheless detected a sense on his part that his patient may be a rich woman with too much time on her hands and not enough to worry about.

'And you say it's like a headache?'

'Sometimes, yes.'

'And other times?'

'More intense than a headache, and my eyes feel irritated.'

He raised his eyebrows and continued his examination. He'd already given her a sight test, which she'd sailed through.

It was late on a Tuesday afternoon and she was in Dr Vogt's private consulting rooms on Behrenstrasse. She'd waited until

January because Karl-Heinrich had arrived home in the first week of December and announced he was staying for the whole of the month.

Dr Vogt concluded his examination. He didn't think anything was obviously wrong, not with her eyes at any rate, and perhaps she ought to visit her physician to discuss her headaches. 'I'm happy to write a letter for your doctor if that helps, Frau von Naundorf.'

She said that would be very helpful, thank you.

'In the meantime, use these eyedrops four times a day – two drops per eye. They're very good for general irritation.'

She thanked him again and asked about payment and he said his secretary would arrange that.

'If the problem persists then please don't hesitate to contact me, Frau von Naundorf, but I'd leave it at least one month before doing so: these conditions have a habit of resolving themselves.'

'Are you here all the time, Doctor Vogt?'

'I'm here on Tuesday and Thursday afternoons and Saturday mornings. The rest of the week I'm at the Charité hospital: I run clinics and operate there and I also lecture at the medical school.'

'I knew a medical student at the Charité but for the life of me I can't remember his name. His father knew a friend of mine, Werner Lustenberger. Sadly, he had to leave before his studies were complete, but he was most charming, a very sweet boy.'

Doctor Vogt smiled politely and shook his head.

'His first name could have been Arno. I'm not sure if I ever knew his surname. Such a pleasant young man, it would have been so nice to have kept in touch with him, especially as one now finds oneself in a position to… help these people.'

Doctor Vogt's consulting room was dark but as far as she could tell he remained impassive. He ushered her towards the door and wished her all the best.

She met Jack the following day, a lunchtime stroll through the Tiergarten.

'He didn't react at all?'

'Not as far as I could tell.'

'And the examination… that went well?'

'I think he may have suspected me of hypochondria: I worry I wasn't terribly convincing.'

'And you say he said you could return in a month?'

'If it's not getting better.'

'Maybe make it a fortnight, say you're worried about your eyes and then tell him you've recalled Arno's surname. If there's no response then he's not our man. In the meantime, we need to think of other ways to find Arno. We could always watch the doctor's house, of course.'

-

She didn't need to wait a fortnight. When she returned home that afternoon her maid said there'd been a telephone call from a Dr Vogt's secretary and please could she call back.

'Doctor Vogt is most apologetic, Frau von Naundorf, but there is one further test he wishes to carry out on you and wonders if you are able to attend his consulting rooms tomorrow afternoon?'

Ludwig Vogt ushered her in and told his secretary that as he had no more patients that afternoon there was really no need for her to stay. He gestured for Sophia to sit down and said nothing until he heard his secretary leave. He then locked the outer office door.

'I am an experienced doctor, Frau von Naundorf.' He looked as if about to chastise her. 'When I examined you, I couldn't understand why you'd come to see me. Your eyesight was perfect and as for headaches, the first doctor one would visit is one's general physician.'

'Well, I—'

'Please. Then you mentioned Arno and a Werner Lustenberger. May I ask why?'

'I recall meeting him and he—'

'I'd appreciate you being honest with me, Frau von Naundorf.'

277

She didn't reply as she watched him carefully: he raised his eyebrows in anticipation of an answer.

'I thought I was being polite: you mentioned you worked at Charité Medical School and I recalled meeting a student there and I—'

'Tell me who you really are, Frau von Naundorf.'

She didn't know how to respond so just smiled back at him.

'A friend.'

'Do you know Arno?'

'I know someone who knows him.'

'I believe you came to see me, Frau von Naundorf, with the sole purpose of seeking to contact Arno. You'll appreciate I'm taking an enormous risk speaking like this so I hope you can trust me.'

'The person who knows him and who wants to know his whereabouts is called Tadashi Kimura. He's…'

A long silence followed. Doctor Vogt's chair had been pushed back casting his face in shadow but now he moved forward. Sophia said nothing but removed a book from her handbag and placed it on the desk.

Dr Vogt picked it up. 'My small contribution to medical science, Frau von Naundorf.'

'There's some writing inside, Doctor Vogt.'

To A – always in my thoughts, T.

'If you happen to know where Arno is, Doctor Vogt, and show him the book then he'll know who has written that inscription.'

The doctor nodded and slipped the book into a drawer. 'I'm afraid we're running out of time, Frau von Naundorf, but we really ought to continue this consultation. Occasionally I see patients at my home in Schmargendorf at weekends. Could you make Saturday afternoon?'

She nodded and the doctor handed her a piece of paper with his address on it.

'Should you be coming by car it would be better to park on Reichenhaller Strasse, but I'm sure you'll take all necessary precautions.'

Sophia and Jack met the following day – the Friday, the day after her meeting with Dr Vogt and the day before she was due to see him in Schmargendorf. It was their third meeting that week – the second one in the Tiergarten. Both knew how risky that was.

'Could it be a trap?'

'It could, Sophia, but I've learnt over the past few years that anything could be a trap, even just walking down the street to the shops. I'm afraid it's in the nature of what we're involved in. We just have to be as careful as possible and then hope we make the right judgement. It sounds as if Doctor Vogt could well be the connection to Arno. Just be careful: I'll go there too and wait within sight of your car. I feel I ought to be there.'

–

She left her apartment in Charlottenburg at half past two and drove the short distance to Schmargendorf in the south-west of the city.

The doctor lived in a small but very elegant-looking house on Kolberger Platz. Doctor Vogt himself answered the door and ushered her in. She noticed him check the street before closing the front door and double-bolting it. He led her through to a sitting room at the rear of the house, a small walled garden visible through the half-closed blinds. They sat down and he asked if she'd had a good journey and she said she'd only travelled from Charlottenburg and could have walked and they both laughed nervously.

'Thank you for the book, Frau von Naundorf. It was very much appreciated.' She noticed Dr Vogt seemed nervous, drumming his fingers on the side of his chair and fiddling with his wristwatch.

'Would you mind if I asked you to come down to the basement? My consulting room is there.'

The young man sitting in the study had dark hair and dark eyes and was nervous looking. He had an unhealthy pallor and stood up quickly when she entered the room and nodded at her.

'Frau von Naundorf, may I introduce you to Arno Marcus?'

Chapter 28

Germany and France
January and February 1941

Matters had moved fast that Saturday afternoon in Berlin once Sophia and Arno Marcus met in Dr Vogt's basement. She explained that a colleague of hers – a man who was in contact with Tadashi Kimura – was waiting in a nearby street.

'If I can bring him in then it would make matters so much easier. He is going to help get Arno out of Germany.'

'To England?'

'Of course, Arno.'

'And who is this man?'

'I promise you he's someone you can trust. He saw Tadashi recently.'

'There's a side gate, tell him to use that and come through the back of the house. I'll unlock it.'

Within minutes the four of them were gathered in the study. It was one of three rooms in the basement, one of which appeared to be Arno's bedroom. The other was a small bathroom. Jack started to speak but Arno stopped him.

'Tell me, how is Tadashi?'

'He's safe, no one suspects him of anything, but he's beside himself worrying about you.'

'I knew he would be and I promise you I was tempted to contact him but Ludo said it would be too dangerous.'

'We couldn't be sure, could we? We didn't know what had happened to him or if he was being watched and I thought if we attempted any kind of contact then it could jeopardise Arno's safety.'

'Let me tell you what happened.' Arno swept a hand through his long hair. 'I left Tadashi's apartment on Brücken Allee in what – the middle of July 1939, so a long time ago now. Ludo thinks I had a breakdown.'

'He'd been cooped up in there for so long and was absolutely convinced the Gestapo were going to arrest him at any moment: he'd become quite paranoid. I tried to tell him he was wrong, but he was in a terrible state. I'm amazed he found me.'

'I remember being convinced I was doomed but thought that if I left Tadashi's apartment at least I'd save him. I left on a Wednesday and the next few days were a daze: I remember seeing a policeman and walking over to turn myself in but then he crossed the road and as far as I recall I slept in a park one night and then went to the Jewish cemetery on Schönhauser Allee. Do you know it?'

Jack shook his head but Sophia replied, 'It's in Prenzlauer Berg, is that correct?'

'Yes, my parents are buried there and I decided to visit their graves and ended up staying in the cemetery for three or four days. Unbelievably the cemetery is still open and occasional burials are taking place, so I hung around during the day and slept in the undergrowth at night. Fortunately, it was summer. After a few days I realised I had to leave the cemetery but had no idea where to go. Then I remembered Ludo. He—'

'May I say something, please?' The doctor was sitting alongside Arno, his foot tapping nervously on the carpet. 'The relationship between Arno and myself... I need to explain that it is... let me put it like this: I was Arno's personal tutor at medical school and one day in his first year he came to see me to – you're all right with me saying this, Arno?' The younger man nodded. 'He came to see me about his feelings: he explained he felt he was attracted to men and that was causing him a good deal of personal conflict. He wondered if he should seek help and wanted to know if that would have an adverse effect on his career. I explained to him how I… you will appreciate I'm taking you into my confidence here… I explained how I had those feelings too and had learned to be very discreet about them. We developed what I would describe as a very strong rapport, but I must stress it was a platonic relationship: it would have been quite improper for it to be otherwise as Arno was one of my students. Do continue, Arno.'

'So, I found Ludo: I looked him up in a telephone directory and saw he had consulting rooms on Behrenstrasse and went there. Ludo was clearly shocked, but very kind – and brave. He brought me back here, where I've been ever since: a year and a half. It feels less restricted than Tadashi's apartment and there's a patio area which I go into when it's dark, no one can see it.'

'I would say for the first few months Arno was in a very bad psychological state, very anxious and even quite paranoid. It took a while for me to get the medication right, but since then there's been a marked improvement. Now he studies hard and eats well and is much better, but…'

'But how long can I stay here? I'm endangering Ludo by being here. If I have the opportunity to leave Berlin and get to England… Can you really help me like that?'

Jack said it was certainly possible but they'd need to come up with a plan and that may take a few weeks.

'It's in your interests to get me to England, isn't it? Once I'm there then Tadashi will start supplying you with intelligence, so you have an incentive.'

Jack said that was true and all the more reason why they'd get a move on. 'I want you to write a letter to Tadashi. Tell him you're well and put in something personal so he'll know it is genuine. Don't give any details about where you are or names, obviously. I'll take the letter to him and then bring his reply. I'm afraid that's the only contact you'll have with him.'

–

'Either you're mad, Sophia, or a genius: I can't decide which.'

She smiled and smoothed out the map on the table between them. She'd come to Jack's apartment on Sächsische Strasse for only the second time. They were plotting Arno's escape.

'Are you sure London won't let us try and get him out through Switzerland? It's the most obvious route... I'm not sure what the best alternative is if they're still not keen.'

'Their concern is not getting him into Switzerland but out of it and then to England. Personally, I don't see what the problem would be with Arno staying in Switzerland: he'd be sorted out with a safe house and he could get the message he's agreed with Kimura back to him, but apparently it has to be England – and London are desperate for Kimura to resume his activities. That's why they're insisting on getting him to France. Your plan's a very clever one.'

–

When Karl-Heinrich von Naundorf left his job as a lawyer in 1934 and joined the SS his rank for the first few months had been that of a Hauptsturmführer, which equated to a captain in the regular army. He'd soon been promoted to a Sturmbannführer but his Hauptsturmführer's uniform remained in a wardrobe in their apartment. With each promotion, Karl-Heinrich insisted on keeping his old uniforms. He also kept his old SS identity cards, a neat pile of them in a desk drawer he rarely opened.

These were at the core of Sophia's plan, along with another document, which would be essential for the journey. Once they got the go-ahead from London and the dates were agreed she moved fast.

On the first Monday in February Jack took the papers to the kiosk on Budapester Strasse. Reinhard winked at Jack and said 'Friday' without his lips appearing to move. The next morning Harald Mettler collected the identity card and the following day took it with him on his courier trip to Bern. At the airport he walked past Noel Phillips and, in an encounter lasting no more than a couple of seconds, slipped an envelope to him. The same happened the following morning – the Thursday – when he returned to the airport for his trip back to Berlin. By the Friday Jack had the documents, and that afternoon he was showing them to Sophia in his apartment.

'I cannot believe how good they look!'

'Apparently they use the best forger in Switzerland. They brought him to Bern and he worked on them right through the Wednesday night. You're sure Karl-Heinrich won't miss them?'

'I doubt it; he has four other identity cards in that drawer and never looks at them. The travel permit – there's no reason why he'd think we even still had it. We used it last summer when we went to Aachen for a few days.'

'And now it permits you both to travel to Strasbourg by car and back to Berlin on one return trip during February. And the identity card… the photograph looks convincing, you agree?'

'Completely. He looks smart in that uniform and cap. It's a good job Karl-Heinrich insisted on keeping them. He'll never know how helpful he's been! And the date of birth…'

'They've changed it from Karl-Heinrich's birthday in 1900 to the exact date of Arno's birthday in 1914. Apparently it's safer if he's ever asked, people tend not to forget their own birthday.'

Sophia's preparation for the journey left nothing to chance. She told her husband she was planning to drive to Mainz to visit her late mother's aunt.

'That old cow – I thought you couldn't stand her?'

'I can't, Karl-Heinrich, but she doesn't have long left. I feel it's the right thing to do. She's got plenty of money and I don't want her to forget me!'

'And you really want to drive there?'

'It's more peaceful than the train, they're so crowded these days, Karl-Heinrich – and the bombing.'

'Telephone me when you return – you promise?'

She left Potsdammer Strasse at six on a Wednesday morning, 12 February. She'd moved the Mercedes from the basement garage the night before and parked it in the street. She told the maid she'd be back late the following day, desperately hoping she'd not miscalculated the journey.

It was still dark when she pulled into the prearranged spot on Reichenhaller Strasse. Within moments a dark figure stepped out of the shadows and slipped into the passenger seat. He looked terrified; sweat dripping down his face and his hands shaking.

She slipped the car into gear and started off, turning right to drive past Doctor Vogt's house on Kolberger Platz. She slowed down enough for the two figures at an upper floor window to see that Arno had made it safely to the car.

Jack Miller had come to the house the previous morning and stayed to see everything went to plan: that Arno was ready in time, that he knew what his story was, that his uniform was right, and at exactly the right time – not too early, not too late – he slipped out of the back of the house and through the side gate and to his rendezvous with Sophia.

–

Just after Wannsee, Sophia pulled in to the side of the road. She'd been explaining as they drove along as much as she could about the car to Arno. She was conscious that an SS officer being driven by his wife looked suspicious and she wanted him to be driving by the time they reached Potsdam.

Potsdam was quiet, just one checkpoint, which they were waved through, and they were in Leipzig before ten. There was very little traffic on the road other than military vehicles and most of them were heading east, in the opposite direction. It was another four hours to Würzburg, which included a long wait to fill up the car with fuel. They ate sandwiches in the car as they waited.

The next stage of the journey was to Heidelberg. There was a checkpoint outside the town and it was half past three when they reached the front of the queue and the questioning was more rigorous than they were expecting.

286

You realise you'll arrive in Strasbourg after dark, sir?

Would it not be an idea to stay over in Heidelberg?

Where is your regiment based, sir?

How long is your leave?

When they were eventually allowed through the tension in the car could be cut with a knife.

'It was crazy to attempt this journey in one day.'

'We're doing it for you, Arno: don't worry, we should be in Strasbourg by six.'

'We still have the border to cross.'

'It's not really a border, I'm told: Strasbourg is now part of the Reich – it's no longer in France.'

–

They headed for the medieval centre of Strasbourg. At the checkpoint on the outskirts of the city a Wehrmacht officer asked if they needed help finding their destination and Arno – who to Sophia's surprise had rather grown into the persona of an SS officer – said that really wasn't necessary and when the policeman muttered something about the Resistance and the city not always being safe, Arno snapped back and said he was surprised the Wehrmacht didn't have these matters under control.

They found the small hotel just off Place du Temple Neuf. As they approached it down a narrow-cobbled street two large doors opened and they drove straight into a covered courtyard. It was only when he stepped out of the car that Arno realised quite how exhausted he was.

–

The hotel was run by a couple who worked for the Resistance and the other four rooms were all occupied by members of the same group. Sophia left Strasbourg early the following morning. She planned to stay in Mainz just long enough for her aunt to realise she'd been there and then head back to Berlin.

Arno Marcus remained in Strasbourg until lunchtime that Thursday. 'It's a full moon and the weather is clear so the collection is on for tonight. But we have to time our journey carefully: we don't want to be hanging around near the pick-up zone, but nor do we want to be out on the road when it's getting dark.'

Arno was dressed as a farm worker as the van headed west out of Strasbourg, through Alsace and towards Troyes. Just before the town they pulled into a farmyard where they parked in a barn. As Arno was transferred to the boot of a car, the man who'd driven the van explained he was now being looked after by another group.

'They'll take you to the pick-up point. You'll be hiding in the woods for five or six hours. Stay close to Hervé all the time. Good luck.'

It was freezing in the wood and deathly silent: Arno and Hervé huddled close, a sheet of tarpaulin covering them. Not long after midnight Arno was aware of someone crouched by the tarpaulin and speaking with Hervé, who stood up and indicated Arno should too. He was in the middle of a small armed group creeping through the wood until it came to a sudden end. Ahead of them was a long field with torches lit along its perimeter. Almost immediately he heard the sound of an aircraft approaching and moments later he saw it, a small plane swaying in the air as it seemed to drop rather than descend and when it landed it appeared to accelerate before coming to a sudden stop, turning round quickly to face the direction from which it had come.

Arno was aware of being hurried towards the plane, its propellers on the nose still running. He waited as cannisters were unloaded and then he was pushed towards a metal ladder fixed to the port side of the fuselage. A pair of hands reached out from inside the plane and hauled him in headfirst as the plane started to taxi down the field.

He found himself slumped in the cramped rear compartment. Opposite him was a smiling man who leaned over and shook his hand warmly.

'I'm delighted to meet you, Arno. My name is Barnaby Allen, but please do call me Barney.'

Chapter 29

Berlin
February 1941

> *Friday, 14 February*

> *My dearest T*

> *I arrived safely yesterday. The journey went well, though it is not one I would wish to undertake too often!*

> *I am being very well looked after and arrangements have been made for me to resume my studies soon. Everyone here is being very kind and treating me like an important guest.*

> *I recall you telling me about your much-loved black cat, Kaguya – what a fine old age he lived to! You clearly loved him very much and I thought of my dog, Hansi: he died when I was ten, but I remember him as clearly as if he was sitting beside me now, I can even hear him panting and feel his warm flank against my leg.*

> *Please be assured all is well with me and I hope with you. I look forward to a time when we shall be together again.*

> *A*

—

Arranging meetings with Tadashi Kimura was always a fraught matter. Tadashi was one of a handful of obviously non-Europeans in the Berlin. Wherever he went heads turned and although Berlin being Berlin meant people avoided gawping at him too blatantly, it was nevertheless obvious he was noticed wherever he went.

Jack Miller tried to avoid visiting Tadashi's apartment on Brücken Allee: it was a quiet street, the kind where comings and goings were noticed, and although the side entrance to the apartments helped, it was a still a risk. The safest place – or the least dangerous one – was Miller's own apartment on Sächsische Strasse. This was a far busier street and on the next block was a specialist stationer, which sold the best-quality writing paper in Berlin. Tadashi had been a customer there for years.

Jack's apartment had its own entrance at the back of his building, reached through a small alley, which ran from the street. And that is where they met on the last Tuesday in February, the 25th.

It was late in the afternoon, an unseasonably warm day where people had overdressed in anticipation of the cold. Tadashi let himself in through the unlocked entrance and Jack's front door.

'You look hot and flustered, Tadashi: have you been running?'

'No, it's turned very warm. May I take my coat off?' He'd already removed his shoes even though Jack told him he needn't bother, a suggestion that clearly horrified his visitor.

'You said you have something, Jack?'

He handed Tadashi a brown envelope that the diplomat opened carefully as if it were something fragile. He put on his reading glasses and Jack watched as Tadashi read the letter without showing any apparent emotion. When he'd finished, he nodded and folded the letter the up.

'Are you satisfied with it, Tadashi?'

Tadashi unfolded the letter and read it once more, and this time there was a trace of emotion as he read, a hint of a sad smile, and when he'd finished, he touched the corner of one eye with his thumb.

'The talk about cats and dogs, that was the agreed code to tell me everything really is fine.' He placed the letter in his pocket.

'I'll need the letter please, Tadashi.'

'I can't keep it?'

'Absolutely not, it's far too dangerous.'

He handed the letter to Jack who tore it into shreds and then dropped it in an ashtray before setting it alight. The two of them said nothing as they watched the letter curl into black ashes.

'Tadashi, now you've been assured Arno is safe I hope you'll…'

The diplomat looked up. 'I gave you my word, didn't I? Do you imagine that for a moment I won't keep it?'

Jack said of course not and if Tadashi was ready, he'd tell him about the dead letter box he'd set up for the handover of documents. They talked it through for the best part of an hour, consulting a map, and by now it was dark outside and Tadashi said he'd better get a move on.

In the hall he put on his shoes and coat and turned to face Jack, standing in an almost formal manner. He appeared to be deep in thought and it was a while before he spoke. 'This is a very serious matter for me, you understand, Jack: even though I am doing it for Arno, the information I will be passing on to you, it could change the outcome of the war… and I will be committing treason.'

He half turned towards the door and hesitated again before turning back to face Jack. 'You know, we did have a black cat called Kaguya; the name means shining night. In our culture we believe black cats protect you against misfortune.'

He paused briefly, then bowed his head and left.

—

Tadashi Kimura's standing at the Japanese embassy on Graf Spree Strasse received a significant boost in February 1941 when Hiroshi Ōshima was reappointed as the country's ambassador to Berlin.

Tadashi had been posted to the embassy early in 1938 and Ōshima had arrived as the ambassador later that year. Even in Berlin it would have been hard to find a more hierarchical institution than the Japanese embassy: everyone knew their place and formality ruled. But despite this there was a connection between the new ambassador and his second secretary. The connection lay within the labyrinthine structure of Samurai clans and the obligations those connected to the clans felt to other members of it.

Hiroshi Ōshima belonged to a prominent Samurai clan from the Chūbu area in Honshu, which Tadashi's mother's family had been prominent members of. The families knew each other. There was a mutual respect. Ōshima soon spotted the younger man's abilities. He was impressed Tadashi was one of the few diplomats in his embassy fluent in German. He found him hard working and unlike many of the other junior diplomats, more independent thinking, more likely to question the official line in meetings.

But Ōshima's spell as ambassador ended abruptly at the end of 1939. The Japanese government was furious it hadn't known of the Nazi–Soviet pact in advance and their ambassador in Berlin took the blame for it. As Tadashi had acquired a reputation as Ōshima's man he did less well under Ōshima's successor, Saburō Kurusu. But to his delight Ōshima was reappointed in February 1941. Ōshima was highly regarded by the Nazi leadership – including Hitler. He was known as a hardliner and an enthusiast for Nazi policies. The word in Berlin was that Germany had requested Ōshima's return.

He was soon making himself comfortable in Graf Spree Strasse. One of his first actions was to reorganise his personal office. He was surprised, he told his chief of staff, that a man of Tadashi Kimura's ability was still a second secretary. He wanted Tadashi working directly to him – and he was to be promoted to first secretary.

Ōshima soon resumed his close relationships with German officials. Tadashi Kimura often accompanied his ambassador to meetings with senior officials, sitting quietly behind him, taking notes, sometimes passing one to Ōshima to prompt him, occasionally helping with translation.

When he returned to the embassy, he always typed up a detailed account of the meeting. Often this would take him late into the night and colleagues would urge him to go home but he insisted on finishing his report: the ambassador would always find a neatly typed report waiting on his desk in the morning.

There'd be other meetings too important for a first secretary to attend – often with Hitler and his foreign minister, von Ribbentrop – where Ōshima would be on his own. These tended to take place later in the day or even at night. They were often informal – more conversations than meetings, and all the more revealing for that. First thing in the morning after any of these encounters Tadashi Kimura or one of the other first secretaries would sit opposite the ambassador as he read out loud from his notes, adding an observation here or a thought there. These would then be written up into a report and as with the others, transmitted to Tokyo after one of the embassy's intelligence clerks had encoded it using the impregnable Type B Cipher Machine.

The documents provided a valuable insight into both German thinking and their plans, and also Japanese plans. Ōshima was a clever man: he knew when to throw a bit more information to the Germans in the hope they'd respond likewise.

And the material Kimura gathered was of extraordinary value. It gave an insight into Japan's growing anger with the Americans and frustration at their economic sanctions. As 1941 progressed, so the relationship between Japan and the United States deteriorated – and Japan's hostile intents became evident. At one of his first meetings back in Berlin, Ōshima told von Ribbentrop that Japan would be prepared to join Germany in an attack on the British Empire and the United States. Ōshima's priority seemed to be to persuade the German government that in the event of Japan declaring war on the United States – which was increasingly feeling like a matter of when rather than if – they should join them in a war against the United States.

And Ōshima was also privy to top-secret Japanese military intentions. These documents were so sensitive that Kimura rarely saw them, certainly not in any detail. The ambassador kept them in his own personal safe, but sometimes he'd take them out when Kimura was in the room. He'd pick half a sentence here, a name or a location there. It was difficult to get more than an inkling at first of what Japan's plans were, but gradually a picture emerged.

What he discovered shocked him to the core.

What Tadashi Kimura passed on to the British was dictated by circumstances: the reports tended to be lengthy and photographing them with the tiny Minox Riga camera Jack had given him was a fraught and time-consuming business. He had to choose a time when he was certain he wouldn't be disturbed – hence his willingness to work late at night. He wanted to be sure they were relevant and some he declined to photograph because he felt that somehow doing so represented a greater treason. These tended to include any reference to the emperor.

He usually waited until he had three completed strips of film, one hundred and fifty frames. He'd wrap the film in tissue paper before carefully placing it inside lengths of cardboard, wrapping them in tape and placing it in an envelope.

And then he'd visit the bar on Hohenzollerndamm.

–

No one was sure if the bar had a name. It was known as Günter's after a long-dead proprietor and its fascia had faded into illegibility. But despite this it had a reputation for being a smart place, located at the northern end of Hohenzollerndamm and somewhere people who wanted to be left on their own could have a quiet drink without being bothered. The toilets were at the rear, across a small, walled yard. In the middle cubicle Tadashi carefully taped the cardboard strip containing the film to the rear of cistern. The gap between it and the wall was so narrow it was impossible to spot.

The following day Jack would visit Günter's and visit the same cubicle where he'd dislodge the cardboard with a metal comb he'd fashioned specifically for that purpose.

The next morning he'd slip it to Reinhard at the kiosk on Budapester Strasse. As he walked away, he was confident it had begun its journey to Switzerland and from there to London. He often wondered what was on the film and determined to ask Tadashi about it one day.

Chapter 30

London
March 1941

Barney Allen had been an MI6 officer for over six years. He had few regrets about joining the Service, even though there were certainly times when he missed the excitement of the racecourse and being out of doors. He rarely strayed from the view that horses made more agreeable companions than his colleagues in Broadway, and human beings in general.

But the knowledge of how effective he was as an intelligence officer more than compensated. 'Your pack of wolves, eh, Barney… jolly good, I hear?' colleagues would remark in hushed tones when they passed in the narrow corridors. In spite of themselves, they found it hard to disguise a sense of admiration, alongside the inevitable envy, which so permeated the building.

But one aspect of the job that Barney Allen disliked was the meetings. They tended to go on for too long and to little purpose, more often about office politics and personal advancement than serving the cause of intelligence.

The meetings inside the Service were one thing, but meetings elsewhere were marked by pointless displays of rivalry and arguments over who controlled what: 'spheres of influence' was how it was termed. This was the case with MI5 and Special Branch and with the different Whitehall departments, especially the War Office and the Foreign Office.

But meetings with the intelligence agencies of other countries tended to be laced with a particularly potent degree of tension and a good deal of mistrust. At first Barney Allen was mystified by this and it took him a couple of years to fully appreciate that if one's job was to be suspicious of enemies, it was hardly surprising when allies were viewed in the same light.

This was especially true with the Americans and it was another reason why Barney Allen wasn't looking forward to the meeting that had been arranged with them at the Foreign Office.

'What was it Oscar Wilde is supposed to have said about the Americans, Piers?'

'I wasn't aware he'd said anything about them, Barney.'

'Something to do with us having everything in common with them except language?'

Piers Devereux laughed and said that was jolly good and he must remember that though perhaps not in this morning's meeting.

'We're on the same side, after all, Barney.'

'Doesn't always feel like it.'

'No, but I suspect that is as much down to personalities as anything else.'

'Will he be at the meeting?'

'Jenkins? Of course. But there's a chap over from Washington who'll be leading for them – and he's the reason for this meeting. I'm told he'll introduce himself as Austin and that is as much as we'll know about him. He's terribly important, apparently, right at the top of the Office of Strategic Services so in MI6 terms senior to me. He outranks Jenkins by some margin so I assume that objectionable man will be on his best behaviour.'

–

Joseph Jenkins was indeed on his best behaviour. He was one of the most senior OSS men in their London station but had a notoriously difficult relationship with his British counterparts. He was an overweight Southerner, prickly and easily offended, especially if he was called Joe rather than Joseph: he had a fear of being confused with Stalin.

But he was indeed on his best behaviour in front of the tall, painfully thin man with the demeanour of an academic who introduced himself as Austin. He and Jenkins were flanked by air and naval attachés from their embassy. Devereux and Allen were joined by Air Vice-Marshal Frank Hamilton from the RAF Intelligence Branch and a rear admiral from the Naval Intelligence Division.

On the walk over from St James's, Piers Devereux had rehearsed his opening remarks – *Delighted you could join us... welcome the opportunity to share intelligence... only right to warn you of the significant information that has come our way pertaining to the United States... Barney here will brief you...*

But before he could speak Austin cleared his throat and thanked everyone for joining him. 'May I say how much the United States appreciates the intelligence you have passed on to us.' He spoke in a manner that was not for interrupting.

'We fully appreciate the significance of this information. We have no doubt your source' – he looked directly at Barney – 'is very well placed and although I wouldn't embarrass you by asking their identity, we're confident we can narrow them down to a handful of people within the Japanese embassy in Berlin.'

'I say, Austin, that is not the purpose of this meeting, surely. We are uncomfortable with this turning into a game of "hunt the agent". Any discussion along those lines is improper and could result in our source being compromised.'

'That is the last thing I intend to do, Mr Devereux.' Piers bristled as the American pronounced the 'x' in his surname. 'Let me put this another way. When I said how much we appreciate your help, I do mean it. We value it enormously. The parts of the reports that you passed on to us certainly corroborate our own intelligence that Japan does have hostile intentions towards the United States of America.

'But I wish to make an important point: the United States remains a neutral country. We are not at war with anyone and as a neutral country we need to be extremely cautious in how we handle such intelligence and how we react to it. Were we to overact we could precipitate a conflict and in so doing be seen as the aggressors.

'You will have noticed I said that the intelligence received from your source corroborates our own intelligence. This is the purpose of my visit to the United Kingdom. The United States would find it helpful if the distribution of intelligence from your source was restricted even more than it is.'

'We hardly give it prominence though, Austin.' It was the first time Barney Allen had spoken. 'It's not as if we publish it in *The Times*!'

'But it has a wider distribution than we would regard as helpful: my government feels it's being pushed into hasty action, the timing of which may not be of our choosing.'

'I'm still struggling to—'

Austin held up his hand for Piers Devereux to stop. He leaned forward. The other seven around the table did likewise.

'What I will share with you now is top secret and not a word of it leaves this room. Since early 1939 – before the start of the war – the Japanese Foreign Office has been using an encryption device called a Type B Cipher Machine which they believe is impregnable. However, since last September we have been able to decode messages passed through that machine, which we have codenamed Purple.

'Since he returned to the embassy earlier this year, Ambassador Ōshima has been a prolific user of Purple. The reason we have been able to narrow your source down to a handful of people within the embassy is that sections of your reports are frequently identical to the material we're intercepting through Purple from Ōshima.

'Don't get me wrong: this is extremely useful to us and it's what I mean in saying it corroborates Ōshima's messages – verifying them, if you like. But the last thing we want is to alert the Japanese to what we know. That is why we're asking you to be more... circumspect with your source. We don't want to frighten the horses, do we, Mr Allen?'

Barney Allen was about to respond. He wondered whether the equine reference was intended to show how much Austin knew about him.

'We know what Admiral Yamamoto is up to. We know they have their eyes on our Pacific Fleet. We know Ōshima's trying to persuade Berlin to join in any war against the United States.' He made a gesture, which could only be interpreted as 'leave this to us'.

Piers Devereux said he quite understood and indeed he very much appreciated Austin being so frank with them and of course the very last thing the British government would wish to do would be to… scare the horses… and there was nervous laughter around the room and everyone stood up to leave.

Piers Devereux asked the rear admiral if he'd be so good as to show their guest out because he and Mr Allen had others matters to discuss with the Air Vice-Marshal.

–

'What do you make of that, Frank?'

Air Vice-Marshal Frank Hamilton shrugged. 'Americans making a lot of noise, as is their want. I think the best course of action is to nod in agreement but carry on as before. We can't have them telling us how to run our agents, can we, Barney?'

'Indeed not. Seems to me they want to have their cake and eat it. They're not in the war, are they? This country is pretty much on its own and it's rather bloody annoying having them on the side-lines trying to call the shots but declining to get their hands dirty. What's your view, Piers?'

'Well… in the normal course of events I'd agree with you both, none of their business et cetera, and in fact, as annoying as that was, in a sense it's rather encouraging, is it not? Shows what Kimura is giving us is spot on, that we're absolutely on the right track. Part of me agrees with Frank, that we should make the right noises to the Americans but carry on as before.'

'And the other part of you, Piers?'

Piers Devereux paused, selecting a cigarette from his packet and then putting it back. 'Roly Pearson had a word with me the other day – Winston's intelligence adviser. He said Winston's well aware of what Barney's getting from Berlin and he considers it to be terribly helpful. Downing Street's view – Winston and Roly, that is – is that having our own line of intelligence on what the Japanese are thinking is absolutely essential, because as Austin has just said, they have their own source and we can't be seen to be at a disadvantage. But – and this was the point he wanted to get across – he wants us to be careful how we handle the intelligence. Evidently Winston and President Roosevelt are working hand in glove on this, much closer than we'd realised. Roly said too much noise could blow them off the course they're plotting, that was the phrase he used.'

'So, what do we do with my source, Piers?'

'Tell him to be even more careful, especially as the Americans have confirmed we're on the right track. Perhaps we'll be even more selective about its distribution. Get Jack to tell him to be even more selective about what he sends us: quality rather than quantity. Don't want to push our luck, do we? While we're here, Frank, do you want to update us on where we are with the German plane?'

'We're still receiving reports from Barney's source in Berlin on the Focke-Wulf 190. Suffice it to say we remain concerned. I think now is the time to see if we can get more on-the-ground intelligence about the Focke-Wulf factories in Bremen and Oschersleben. Are your wolves ready to prowl round there, Barney?'

'They're waiting for the right moon as I understand it, Frank.'

Chapter 31

Germany
April 1941

'You mean to say you've never been to Bremen, Herr Miller?'

'I'm afraid not, Reichssportführer, but with Werder Bremen doing so well in the Gauliga Niedersachsen I decided I really must go up there and when I noticed they're playing Eintracht Braunschweig at the Weserstadion next week I thought this would be an ideal opportunity, given the two teams are such close rivals.'

Hans von Tschammer und Osten nodded. Jack Miller had noticed how his chest swelled when Jack called him Reichssport-führer.

'And you say the Propaganda Ministry refuse to grant you a travel permit.'

'Apparently Bremen is a particularly sensitive area. I'm only interested in football, you know that.'

'There was the incident in Hamburg when I was required to—'

'That was a misunderstanding, Reichssportführer. I got lost.'

'As you told me, yes. I'm not sure why Bremen should be any more sensitive than Berlin. Leave it with me, but, Herr Miller...'

'Yes, Reichssportführer?'

'Do me a favour and don't get lost in Bremen, eh?'

–

'Do you think it's a good idea, Karl-Heinrich?'

'Is what a good idea, my dear?'

'What I was just telling you.'

'I'm sorry, it was a long journey from Poland. Please start again.'

Sophia held up a copy of *Frauen-Warte*, the magazine of the *Frauenschaft*, the Nazi women's organisation. 'I was reading this article about how desperate they are for more volunteers and I thought perhaps I should do more. It seems that children's homes are in particular need of volunteers. The ones in Berlin have all the help they need, but there's one near Magdeburg…'

'It will take you half a day to drive there.'

'I hope you don't mind, Karl-Heinrich, but I've already spoken with the matron. I could drive down on a Tuesday morning, stay overnight – they need women to stay there at night – and drive back to Berlin on the Wednesday afternoon. I would feel I'm doing my bit for the war effort and if it works out I could visit more often.'

She'd moved closer to her husband and placed her hand on his thigh. He smiled and placed his hand on top of hers.

'You're a very good woman, Sophia.' Her brushed his hand across her hair and tucked a strand behind her ear. 'You are unable to have children yet are willing to work with them. Surely that is what the Führer means when he says he expects every citizen to make sacrifices. Of course you should do this. It is your duty.'

–

They'd had to abandon using Kaiser Wilhelm Memorial Church on Auguste-Viktoria-Platz for Oberstleutnant Ernst Scholz to leave documents for Jack Miller to collect.

It had worked well until the young man in the storeroom was conscripted. Scholz and Miller had decided to use the Luftwaffe officer's storage cage in the basement of his apartment block on Düsseldorfer Strasse. It wasn't ideal, but then Jack Miller was struggling to think of places that were.

Scholz left a package every four or five weeks. After he'd collected the report, Jack walked up to Kurfürstendamm and wandered around the shops, so by the time he returned to his own apartment on Sächsische Strasse he could be sure he hadn't been followed. He'd wait until it was dark and draw the curtains before he locked and bolted the front door and spread the pages of the report on his table. It could take over an hour to photograph it on his Minox Riga – making sure the light was right, turning the pages over, checking the film was moving properly between exposures. He'd place the strips of film in a cardboard sleeve and then destroy the document, tearing it into shreds and burning them in the bath. The following morning he'd send the film on the next stage of the journey when he slipped the envelope to Reinhard at the kiosk on Budapester Strasse.

There was precious little time for him to study the documents but he was certainly able to pick up that the development of the Focke-Wulf 190 was going well. He read how the BMW 139 engine was replaced with the 801 and once the cockpit had been moved the fuselage became more robust and this was regarded as a significant improvement. There was a new cooling unit, which was also seen as a big success although the high temperatures generated by the radial engine were still seen as a problem that needed to be sorted.

Kurt Tank was very pleased with the new wing design – it was larger than the previous wing and did slow the 190 down by around six miles per hour but made the plane far more manoeuvrable and significantly increased its climb rate.

There were references to production, which caught his eye. The trials at the Luftwaffe's Erprobungsstelle test facility in Rechlin were going well, so much so that the next stage of production was now underway. They expected the plane to fly in combat by the summer. The main production centre would be Focke-Wulf's factory in Bremen, but there was concern about concentrating all their efforts on one location, especially one well within the reach of the RAF, so the AGO Flugzeugwerke factory in Oschersleben would also be used.

It came as little surprise to Jack Miller when messages from London became increasingly insistent.

We must have ground-level photography from Bremen and Oschersleben.

That is an absolute priority.

−

Two days after his meeting with Hans von Tschammer und Osten, Jack Miller received a travel permit allowing him to visit Bremen: attached to it was a letter from the Reichssportführer asking that every courtesy be afforded to Herr Jack Miller.

One week later he was in Bremen. He arrived the day before the game between Werder Bremen and Eintracht Braunschweig, allowing himself time to look around the city. It was a short walk from the main station across the Stadtgraben Lake into the Altstadt, the old town. His hotel was off Bredenstrasse, in what locals called Mittenmang, which meant being at the centre of everything.

And he certainly was at the centre of everything.

It was a pleasant walk heading east from the Altstadt along the north bank of the Weser River to the Weserstadion, the home of Werder Bremen. He collected his accreditation for the match and sought out one or two people to interview. There was a coach who was in a hurry but predicted a tight game and said they were taking nothing for granted − every coach he'd ever interviewed before a game said the same thing. An older official wanted to tell him the history of the club and helpfully showed him around.

Would you mind if I took some photographs of the ground?

Of course not!

May I take one with you pointing to the goal?

Of course not!

When he left the ground, he took a tram heading east, into Hastedt, the location of the Focke-Wulf factory. He'd hoped he wouldn't miss it but it was so large it dominated area. The tram route ended close to the factory and Jack got off to catch a local bus. It was around three o'clock, a quiet time, and the bus − which as far as he could tell was on a circular route − was more or less empty. He found a seat at the back with no one near him and knew this was an opportunity he couldn't miss.

He took out his Leica camera – the one he'd just used in the Weserstadion – and replaced the 35-millimetre film with a new one. He held the camera low against the window of the bus, taking a series of photos as they drove past the factory. It was only when he'd taking all thirty-six exposures that he realised he wasn't alone. A large woman, perhaps in her forties, was sitting in the row in front of him on the other side of the aisle. He had no idea how long she'd been there but she seemed interested in him. If pushed he'd have said she was curious rather than suspicious, but he didn't want to put it to the test.

'Heil Hitler!'

The woman hesitated and then looked shocked at not replying immediately. She said sorry and 'Heil Hitler' and looked away.

A cold fear gripped him. He needed to remove the film he'd just used and replace it with the one from the football ground, but that needed to be done carefully. It would take a couple of minutes and was not an altogether silent procedure. By his reckoning they were two stops away from the tram stop. He decided not to risk changing the film then.

The same woman left the bus at the tram stop and was on the same tram as him as it heading back to the Altstadt. He got off the tram at the Weserstadion and walked back from there, stopping at a bar along the way for a cold beer.

He was still shaking when he arrived back at the hotel. This was all becoming too much. He felt as if he was riding his luck on every mission. He was also making mistakes – how could he not have spotted the woman on the bus? Could she now be telling someone about the strange man she saw on the bus? *With a camera, I'm sure of it – yes, as we went past Focke-Wulf!*

In the hotel room he looked in the mirror. He seemed to have aged by about ten years. There were lines around his eyes and the skin on his chin now sagged. His hair was beginning to thin and was greying at the temples. He was constantly anxious, drank too much, slept badly and the happy-go-lucky Jack Miller – the charmer from Philadelphia, the man with the smart sense of humour and an impressive success rate with beautiful women – that Jack Miller was a stranger, a shadow in the past.

His mind turned to his retirement plans: leaving Germany, returning to the States – the Lisbon route was the one he preferred – and only letting Barney know once he was back in Philadelphia and by the time he received the letter Jack would be visiting his brother at whichever port he'd ended up at. Just the thought of that calmed him down. He knew he didn't have much longer in Berlin before he'd make a fatal error, a mortal misjudgement.

He carefully placed the film in its hiding place in his shaving kit and decided that as far as Bremen was concerned, that was it. If they weren't satisfied with the film, hard luck. He'd cover the match the next day and then head straight back to Berlin and once there he'd check out the best way to get to Lisbon. Someone mentioned something about being able to fly there via Zurich and Barcelona. There'd certainly be an article or two in that.

As he lay awake in bed that night, he reflected how ironic it was that Berlin felt safe compared to the trips outside it.

–

Sophia had told Karl-Heinrich as little as possible about the children's home where she was going to volunteer. In truth, he wasn't terribly interested. He'd come back to Berlin the weekend before her trip there and he was in as bad a state as she'd ever seen him.

In the early hours of the Saturday morning, she'd woken to find his side of the bed empty. She found him in his study staring at the wall. He had a cigarette in one hand and a bottle of brandy in the other. When he turned round his eyes were red and his skin grey.

Thank God you have no idea what it is like, Sophia. We are doing our duty and it has to be done, but… at what price.

She'd asked him what he meant and he said he just wanted to forget.

Before he left on the Monday morning, she reminded him she was going to the orphanage on Tuesday.

'I'll be back Wednesday.'

'Where is it again?'

'Near Magdeburg.'

'In the city?'

'Nearby, a town called Wanzleben.'

He nodded and then told her it may be a month before he returned, perhaps longer. He said he worried she must be at a loose end while he was away and she said he mustn't worry about that, she managed to keep herself busy.

She left Berlin on the Tuesday morning, driving west through Potsdam, Magdeburg and Wanzleben. The orphanage was actually further west, just outside the smaller town of Klein Wanzleben. But she carried on, straight past the entrance to the orphanage – which was set back from the road in an old country house – and continued to drive south-west. Eight miles later she came to her destination: the outskirts of Oschersleben and the looming mass of the enormous AGO Flugzeugwerke factory.

She found an elevated area by the road in the shade of trees that offered good views of the factory. Cranes dotted the skyline: it was clear sections of the complex were still under construction.

She checked she wasn't being observed and removed her camera from the glovebox and took a dozen photographs before driving on. She repeated the excrcise twice more and was on the final exposure of the film, debating whether to push her luck and load another film, when the decision was made for her. In her rear-view mirror she watched as a police car pulled up. She had just enough time to slip the camera under the car seat.

Thank God you've turned up, officer! I am looking for the orphanage in Klein Wanzleben and I know it's on this road but I can't seem to find it – I keep stopping every time I see what looks like a turning!

She adjusted the red beret which matched her lipstick and smiled sweetly as she handed the officer a sheaf of papers: a letter from the orphanage, her own identity card, the car documents and a card identifying her as the wife of SS Brigadeführer Karl-Heinrich von Naundorf. When he saw the last one the officer clicked his heel and gave a small bow.

No problem Fraulein, no problem at all... you've driven past the orphanage... it's easy to miss... this is a town called Oschersleben... please don't worry, I'll escort you back there myself.

Chapter 32

Berlin and Bern
April 1941

This time it wasn't a thin strip of cardboard behind the cistern at Günter's on Hohenzollerndamm but rather an envelope containing a note with a single line of type.

I must see you urgently! I will come tomorrow!

As a journalist Jack Miller had an aversion to exclamation marks. He'd been taught they should only be used in the most extenuating of circumstances. He hoped that their use in Japanese signified less urgency.

Tadashi Kimura arrived at his apartment on Sächsische Strasse the following afternoon clutching a bag from the stationery shop he'd just visited. Jack noticed he was wearing a large pair of dark glasses, which made his features less obvious.

What was obvious though was the diplomat's agitation. Jack had always found him unflappable.

'Is something the matter?'

'May I sit down, Jack?'

'Please do, you don't need to ask. Just put those books on the floor. Don't you want to take your coat off?'

'I can't be long Jack. I am very worried.'

'About what?'

'About the fact that based on my assessment of the political and military situation nothing seems to be happening in response to the intelligence I'm passing on to you. Remember, I'm based in Ambassador Ōshima's office. I see almost everything. My real worry is that I pass on all this vital intelligence to you and I assume it is shared with the United States and yet… it appears it is being ignored. Japan is showing hostile intentions to the United States, the Japanese Imperial Navy is making plans to attack the United States Navy but I see no evidence the Americans or the British are reacting to my intelligence. I'm risking my life every day, Jack, and yet it seems no one is interested.'

'I'm here in Berlin, Tadashi, so I don't know all the ins and outs but my feeling would be just because you don't see in your reports how the British and Americans are reacting to the intelligence doesn't mean they aren't. We just have to assume they are, but being very careful.'

'I often ask myself if it's worth me carrying on? After all, I promised to supply intelligence if the British helped Arno and that happened, we both kept to our sides of the bargain. But now…'

'You said you want to join Arno in England and—'

'Do you think that will ever happen, Jack? I've been in Berlin for three years now. If it wasn't for Ambassador Ōshima I'd have been posted elsewhere. I worry I'll be recalled to Tokyo or sent to another part of the world and I'll never see Arno again. This war could last forever and—'

'I'm sure you'll get to see Arno again and I—'

'You probably think it's wrong, don't you, Jack – my feelings for Arno and his feelings for me. I would imagine you think it is a perversion and—'

'Tadashi, it's none of my business and all I—'

'I don't expect people to understand. There is a long tradition of male relationships like ours in Japan: it is called *nanshoku*. It is only since the turn of this century that it's become less tolerated. I would find it hard to explain my feelings to people and in any case, in my position it is impossible to do so. Part of Japanese tradition is to avoid drawing attention to oneself. But for me the idea that I won't spend the rest of my life with Arno, that maybe I'll never even see him again… that is an intolerable thought. It is the reason why I take these risks. And then to feel like no one is listening to what I say... There's an ancient saying that is very difficult to translate but roughly it means shouting at empty ears. This is what it feels like to me.'

Jack had half a bottle of whisky left and poured a generous measure for his guest. Tadashi glanced at his watch before drinking it in one go and holding the glass out for a refill. Jack said he quite understood how his good friend – because that was how he regarded Tadashi – felt. He himself often felt like that. It was, he said, in the nature of what they did, which was lonely and dangerous and being so... isolated inevitably gave rise to these feelings of... doubt and uncertainty. It was easy to feel ignored but he really mustn't feel like that: the information he was providing was of such high quality that he had no doubt it was being acted upon.

'I'm going to Switzerland later this week and will be able to tell the British about your concerns – and I can also see what we can do about getting you out of here. Leave it to me.'

'How come you're going to Switzerland?'

'It's a long story.'

–

Jack Miller rarely visited the United States embassy on the corner of Pariser Platz and Hermann-Göring Strasse. He found them to be offhand and officious and had the impression they preferred to deal with American correspondents they knew well and trusted. Jack Miller had kept a distance from them and they clearly didn't like it.

At the beginning of April, a message had come through from London: they wanted to debrief Jack in person. Could he make it Switzerland by any chance? As it happened, Jack had spotted a perfect opportunity to go to Switzerland, but he needed the advice of the embassy. The press attaché was an asthmatic young Bostonian who dressed formally and acted like a member of the British aristocracy. He and Miller held each other in mutual disregard.

No, he replied. *I can't help. I'm not a travel agent. Go and see Lowe in Consular.*

It was the first time Jack Miller had met Frank Lowe, who turned out to be a most pleasant if rather put-upon Californian.

'You realise the problem, don't you, Jack – I can call you Jack?'

Jack said he wasn't sure which problem he meant, he had so many of them. And sure, call me Jack, Frank.

'You're an American citizen. You can leave the Reich easily enough, assuming all the paperwork is in order and you don't owe anyone any money and aren't wanted by the Gestapo. But the problem will be getting back into Germany. I assume you'll be wanting to return here?'

Jack said of course.

'Don't blame you. I know this place is hell on earth but we're at the centre of it… every day feels like we're witnesses to history. I'm keeping a detailed diary, you know. I don't know if you know any publishers in the States? Look, there's no guarantee you'll get back in. My advice would be to find someone high up to endorse you. That should help.'

–

He took Frank Lowe's advice and that afternoon made a telephone call, the result of which was a journey the next morning to the Reich Sports Office on Westend Allee and a meeting with Hans von Tschammer und Osten himself.

The Reichssportführer listened to him carefully, if slightly bemused, and when Jack had finished, picked up his phone and asked his secretary to bring coffee and then leaned back in his expansive leather chair and lit a cigar, puffing on it a few times before replying to the American.

'What makes you think people in the United States will be interested in me?'

'Because through your efforts, Reichssportführer, you have ensured sport and physical activity is at the forefront of national life. I cannot think of another country where that is the case. A profile of the man who is behind this will be unquestionably of interest to Americans.'

'I think you're trying to flatter me, Herr Miller.'

'Why would I do that?'

'Because I imagine as usual you want a favour.'

Jack Miller shrugged as if nothing could be further from his thoughts. He said he quite understood if the Reichssportführer would rather not be interviewed and—

'I didn't say that, Herr Miller. I would be delighted to be interviewed. The only thing I would ask… indeed, insist upon is that you use my official photograph to accompany any article. Now, tell me what is the favour you require?'

'Germany are due to play Switzerland at soccer – football – in Bern on the twentieth of April, I believe?'

'That is correct. Our victory will be a fine gift for the Führer on his birthday.'

'I would be most grateful if I could receive official accreditation for the match and a letter from you endorsing my travel permit, Reichssportführer.'

The German looked at him for a moment or two behind the curling brown smoke of his cigar. Then his face broke into a broad grin.

'Of course, Herr Miller. I admire the way you operate. But the profile of me… if it isn't flattering then I will withdraw the accreditation!'

–

Jack Miller shuddered when he thought of the damage the profile of Hans von Tschammer und Osten would do to his reputation. However carefully the article was written there was no hiding its main purpose: to appeal to the Reichssportführer's vanity. He was amazed Ted Morris had managed to place it in a dozen newspapers: he wondered if he was paying them to run it.

But it worked. His accreditation duly came through for a match billed – not least by himself in an article breathless with enthusiasm – as part of an unofficial World Cup. The Germans could not have been more confident: they'd just thrashed Hungary 7–0 in Cologne. Little Switzerland surely wouldn't present much of a problem.

Thirty journalists were flown to Bern on a special charter flight on the Wednesday before the match and taken by coach to the Schweizerhof on Bahnhofplatz. The group was accompanied by half a dozen officials from the DFB, the German Football Association. Three of them, Miller guessed, were Gestapo – there to ensure the journalists kept in line and avoided contact with people who had nothing to do with football.

Basil Remington-Barber knew how closely Jack Miller would be watched. He'd told him not to contact him, just to act normally and do everything the group did. He'd find him.

On the Friday they were taken to watch the Swiss team train at the Stade de Suisse and then attended a lengthy press conference where the proceedings were conducted in German, Swiss German, French and Italian. The Swiss coach said he was confident but taking nothing for granted.

The journalists had no commitments that afternoon. There was a walking tour of the old town or they could return to the hotel but were told if they left it they'd need an escort. *For your own safety.*

In Bern, perhaps the safest place in Europe.

He was resting in his room that afternoon, checking his notes from the training sessions and press conferences and wondering whether to file anything that evening. He decided against it, he doubted anything would run before Sunday's match. He answered a knock at the door and let in a man from housekeeping who'd come to fix a leaking tap. The man turned it on and the bath tap too and then beckoned Jack towards him.

'Someone wants to see you. When I leave the room, I'll check the corridor and if it's clear, follow me to the service lift. We'd better get a move on. Don't forget to turn the taps off.'

Five minutes later he was sitting in a suite on the top floor admiring the views over the old town with the River Aare behind it. Basil Remington-Barber was fussing over something in the drinks cabinet while explaining something about one of the bridges.

'You realise the Gestapo is all over your group?'

They were sitting in a lounge area, nursing the very large measures of whisky that Basil had served. Jack nodded.

'Hence my having to spend London's money on this room and disgracefully over-priced malt and bring you up here in a goods lift. Barney tells me you're a bit uneasy about things? Perfectly understandable. Gets to us all and you're in—'

'It's not so much me, it's our Japanese friend.'

'In what way? We got his chum to England safely enough… surely he's happy with that?'

'Indeed: he wouldn't be passing all these documents on to us if he wasn't. But he's worried that there doesn't seem to be much reaction to what we're sending over. I've another film for you here.' He handed an envelope over. 'It's first-class material, apparently, Basil, brimming with evidence of Japanese plans to attack the United States and drag Britain into it to. I think his worry is that he's risking his life and yet the material is being ignored.'

'Just because he sees no evidence it's being taken account of doesn't mean it is being ignored.'

'I tried to tell him that too, Basil. It's very difficult in Berlin, Basil, which I know is stating the obvious, but the atmosphere is very intimidating. People live on their nerves and I sometimes wonder how much longer I—'

'Look, Jack.' Basil shifted his chair closer to the American's. 'How can I put this? I'm a pretty important chap: I fought in France throughout the Great War and ended up as a major in a Guards Regiment. I joined the Service soon after that and have run our operations in some important places including Cairo and Paris. Bern was meant to be my last posting before retirement, which is now a distant prospect. I'm also well-connected: it may not mean a lot to you but my family are aristocracy – there's an

Honourable in front of my name. Half the people who run the country went to the same school as me. In Britain that counts for a lot.

'I tell you all this not to impress you but to make this point: notwithstanding everything I've just told you, I'm just another cog in the wheel, I barely matter. I've had to accept that when I pass on intelligence or get an agent or one of our aircrew back home, I don't hear any more about it. That is how it is. As much as I may think I'm important, in the great scheme of things I'm just someone else in the crowd. We all have to accept that, I'm afraid, which isn't to say that what we do isn't important. The fact we may sometimes feel ignored should not lead us to be disheartened. You need to understand this and Tadashi should too. I hope you catch my drift; I do rather ramble at times. Something to do with age. You mustn't feel disheartened.'

Jack said he was very grateful for all that but he did nonetheless have a nagging concern that maybe… he wasn't sure how to put it… but that possibly London was overwhelmed and perhaps some vital intelligence was stuck in an in-tray?

Basil said he quite understood and he promised to put these concerns to London but in the meantime, Jack really wasn't to worry and nor should Tadashi. The relationship between Britain and the USA was an absolute priority and therefore anything to do with it was bound to be acted upon.

'It's quite evident that it's treated as first-class honours material, Jack. Neither you nor our Japanese friend should worry. It's giving Winston all the ammunition he needs.'

'And Tadashi wanting to come to England?'

Basil Remington-Barber shook his head. 'That clearly isn't going to happen while the war's on, is it, Jack? Not that we tell him that of course. I can't see him passing off as an SS officer, can you? He'll stick out like a sore thumb wherever he is. Just assure him it is indeed our intention to reunite him and his friend, but don't promise when.'

The game between Switzerland and Germany turned out to be a great sports story and Ted Morris managed to place it in virtually all their newspapers in the States. Against all the odds Germany were beaten 2–1 by the Swiss and Jack wrote it up as one of the greatest ever upsets in international soccer.

And as one of his editors would have described it, the story had legs. The reaction in Germany was furious. Goebbels threatened to sack Hans von Tschammer und Osten and take on the post of Reichssportführer himself. There would, he declared, be no more international sporting events where the result was in any way unpredictable. The German team was told that one more performance like that and they'd all be sent to the Eastern Front.

Jack Miller knew how they must feel.

Chapter 33

Oberstleutnant Ernst Scholz retired in June 1941.

His work as a Luftwaffe officer at the Air Ministry in Berlin continued – in fact, it flourished. But his retirement was as a British agent, something he'd been contemplating for a while.

There was no single reason for his retirement. Although he was opposed to the Nazis and wanted revenge for his wife's death, he didn't see himself as a traitor, even though he knew full well what he was doing was treason. It was a tricky paradox to live with but he rationalised it by believing it wasn't in Germany's interests to be ruined by the Nazis.

Then there was Magda. After his wife's death he'd found it hard to imagine he'd remarry, but he'd met Magda at a New Year's Eve party and they'd become very close. She worked as a nurse at a psychiatric asylum just outside Berlin and although he didn't love Magda in the intense way he did his late wife, she was very sweet and pretty, even if a bit quiet at times. She avoided any discussion related to politics – that was common in Berlin, even between lovers and within families – but she clearly wasn't a Nazi. He soon realised she'd be a good companion and maybe in time – who knows, he may even grow to love her. Their wedding date was arranged for July and she'd then move into his apartment on Düsseldorfer Strasse.

But perhaps the main factor was the increased risk at work. A new head of security had arrived at Wilhelmstrasse at the start of the year and had soon made his mark. Even the most senior person was liable to be searched when leaving or entering the building. Scholz's modus operandi with documents he was providing for the British was to identify those where multiple copies had been made, which applied to ones where more than one department was involved and extra copies had been made before they were sent to Registry.

The American had tried to persuade him to take a camera into work, but he was having none of that. Instead, he'd wait until he found a 'spare' document from one of these FW190 files and slip it into his coat. He'd only done this once since the new security regime and that had been nerve-wracking enough. But one night at the end of February he'd stayed late at work and was just about to check the FW190 files when a team of security officers came in and explained this was a routine check and please could he remain where he was and not touch anything. They made notes of everything on all the desks and then went through all the contents of his. They checked his jacket, coat, briefcase and desk drawers.

Everything is in order, Oberstleutnant. Thank you for your understanding and apologies for the disturbance.

Ernst Scholz said not at all, he was pleased to see they were being so diligent.

He realised his time as a British agent was coming to an end. He'd done his bit. The FW190 was due to start flying operationally any time now, just a matter of weeks, and it appeared the British were beginning to react to his intelligence. There'd been a series of RAF bombing raids on Bremen since the end of 1940 and some particularly heavy raids early in January, which had hit the Focke-Wulf factories. The American had even asked him if he could request a site visit to the factories and take some photographs while he was there. He'd responding by suggesting while he was at it should he could take a camera crew?

It was a meeting at the beginning of May that proved to be the final straw.

He'd arrived early at work on a Monday morning and the general-major in charge of his department took him aside and said he was being attached to another unit for a few weeks. He must have looked concerned because the general-major told him not to worry.

'You've done a first-class job, Ernst, but there's something big going on and we need senior officers with your grasp of organisation and logistics – and who we know we can trust.'

In a secure room on the fourth floor, where he was relieved to find himself in the company of a dozen fellow officers of similar rank, the lights dimmed and a slide show began and the first slide said: 'Operation Barbarossa'.

The presentation lasted over an hour. Any day now, they were told, Germany would begin its invasion of the Soviet Union. Three Army groups would attack along a border stretching from the Baltic in the north to the Carpathian Mountains in the south. Seven German armies, four Panzer groups, three Romanian armies under German command. It was a formidable force and the aim was to conquer the Soviet Union in a matter of weeks.

Their role, they were told, was to assist with planning the Luftwaffe's part in Operation Barbarossa. They were to identify and prioritise Soviet airfields to be attacked. Air supremacy was the priority, they were told. Each officer was then handed a folder with details of the sector they'd be looking after.

Ernst Scholz's sector was in Army Group Centre under the command of Generalfeldmarschall von Bock and specifically the 4th Army, commanded by General von Kluge. He would be looking at targets and objectives in the area running from Brest to Kowel.

One of Scholz's colleagues asked how imminent the invasion was and the general taking the briefing repeated what he'd said at the beginning: *any day now*. Another Oberstleutnant said it had better be imminent and the general asked what he meant.

'It's what… six hundred miles from Brest to Moscow? Across hostile terrain. Sure, we'll have the benefit of surprise and of course the Luftwaffe will ensure we have air superiority, but the Red Army is tough and it's enormous… and if we move too fast there'll be problems with supplying our front line. If we leave it much longer then before we know where we are it will be winter and…'

–

Their concern turned out to be justified. By the time the invasion began on 22 June, they knew they'd be facing a familiar enemy, the Russian winter. But Ernst Scholz didn't mention a word of this to the British. He was aware that if there was any suspicion about information being passed to the British about the FW190 and Barbarossa then he'd soon be spotted as the man who'd worked on both. Instead, the night after that first briefing at the beginning of May he went straight to the basement under his apartment on Düsseldorfer Strasse and pulled out a dusty red rug from the back of his storage cage and placed it over the box of paints at the front.

When the American saw that he knew it meant danger.

Oberstleutnant Ernst Scholz had retired.

Chapter 34

London and Berlin
November 1941

Endless meetings in dimly lit and stuffy rooms, the attendees invariably distrustful of each other, the proceedings like a complicated Greek drama, with obscure speeches apparently setting the scene for what was to follow.

By now Barney Allen was resigned to the fact a good deal of his life was destined to be spent in such meetings. The meeting this afternoon was at the Foreign Office and the two officials from that great department of state were the head of the Political Department and a man called Brookes who'd been two years above Barney at school.

'We have a request, Piers… your chap in Berlin.'

'Barney has a number of chaps in Berlin.'

'Ah yes, his famous wolves… we know one runs a highly placed source at the Japanese embassy and we are exceedingly grateful for the intelligence gathered from that source. It corroborates everything else we see in connection with Japan's intentions vis-à-vis the United States – and us of course.'

As he spoke, Barney remembered Brookes had been a very convincing Cordelia – lipstick and all – in a school production of *King Lear*. It was hard to disassociate him from that role.

'Without wishing to involve you any more than is necessary in the unpleasant world of international diplomacy we would like you to request this source do something that would be of immense benefit to this country.' Cordelia held out his hand for his colleague to pick up the baton.

'Would we be right in assuming your source has the ear of Ambassador Ōshima?'

Neither Allen nor Devereux responded.

'We are of the view – assisted in no small part by the intelligence you pass on to us – that a Japanese attack on the United States and a subsequent declaration of war by them on both us and the USA is now a matter of timing. I am of the view it will be by the end of this year at the very latest.' The head of the Political Department spoke in an over-mannered way, as if delivering a sermon. 'It would be of enormous help if your source could prevail upon his ambassador to persuade the German government that when that happens it would be in their best interests to join Japan in declaring war against the United States, ideally with minimum delay.'

'Really?'

'Yes, really, Piers. This is the view of the prime minister who's in daily contact with President Roosevelt and they are very much in agreement regarding the approach of both countries. The issue of how Germany will react to a Japanese declaration of war on the United States has been a constant topic of conversation. The question is: in the event of a Japanese attack will the president be forced to declare war against Germany? This will be problematic for him as a majority of Americans currently oppose such a war. This dilemma will be solved if Germany declares war against the United States first. It would also be the preferred option of this country: having the United States drawn into a war against Germany means we will no longer be alone in our struggle against them.'

'You mean it is in the interests of the United Kingdom for Japan to attack the United States?'

'We are saying we believe that to be inevitable and therefore it is incumbent upon us to ensure the outcome of such an attack is in the best interests of the United Kingdom.'

'The intelligence from Berlin,' said Barney, 'is gathered at considerable risk. We would hope it is being used to prevent war rather than increase its chances.'

The head of the Political Department waited a while before responding. 'The intelligence you are gathering from Berlin is being used for the benefit of the United Kingdom, Barnaby. How the British government chooses to use that intelligence is a matter for the government. Gathering the intelligence is not an end in itself, is it? It is part of a bigger picture. We are asking you to get a message to your source and prevail upon them to make out the case for Germany to declare war on the United States.'

'Do you have any suggestions?' Piers Devereux leaned back in his chair, looking confused. 'After all, it's hardly in Hitler's interests to declare war on such a powerful country, is it?'

'Maybe not, but the Germans need Japan to enter the war and engage us and Russia. I would imagine the Japanese diplomatic position would be that they are hesitant in doing this if they cannot be sure they won't be acting alone.'

'Furthermore,' said Brookes, 'our understanding is that Hitler regrets the fact that this country and France declared war against Germany in 1939 rather than vice versa. We think persuading him to declare war against the United States will appeal to his vanity, to his desire to be seen as a powerful military leader, a man in control of his country's destiny.'

–

Pssst!

Sophia von Naundorf was hurrying home from swimming on a bitterly cold Wednesday morning. Since the invasion of Russia people commented wryly that the weather had worsened – a convoluted joke along the lines of forgetting to close the windows. Her hair was damp and she just wanted to get home and have a hot bath.

Pssst!

She heard it as she walked past a deep doorway on Schloss Strasse but carried on and ignored the sound once again as it appeared to follow her and when she quickened her step, she became aware of a figure coming alongside her, its shoulders hunched and head bowed low as was hers, meaning that for a moment she couldn't make out who it was.

'I presume you're heading back to your apartment?'

A scarf covered the lower part of Jack Miller's face, making his voice slightly muffled. She said she was.

'Is your maid in?'

'I expect so.'

'Send her on an errand that will keep her away for at least an hour and then leave the door to the back staircase open: I'll come up in half an hour. You could have a coffee waiting for me if you wish.'

Thirty minutes later they sat opposite each other in the sitting room, the fire blazing away.

'You're able to get coal?'

'What do you think, Jack – that SS officers are deprived? But don't think our lives are free from hardship – this is the last of the proper coffee. You look worried?'

'I could be wrong and I've said nothing to London but I'm worried they may be on to me.'

'Who?'

'Who do you think – the social democrats? The Gestapo of course!'

'What makes you say that?'

'It's only a suspicion, Sophia, but the other day I was followed when I left the Propaganda Ministry. I even walked all the way back to Sächsische Strasse, which stretched them a bit, but certainly I recognised three faces who were with me all the way. And most days I see someone watching the apartment. I managed to get a message to Tadashi that under no circumstances should he come anywhere near the place. Of course, it could be my imagination. It's possible that with the strain I've been under I'm sensitive to anything like this – paranoia, I think they call it. But I don't think it's my imagination.'

'Are you sure they didn't follow you today?'

'I managed to catch a tram on the Kurfürstendamm and then get off it while it was moving. I walked for another hour before

I went to wait opposite the *stadtbad* on Krumme Strasse. Could I have another coffee?'

He followed her into the kitchen and leaned against the sink.

'I know you're going to tell me that I'm an American journalist in Berlin and it would be surprising if they weren't keeping their eyes on me but... this seems more serious, if that's the right word: sinister, maybe? I think someone may have been in the apartment last week, though it's such a mess I can't be certain. Since then, I've avoided passing anything on to the courier, not even a message telling them I'm laying low for a while.'

'Should you leave Germany maybe?'

He'd spotted a bottle of schnapps on the side and was wondering whether to ask for some. 'Not yet, not yet... there's still too much to do, Sophia. The situation with Japan and the United States... it's heading towards war. I can't leave now. In any case...'

'Are you all right?'

'Yes, I'm sorry... I'm not sleeping. I spent most of last night watching the street from a gap in the curtain: I'm certain a Gestapo car was parked opposite for a couple of hours around three o'clock. London have ordered me to brief Tadashi about something, they say it's very urgent, an absolute priority. I've already told you I've instructed him not to come to my place but this briefing, it needs to be in person and...'

'And you want me to do it?'

–

At the last meeting of the *Frauenschaft* Sophia had attended they'd impressed on those present how the organisation needed a higher profile. One way of doing that, they said, was to distribute copies of *Frauen-Warte*: 'then people will see all the good work we do!'

She'd taken a bundle of copies and volunteered to distribute them, which was why just two nights after meeting with Jack Miller in her apartment she was at the side entrance of Tadashi Kimura's apartment building on Brücken Allee. The old man on the first floor refused to come to the door; the woman on the second floor – Jack had warned Sophia about her – was polite enough and of course took a copy but Sophia got the impression she was frightened more than anything else. There was no one on the third floor so she posted a copy through the letterbox and then knocked on the door of the fourth-floor apartment.

Tadashi Kimura was calm when he opened the door and saw her. She asked if he was interested in a copy of *Frauen-Warte* and gestured that he should invite her in.

'I can't stay for more than five minutes, any more than that would look suspicious.'

'Is it about Arno?'

'No – you don't need to worry about him.'

'Jack told me not to contact him. I have some film here: can you pass it on?'

'Give it to me. You need to listen carefully. Jack is busy but has a message for you from London...'

In the end she was in the apartment for ten minutes as she explained carefully what Jack had told her. *If Japan is to declare war on the United States, then it would be desirable for Germany to declare war on them too... this should be presented of course as being in the interests of both Japan and Germany and...*

'...and of the United Kingdom too?'

Sophia shrugged. 'Jack asks what the atmosphere is like at the embassy at the moment?'

Tadashi laughed. 'Frantic and very tense. Something is clearly imminent. Ambassador Kurusu is heading to Washington but there's no expectation of a diplomatic solution. In the last week there's been a tightening of security – whether they suspect someone is passing on material or whether it is to do with the military situation, I don't know. What I do know is that I'm seeing less sensitive material so I'm being more cautious. The film I've just given you, it's from last week. I don't know when I'll next have something to pass on. You can tell Jack that as of yesterday Admiral Yamamoto's fleet was still at Hittokapu Bay. They need to be aware of that.'

She promised to return in a week or two and he urged her to be careful.

The following morning, she went for a swim at the *stadtbad* where in the Member's Club she slipped the film and a note about what Tadashi had told her into Jack's locker.

–

Very early that same morning a slight man wearing a suit too big on him met with Ambassador Ōshima in his private residence.

Kuzumi Kobayashi had arrived in Berlin at the beginning of November with the cover of a clerk in the consular department. Ōshima and the military attachés were the only ones aware of his true identity as a senior officer in the *Kenpeitai*, the Japanese secret police.

'Have you concluded your investigation, Kobayashi?'

Kobayashi removed his spectacles and then put them back on before licking his thumb and turning over a page in his notebook. 'I have concluded the first stage in my investigation, Ambassador.'

'And your conclusions?'

'My interim conclusion is that I agree with Tokyo that someone in this embassy is leaking material to the British and that material is reaching Washington.'

'Which I've already told them is ridiculous – do you have proof?'

'Not as such, sir, but I—'

'Well there we are then – as I thought, no proof! Maybe the leaks are in Tokyo.'

Kuzumi Kobayashi stood up and ceremoniously handed a sheet of paper to the ambassador, bowing as he did so.

'What is this?'

'A list of suspects, sir.'

'You have no proof but you do have suspects? That's ridiculous!'

'All of the people on this list had access to the documents we know may have been leaked.'

'Half of my diplomats are on this list: maybe I ought to be on it too!'

'I have compiled it in order, sir – the diplomats who have had access to the largest amount of leaked information are at the top.'

'That is plainly ridiculous: Tadashi Kimura is up there – he's one of my most trusted men. We have a clan connection, for heaven's sake.'

'I require you to allow me to place the diplomats at the top of the list under special surveillance, sir.'

Hiroshi Ōshima said very well, but this was going to be a waste of his time and he didn't want anything to disrupt the important work these men were doing.

Chapter 35

Berlin
November and December 1941

Eleven... twelve days spanning the end of November and start of December, during which time Jack Miller felt like a reluctant witness to the last days of the world.

The enormity of the information he was privy to was hard to bear and he occasionally felt a mad urge to share it with people he barely knew like the cafe owner on Berliner Strasse who served him the freshest rolls and topped up his coffee for nothing, or the old woman in the threadbare shawl who spent all day sweeping the front of the apartment block next to his.

All this was a consequence of Tadashi Kimura's behaviour, which had become increasingly manic during the course of November. On her second visit to Brücken Allee Sophia had been shocked at the diplomat's behaviour. He'd hurried her into his apartment, tearful and panicked, and paced the room with a glass of whisky shaking in his hand.

It will be any day now... why aren't you passing on these messages? Whose side are you and the American on? The atmosphere at the embassy... everyone is suspicious these days... I don't trust you... you're German... and a woman...

Sophia and Jack met the next morning, he entering her apartment through the basement and the side door, which opened onto the back staircase.

'He's panicking, Jack – he's in a terrible state – and drunk.'

'Hopefully it was just the drink talking and once he sobers up... maybe he needed to get things off his chest.'

'He doesn't trust me, that's clear.'

'I think he's just on edge, Sophia, we all are and—'

'He clearly doesn't like women. I'm not sure it's a good idea me going to see him again. I think you need to go and tell him to lay low for a while, not to pass on any intelligence for a week or so and then see how he is. What do you think?'

Jack shrugged.

'Do you still think you're being followed?'

'Funnily enough there's been no sign of it for the past week, maybe it was my imagination after all!'

–

It hadn't been Jack Miller's imagination.

The Gestapo officer assigned to investigate Jack Miller was none other than Karl Henniger, the man who'd handled the British woman Maureen Holland and had arrested and interrogated Werner Lustenberger.

Since the inconvenience of Werner's death, Henniger was only trusted with routine cases, one of which was Jack Miller. The American had become a suspect only because the Propaganda Ministry had taken exception to the tone of his coverage of Germany's defeat in Switzerland. They'd detected the use of humour and took offence at his references to the Eastern Front and were particularly offended by the phrase 'Germany's normally lightning-paced attack'.

What annoyed them most though was the protection he seemed to enjoy from the Reich Sports Office and especially the Reichssportführer. They persuaded the Gestapo to investigate him, though a growing backlog of cases in Berlin meant this took a few months to sort out.

Karl Henniger began his investigation in the middle of the September. He had the American's apartment on Sächsische Strasse watched, questioned his neighbours and when he could get his hands on enough men, had him followed. It was all rather intermittent and somewhat half-hearted. From the outset there was nothing to suggest Jack Miller was anything other than what he appeared to be – an American journalist covering sport and scratching a reasonable living out of it.

Everyone they spoke to commented he was a nice enough person who never broached any awkward subjects. The cafe owner on Berliner Strasse insisted he never mentioned politics – or rationing. Henniger had even managed to get into the apartment one day and although he had to keep the search quick, there appeared to be nothing suspicious, though he had to say it would have been difficult to find anything given the state of untidiness.

In October Henniger put a request in to the Abwehr station in Washington DC for them to check whether Miller's articles were indeed being printed in any American newspapers. After initially saying they had more important things to do, by mid-November they came back and said he was actually quite prolific.

Henniger's report to the Propaganda Ministry said Miller appeared to be above suspicion and it was agreed he no longer needed to be watched. But as Jack Miller faded from suspicion Tadashi Kimura came under the spotlight.

Kuzumi Kobayashi – the Japanese secret police agent – was unimpressed by Ambassador Ōshima's insistence that Kimura was to be trusted because of a clan connection. Kuzumi Kobayashi came from a humble background with no links to the Samurai and invoking it only made him look harder.

Tadashi Kimura was at the top of his list because the material he had access to correlated with the information the *Kenpeitai* suspected had been passed to the Americans. Kimura seemed to be on edge and nervy, the security staff reported he was often the last diplomat to leave the embassy.

There were even rumours about him having been seen in the past at clubs in Berlin frequented by homosexuals. Kobayashi treated these as just rumours: the man was, after all, married, although it was some time since he'd seen his wife. He'd not applied for home leave though, which was odd.

Henniger could have asked for Kimura's apartment on Brücken Allee to be searched but decided to wait until he had more evidence. The Gestapo had a small unit that worked with the friendly diplomatic missions and they agreed to have Kimura followed. They promised to follow him from work for a few days and watch the apartment. They'd speak to neighbours.

–

It was a Friday evening – 28 November – when Jack Miller visited Tadashi Kimura's apartment. He knew full well he was taking an enormous risk but felt he had no alternative. He planned to ask the diplomat to give him all the latest intelligence and then suggest he keep his head down for a couple of weeks. He managed to enter the block through Bellevue Park at its rear, climbing through a hedge and creeping along the small garden to the side entrance and then up to Kimura's apartment.

Tadashi Kimura seemed calmer than Sophia had described him. He was still wearing his dark suit and explained he'd only just returned from work and how was Jack and was there any news on Arno?

He replied that as far as he was aware Arno was well and Tadashi asked what he meant by 'as far as he was aware' and Jack said it was just a turn of phrase – what he meant was no news was good news and he was sure Arno was looking forward to seeing him.

'But you wouldn't tell me if it was bad news?'

'I can't imagine what bad news there could possibly be, Tadashi: Arno is in England, which is as safe for him as anywhere in the world.'

'And what about me – when am I going to England?'

Jack noticed the diplomat was becoming agitated now, removing his jacket and tie and walking up and down the room before pausing by a shelf to remove a whisky bottle from it.

'After Christmas.'

'Really – why didn't you tell me?'

'That's the reason I'm here: I wanted to tell you in person. Early in January, we'll get you to England.'

Tadashi stopped pacing the room and sat opposite Jack with a disbelieving look on his face. 'No sooner?'

'It takes time to make arrangements but London wanted me to tell you it's all being sorted. Please don't ask too many questions, Tadashi, because I don't know the details yet.'

His mother used to call it a white lie, which he'd always understood as a lie that your parents told you. In his book, a lie was a lie but this one appeared to have served its purpose, whatever its colour. Tadashi appeared calmer and Jack told him that although there was nothing to worry about, he ought to stop gathering any intelligence for a few days, maybe even a week or two.

Tadashi shook his head. 'It will be too late!'

'What will?'

'It is very difficult in the embassy – there is more tension and I think more security. The last material I gathered for you was a week ago, I haven't felt able to risk it since. I have a film here I can give you. Since then, I have memorised much of what I've seen and heard. If I told you now, would you be able to make notes?'

Jack said he had very good shorthand so, yes… please tell me what you can.

Over the next hour Tadashi spoke in a quiet voice, pausing only to sip his whisky or answer questions.

Admiral Yamamoto's fleet sailed out of Hittokapu Bay on Kasatka two days ago… the 26th… There are six aircraft carriers, including Sōryū, Zuikaku *and* Hiryū… *they're carrying more than four hundred aircraft – yes, four hundred… It's heading east, the objective is to attack the United States Navy but I'm not sure of the intended target… I do know the voyage will take a few more days… I overheard Ambassador Ōshima talking with the Naval attaché this morning and they said something about the 4th December…*

Jack asked him to be more specific about that date.

'I was in the outer office and the door was shut some of the time but I did catch a glimpse of them looking at a map and I think I heard the Naval attaché say that was when the fleet would change direction.'

'To where?'

'I don't know: but I do know that the emperor has already approved the attack and that Japan will certainly declare war on the United States.'

'But what about all these talks to reach a diplomatic solution?'

Tadashi Kimura pulled a face. 'Japan wants the Americans to believe there's the possibility of a diplomatic solution. We all know Ambassador Kichisaburō Nomura has been putting various proposals to the United States government – ending the war with China, withdrawing our troops, supplying us with oil, more troop withdrawals in Indochina... I could go on, but all this diplomacy, it's just designed to buy us time. Maybe the Americans know this because on the same day Yamamoto's fleet set sail the Americans demanded Japan withdraw all its troops from China and Indochina, which they must know we'd never agree to.'

'So war is inevitable?'

'Absolutely. You must tell the British about the fleet and they must inform the Americans. Who knows where it's headed, but maybe they can work it out? My guess – it's only a guess, but remember I was an officer in the Imperial Navy – is that if the fleet changes direction on the fourth of December it could well head south to the Midway Islands or west to Wake Island or even Guam though of course, they could...'

He hesitated and then shook his head as if dismissing the thought.

'They could what?'

'They could of course head south east towards Hawaii and to Pearl Harbor on Oahu Island which is where the main US Navy Pacific Fleet is based but... no... even with four hundred planes that's far too ambitious a target given the distance and the fact it's very heavily defended. The Americans are bound to spot them way before they get there.'

A feeling of fear fell over Jack Miller as he recalled the letter from his brother he'd received a few months before. Tom told him he was being transferred to Pearl Harbor. 'Come and visit me in Hawaii!' He wondered whether to push Tadashi on this but thought better of it. After all, hadn't he just said it was too difficult a target?

–

The atmosphere in Ambassador Hiroshi Ōshima's office was heavy with suspicion.

The head of the Gestapo unit that had been investigating Tadashi Kimura was there and to the ambassador's left sat Kuzumi Kobayashi with the restrained disposition of someone confident they've been proved right.

It was the Monday morning – the first day of December – and the ambassador was looking at the Gestapo officer suspiciously. 'Go on then.'

'At your request, sir, we put Tadashi Kimura under observation, which included following him after he left the embassy, watching his apartment and questioning the neighbours. One of the neighbours is a Frau Sauer who lives two floors below him in Brücken Allee. She told us that on a number of occasions in 1939 she saw a younger man – a German – entering and leaving Kimura's apartment and she believes he may have been staying there. Frau Sauer says there have been one or two other visitors too, but she was unclear about who or when. She told us that around two weeks ago a German woman knocked at her door to give her a copy of *Frauen-Warte*. She then noticed the woman knock on your colleague's door on the fourth floor and enter his apartment and remain there for at least ten minutes. She was unable to give us a useful description of the woman other than she was smartly dressed and wore a hat, which made it hard to make out her face.

'We gave Frau Sauer our telephone number and asked her to contact us if she noticed anything suspicious. She rang on Saturday morning to report that the previous night she'd heard someone on the stairs and when she looked out a man perhaps in his thirties was climbing to Kimura's floor. He remained in Kimura's apartment for over an hour.'

'She's sure of that?'

'Yes, sir.'

'And she didn't think to call you that night?'

'Apparently she didn't think anyone would be there. However, two of my officers were watching Kimura's apartment when they spotted a man matching that description leaving his apartment block. They thought it odd as they'd not seen him enter so they questioned him. He said he'd been to visit a friend called Hans – he didn't know his surname – who wasn't in and he thought he may have got the wrong address. They asked how come they'd not seen him enter and he said he didn't know as it had only been a few minutes before. They asked to see his papers and it turns out he's an American journalist called Jack Miller with an address in Sächsische Strasse in Wilmersdorf. You don't know of him, I suppose?'

The ambassador shook his head.

Kuzumi Kobayashi coughed before speaking. 'If you don't mind, sir, when I was informed about this earlier this morning, I did speak with our press attaché who assures me neither he nor anyone in his department have ever had any dealings with this gentleman.'

'Why have you not arrested him? And surely we should bring Kimura in for questioning?'

'A colleague of mine was asked to investigate Herr Miller and earlier this month he concluded there was no need to proceed with the investigation. However, things change as new inform-ation comes to light. My advice is to wait for a few more days if we can, during which time we will have the opportunity to investigate this man further.'

'And we will be able to take a closer look at Kimura.'

'Exactly: it may be that other people are involved – I'd be most surprised if they aren't – and this will give us an opportunity to spot them: we've learnt that arresting people too soon can be a mistake.'

Ambassador Ōshima impatiently tapped his pen on his desk. 'How many more days?'

'Ideally another week, sir.'

'No, no... no – today is Monday: the latest I can agree to is Thursday.'

'The fourth of December, sir?'

'Yes, the fourth of December.'

–

It was almost as if Basil Remington-Barber had known what could happen.

Not that one is saying you're going to be arrested, Jack, but of course in this business one never knows so my advice is to always have an escape plan up your sleeve. Keep in mind where you can go in an emergency and – and this is terribly important, Jack – have a bag!

There were times when he wondered what on earth the Englishman was talking about.

'Not much you can do if you're arrested, of course, but sometimes agents catch wind that they're being hunted. If you have somewhere to go and – importantly – a bag stashed away with some essentials in it then that can make all the difference: it means you'll have the resources you need to escape. Wolves do that, you know; they have different dens they use when they need to hide. Remember to have new papers because your identity will most likely have been compromised, otherwise you wouldn't be on the run, would you? Use a smallish rucksack and if you can hide a spare coat and hat: that's terribly useful, you'll be surprised how effective changing your outer clothing can be.'

–

Jack first wondered if he was being watched again when he left his apartment on the Monday morning. He'd been on his way to leave the envelope with the film in at Reinhard's kiosk on Budapester Strasse when he noticed a couple behind him. He'd turned round rather suddenly and was surprised at how close they were.

He'd smiled and carried on and when he next turned round an overweight man was walking breathlessly behind him, struggling to keep up.

He'd dismissed the idea he was being followed at first: he'd decided he was worrying too much and nothing had come of his suspicions before and it didn't help matters by worrying so much.

But as he was on Ranke Strasse and not far from the kiosk on Budapester Strasse he turned round once more and spotted the couple again, this time talking to a tall man and appearing to gesture in his direction. Jack was convinced the tall man was one of those he'd thought had been following him earlier in November. He didn't go anywhere near the kiosk, instead carrying on into the Zoologischer Garten.

He bought a cheese roll from a vendor at the entrance and then sat on a bench and took his time over eating it. During that period the same couple walked past twice, as did the overweight man and the tall man.

He took a tram to the Propaganda Ministry for the daily briefing – events on the Soviet front were not worthy of comment, apparently – and then returned to his apartment. He didn't think he was followed back and nothing in the apartment appeared to have been disturbed, though that was hard to tell.

But the next day – the Tuesday – was the same and he again had to abandon his visit to Reinhard's kiosk. This time he was followed back from the Propaganda Ministry and that night he was certain his apartment was being watched from the street. He composed a coded communication telling London he was in trouble and slipped it into the same envelope as Kimura's film and his report on what the diplomat had told him on the Friday night.

He left Sächsische Strasse just before ten on the Wednesday morning and instead of heading north went in the opposite direction. As he passed the apartment building next to his he wished the old lady sweeping the pavement a good morning.

'Be careful,' she said in a hoarse whisper, 'I heard them asking about you.'

Before he could ask her who she'd turned her back, hunched over her broom. He headed to Berliner Strasse and stopped at his favourite cafe, the first time he'd been there for a few days. The owner wasn't nearly as jolly as he normally was: just giving him the briefest of nods as he entered and sending the waitress over instead of himself.

Jack Miller wasn't too surprised: he'd noticed in recent months how fickle Berliners had become. The city seemed to live increasingly on its nerves and one consequence was people could be unpredictable: friendly one day, quite distant the next. At eleven o'clock he decided it was time to move on and slipped into the back of the cafe to use the toilet. In the narrow corridor he was aware of the door into the cafe closing and a large figure following him.

It was the owner.

'Upstairs, quick.'

He hurried up the narrow staircase to a tiny room on the top floor, most of it taken up by an untidy desk. The owner beckoned Jack in and closed the door.

'The Gestapo are asking about you. They came a month ago and wanted to know if you ever discussed politics and I said no but I thought better than to say anything to you, I thought it was just routine, you know – with you being a foreigner. But on Monday they came back and wanted to know more: were you ever in here with anyone else, did you ever leave anything here for someone else to collect, did you ever talk to any other customers… I don't want to get involved in anything but I've always liked you and I just wanted to warn you. You'd better leave now. And can I ask you a favour?'

Jack said of course.

'Please don't come back.'

He moved quickly after that. He left the cafe and headed south to Schmargendorf to catch the U–Bahn and changed trains three times. An hour later he finally exited at Wittenberg Platz and although he was as certain as he could be that he'd lost whoever was following him he still took a longer route on to Budapester Strasse. Reinhard was closing up as he arrived at the kiosk and gave him an anxious look, as if to ask whether there was a problem.

Jack used the code to indicate he was in trouble.

'Matches, please, I've run out of matches.'

Reinhard didn't react as he handed a box to him. Jack had meanwhile placed the envelope under a magazine and tapped it, telling Reinhard 'this is urgent'.

'You mustn't look so worried; I could tell something was up. I'll get this to the courier but if you're in that much danger my advice is to not hang around. You should get the hell out of this damn city.'

–

He'd hidden his rucksack in the basement under the apartment block on Düsseldorfer Strasse where the Luftwaffe man Scholz lived. He'd not had contact with him since June when he'd spotted a red rug on top of the box of paint cans and knew that was the warning sign to stay away.

But he'd found a perfect hiding spot there in a part of the basement well away from Scholz's storage cage – a tunnel connected two parts of the basement, a dark area where the wall was caked in a thick layer of soot and on the ground a metal grate appeared to lead to a foul-smelling and noisy sewer just a few feet below. It wasn't somewhere people would choose to pry around and Jack had found a loose block at the foot of the wall and had hollowed out enough space to hide a rucksack and a bag containing a change of clothing, both wrapped in tarpaulin.

He hurried there from Budapester Strasse: fortunately, the basement was deserted, and he went to his hiding place, crouching down opposite it for a while to be sure he'd not been followed.

He waited a few minutes before crawling over to the wall and prising away the block he'd loosened and sure enough, behind it was the tarpaulin and in that his rucksack and the change of clothing. He quickly removed his light brown raincoat, trilby and smart shoes and wrapped them in the tarpaulin before stuffing it in the void and replacing the block.

He put on a heavy black workman's jacket, a dirty cloth cap and workman's boots. They matched his new identity papers, which Basil had supplied: Hans Klein, a manual worker from Brandenburg, exempt from military service due to poor hearing.

It will get you through most checks, Jack… but if they're looking for you it won't stand up to an awful lot of scrutiny: they rarely do.

He checked his watch. It was four o'clock now and soon the curfew would begin. He toyed with the idea of remaining in the basement overnight but decided he couldn't risk Scholz spotting him if there was an air raid.

Then he remembered how Arno had mentioned he'd hidden in the Jewish cemetery on Schönhauser Allee when he was on the run. He couldn't think of anywhere better to go and it would only be for one night.

On Thursday he'd make contact with Sophia.

For now, he headed to Prenzlauer Berg, the burdens of being an exhausted, manual worker coming naturally to him.

Chapter 36

It was a wonder what two nights in a cemetery could do for one's appearance — and to one's chest.

Jack Miller had left the basement on Düsseldorfer Strasse just after four o'clock on the Wednesday afternoon. At the end of Pariser Strasse, he took a tram as far as Tiergartenstrasse, from where he walked a couple more blocks and then caught the U-Bahn.

Half an hour later he got out at Horst-Wessel Platz and walked up Prenzlauer Strasse. It was just before five-thirty and fortuitously this part of his journey coincided with people travelling home from work. He was certainly not the only worker trudging along exhausted and dirty from the day's exertions. He turned left into Treskow Strasse, which took him to the north-east tip of the Jewish cemetery, away from the main entrance on Schönhauser Allee.

Without pausing he turned into a small alley, beyond which were low railings in front of a tall row of trees. He glanced round: with no one in sight he climbed over the railings and hurried into the cemetery. If he was stopped, he'd decided, he'd say he urgently needed to use the toilet.

The Jews can hardly object!

But no one stopped him. It felt more like a wood than a conventional cemetery, with individual graves set between the trees, small rows crammed together where the space allowed. He headed to the centre and found an area with thick undergrowth and settled down in it. He remained there until the following morning. He hardly slept thanks to the cold and the sounds – real and imagined – around him. At one stage he was convinced he caught sight of two figures passing a few feet in front of him and around four in the morning he heard what sounded like laughter nearby.

He left the cemetery just after six on the Thursday morning. He was filthy and coughing heavily, but his instinct was not to remain in the cemetery during the day. He found a cafe on Wiesenberger Strasse which looked down on its luck, but evidently not as much as him because the woman behind the counter seemed appalled when she saw the state of him and said he'd have to sit at the back, in a draughty space next to the toilets, which suited him fine. He had plenty of money on him, which meant he was able to remain there for a good hour and before he left, he bought a large sausage and some bread. He'd had a good look at himself in the mirror and was impressed at how his appearance had already changed. His face was filthy, stained with dirt, and as he'd not shaved the previous day the stubble made him look older. Not only did he not look much like Jack Miller, he didn't feel like him either. He was, he reminded himself, Hans Klein.

He left the cafe and headed south, arriving in Sächsische Strasse around ten-thirty, driven by an urge to see if his apartment was being watched. It was an obvious risk, but from a block away he could see Gestapo cars parked in front of his building and plainclothes officers and uniformed policemen milling. He moved just far enough forward to spot more activity down the alley, by the entrance to his apartment.

He decided not to hang around, vindicated he'd made the right call the previous day, that he'd acted on the danger signs. He'd needed to be sure. He headed north to Potsdamer Strasse, which he tentatively entered from the east, relieved to see no sign of activity outside Sophia's apartment building. He walked past it on the opposite side of the road, glancing up at the small window and saw that the curtains were drawn, Sophia's signal that all was safe. But it wasn't a fool-proof signal – if she'd been suddenly arrested, she wouldn't have had time to open the curtains. And it was a Thursday, there was always the possibility Karl-Heinrich could come home for the weekend.

On the long walk back to the cemetery he realised how bad his cough now was. It was one of those that could be sorted by a hot bath, a hot drink and whisky and a good night's sleep, none of which were likely to be found in the cemetery.

He found another patch of undergrowth in the centre of the cemetery; this one had been hollowed out and someone had clearly been there before. As it got dark a man appeared a few feet alongside him, nodding at Jack. They said nothing all night: silent companions, unspoken conspirators, each deliberately ignorant of the other's predicament. The man offered Jack his flask of schnapps and the only time he appeared animated was when Jack handed him a chunk of sausage.

He must have slept for a couple of hours because when he woke it was seven-thirty and he was alone. He brushed himself down and headed back to Charlottenburg. The curtains were still drawn and all seemed quiet outside. The Mercedes wasn't in the street where it was usually parked when Karl-Heinrich was home and he could see the maid in the front room wiping the windows.

He was about to find a telephone box when he saw Sophia leave the building. He crossed the road and came alongside her.

'I'm in trouble, Sophia, I need your help.'

'I didn't recognise you!'

'That's the idea. Are you safe – no problems?'

'Are you being followed?'

'No, but they're after me.'

She stopped and allowed herself a moment or two to think. 'You look dreadful... let me think... I'll have to wait a while: I'll tell the maid she can have the rest of the day off and won't need to return until Sunday night. Fortunately, Karl-Heinrich isn't home this weekend. Here...'

She opened her handbag and made a play of giving him some coins, at the same time slipping her car keys into his hand. 'Hide in the car. There's a rug on the backseat. Stay on the floor and cover yourself with it. I'll come for you around four.'

–

Tadashi Kimura's world came crashing down that Friday morning.

On the Wednesday night he suspected he was followed from the embassy to Brücken Allee. Back in his apartment he picked up the telephone to call the American but there were odd clicking noises he'd not heard before so he put the phone down.

The following morning, he was certain he was followed to work. When he arrived, he was told he was needed in the consular department for a day or two. He wasn't quite sure why he'd been sent there – something to do with a problem over the issuing of passports, though he couldn't quite work out what the problem was or what he needed to deal with. He spent the day sitting opposite a clerk recently arrived from Tokyo, a man called Kuzumi Kobayashi. They hardly spoke, but whenever he looked up Kobayashi was staring at him.

It was the same on the Thursday night: a suspicion of being followed and when he arrived home, he suspected someone had been in his apartment. He'd always been meticulous about where he kept things and he was certain the fountain pen on his desk had been moved, as had the books on his bedside table.

He slept fitfully that night, getting up to check the road outside and then to write a long letter to his wife, the first he'd written for a month. He explained his life had been complicated and whatever happened she mustn't think badly of him.

But on Friday morning he was sure no one was watching him and when he arrived at Graf Spree Strasse he bumped into Kuzumi Kobayashi in reception who told him he was no longer needed in the consular department. He was to go to the ambassador's office. It was only as he entered it that he realised Kobayashi was behind him and before he had time to react, he was ushered into a side room, where the blinds were drawn and the head of security at the embassy was sitting at the front next to Ambassador

Ōshima. Tadashi was told to stand at the other end of the table and noticed two security officers appear either side of him. Kuzumi Kobayashi was now next to the ambassador and he spoke first.

…under suspicion… access to sensitive, top-secret material… being passed to the British… possibly the Americans too… do you know this man…?

At which point Kobayashi showed him a photograph of the American, Jack. Kimura was too shocked to react: he knew he ought to deny all knowledge immediately but he was so paralysed with fear he couldn't even shake his head. At one point he felt himself sway and a security guard grabbed his elbow.

When he tried to speak, he struggled to form his words: he was aware of standing there with his mouth open.

'Well then, Kimura, what do you say?'

For a few more moments, nothing. Then it was as if someone else had taken control of his body. He felt his knees buckle and heard himself sobbing, so loud at first it was impossible to talk, but then he heard himself: 'I'm so sorry… I apologise for my indiscretions, for all of them. What I did was wrong, I wanted to prevent a war. I…'

He managed to stop himself at this point, though of course by then it was far too late. He had absolutely no idea what had come over him. Events moved fast after that: the ambassador came over and told him he was a disgrace and then he was marched out of the room and down to a small room in the basement where he was strapped to a chair and the lights were turned out before the door was locked.

When the door opened a few hours later Kuzumi Kobayashi told him he had a choice. 'If you give a full confession now, you'll be taken back to Japan to face justice. If you don't co-operate, you'll be handed over to the Gestapo. Would you like some time to think about it?'

Minutes later he was telling them what he hoped they'd believe was a full confession. It was actually a very partial confession – he was determined not to mention Arno. From their questions it was clear they didn't know where Jack Miller was so he concentrated on him, not mentioning the woman or Doctor Vogt, the man who'd hidden Arno. Kobayashi also asked him about the kind of clubs he visited: where any of them the kind of places where only men went?

Tadashi Kimura admitted he'd been to those clubs – out of curiosity, he insisted, he'd never felt comfortable in them but unfortunately, he wasn't sure what happened, but he may well have got drunk and one thing led to another and that's when he met the American and… after that the American started to blackmail him and soon it was too late and he was trapped and he was so ashamed and…

Kobayashi asked him where they met and he said in his apartment or the American's – he gave him the address.

They kept him in the basement for a few more days. Kimura lost track of days but sensed he was handling the questioning well. Each day Kobayashi returned with more questions – usually a variation on ones he'd asked before – and Kimura kept his story simple and resisted any temptation to elaborate on it. As long as he didn't mention Arno. He had little doubt about the fate that awaited him in Tokyo but he felt he could handle it, not least because he deserved it.

Anything would be preferable to ending his days in Prinz-Albrecht-Strasse.

–

Jack Miller remembered little after Sophia shepherded him to her apartment that Friday afternoon. He recalled her saying that Karl-Heinrich rarely came home these days and the maid would be back on Monday morning and he had a high temperature and a terrible cough and perhaps he should rest and take some of the very strong medicine her husband swore by.

His next memory was waking up in a dark room, unsure of where he was or whether it was day or night. He was covered in sweat and felt as if he'd been drugged. It was not an altogether unpleasant experience.

He must have drifted off again because when he next awoke thin shafts of bright light speared the room. He sat up and as soon as he started coughing the door opened and Sophia came in. It was nearly ten o'clock in the morning, she said: Saturday. He'd been asleep since five o'clock the previous afternoon, she said: Karl-Heinrich's medicine had obviously worked – it contained morphine and cocaine and Jack said they ought to bottle it.

He had a hot bath and when he sat down to eat he told Sophia the whole story – his suspicion on the Monday that he was being followed turning into a certainty on the Wednesday; how he'd managed to lose them, dropping a message at the kiosk and then changing his clothes and picking up his rucksack in Düsseldorfer Strasse before spending two nights in the cemetery. He told her how he'd watched her apartment on the Thursday and only returned the following day because it seemed safe and now...

He shrugged and then quite without warning felt tears well in his eyes and roll down his cheeks and soon he was sobbing uncontrollably. He felt Sophia stroking his forearm and then touch his shoulders, telling him not to worry, this was quite natural and the medicine made him less inhibited and he'd been under so much pressure...

And then she was silent. When he looked up and smiled apologetically, she smiled too, a sweet smile full of affection, and she used her thumb to wipe away the tears under his eyes and gently brushed her hand across his face and he assumed it was either his imagination or the medication, but there seemed to be an intimacy to her touch. When he stopped crying, they remained sitting together at the table, moving their chairs closer to each other and he took her hand and that's how they sat for a long while, saying nothing until they heard the clock in the sitting room strike twelve.

'I need to leave Berlin, Sophia.'

'My maid will be back around eight-thirty Monday morning: you'll have to be gone by then. Where can you go?'

'I have Swiss papers and currency in my rucksack. If I can get over the border, I'll be fine. But…'

For the next hour they pored over a large map. The Swiss border was at least five hundred miles from Berlin, which meant the drive there and back would take her at least three days. They agreed that travelling by train would be the best way, though still a dangerous one.

At six-thirty on the Monday morning Sophia drove the Mercedes from the basement garage and headed towards the centre of the city. At the end of the road, she told Jack Miller it was safe and he got up from the floor and sat on the back seat. He was dressed in a smart black overcoat, a suit and shoes, all belonging to Karl-Heinrich. In his small suitcase was the rucksack and the clothing belonging to Hans Klein: they'd agreed this was more suitable attire if he got as far as the border.

The short journey was conducted in silence: there was too much to be said and both knew now wasn't the right time, though whether there ever would be a right time seemed unlikely and both of them clearly sensed that too.

When the car stopped on Viktoria Strasse, she told him where Potsdamer station was and he said he knew and told her to take care and they would see each other soon and she bit her lip and said that was her hope too and he'd better hurry. Moments later he was crossing the road and by the time he reached the other side the Mercedes was a dark blur.

The train to Nuremberg left at seven and his papers were only checked once on the journey. It was the fastest train of the day on that route and it pulled into Nuremberg on time at noon. He'd decided not to buy a through ticket just in case the Gestapo picked up his trail in Berlin.

The next stage of the journey was more difficult: twice he was asked why he was going to Stuttgart and on the second occasion he was pressed as to which factory he was being sent to work at.

The policeman looked unimpressed when he replied he'd only been told to report to the city's labour office.

They arrived in Stuttgart just before five that Monday afternoon. The ticket office was about to close but he was just in time to buy a ticket for his journey the following day.

He found a small hotel off Königstrasse run by a mother and daughter who seemed to be so grateful to have a guest that when he appeared flustered at all the forms he needed to fill in they said not to worry, just fill in the name, address and identity-card number and they'd do the rest and he said he was most grateful and gave them a generous tip and they asked if he'd like a meal brought up to his room, which he said sounded wonderful.

When he left in the morning, he asked for directions to the labour office and took some time carefully writing them down. The mother and daughter waved him off and only when he'd turned the corner did he turn in the other direction to the station. His first stop was the ticket office and after that the kiosk selling confectionary.

The journey from Stuttgart on the Gäu line took the best part of the day and became more fraught each mile they headed south. In other circumstances it would have been a pleasant journey: the train not as crowded as he was used to and the scenery was spectacular. But he spent the whole journey picking holes in his cover story, which was not too difficult.

The biggest flaw as he saw it — apart from the lack of papers — was how come a manual worker had travelled from Berlin to Stuttgart dressed so smartly: one railway policeman had mentioned it and he'd insisted he was a manager now, no longer a manual worker. And now he was heading towards the Swiss border, the most closely guarded one in the country. What was Hans Klein doing there?

The first check came between Herrenberg and Bondorf and was straightforward enough but at Sulz am Neckar the railway policeman wanted to know if he had papers allowing him to travel that far and he said of course not, this was a journey he did regularly and it was the first time he'd been asked for them.

The next check came after the train left Rottweil. A policeman in plainclothes, probably not Gestapo but he was in a mood to have a discussion about his career path.

'Papers, please.'

He looked at Jack then at the papers then back again and nodded. 'And you're travelling where?'

'Engen.'

'Purpose of visit.'

'A job interview, sir: I work in specialist areas – to do with defence.'

'And you have no letter or permit relating to that?'

Jack Miller apologised and said of course he did but like a fool had left it in his hotel in Stuttgart and he was damned if he could remember the name of it, though it was around Königstrasse if that was of any help and the policeman said it wasn't, it would have been of more help if the hotel *hadn't* been around Königstrasse.

'You don't sound as if you're from these parts?'

'I'm from Brandenburg.'

'So I see: but you don't have the accent.'

Jack said that was probably because he'd lived in the Netherlands for a long while and then for the second time that journey slipped into his mouth one of the strong mints he'd bought at the kiosk in Stuttgart and it quickly had the desired effect. Mints always caused him to cough, usually quite violently: it was a trick he'd used since his schooldays. This time the cough was so violent tears streamed from his eyes. The policeman looked uncomfortable and stepped back from him, evidently in a hurry to move on.

'I'm not satisfied with you having no papers about being in Engen. Where are you staying there?'

'I'm being met at the station apparently.'

'I'll contact our office in Engen and make sure they also meet you when you arrive. They can verify everything then.'

Jack said he quite understood and he was very sorry for any inconvenience.

At his training in England, he'd been taught how railway staff were trained to examine tickets closely to spot someone leaving a journey early. This was why the previous night he'd bought a ticket from Stuttgart to Engen and if all had gone well, he'd have then taken the branch line to Singen, right on the Swiss border. But that morning he'd bought another ticket, this one to Tuttlingen, in case he needed to leave the train early. He took care as they approached the station: as far as he could tell the policemen were further up the train, so he headed to the rear and removed his overcoat and took out the workman's jacket and cap and put them on. He waited until the train started to pull out of Tuttlingen before jumping off.

The station was quiet as he left it. He half expected a shout to call him back but the town was quiet too and he hurried along, anxious to put as much distance as possible between himself and the station. He found a small park and sat on a bench to take stock. He was some twenty-five miles from the Swiss border and it was getting dark and any time now the police at Engen would realise a Hans Klein hadn't arrived at their station. He needed to keep moving.

Under cover of the trees in the park he changed into the rest of his workman's outfit and hid the case containing the smart clothes in the undergrowth. He felt more comfortable as a manual worker and the boots were certainly more suited to his plans. The Swiss border was to the south-west and he headed in that direction with a vague plan to walk until it was dark and then hide until daylight. He'd been walking for ten minutes when he came across a Daimler lorry parked on the verge. It was caked in mud, as was the driver who was sitting in the open cabin enjoying a cigarette. He called out as Jack walked past.

'Where're you heading at this time of the day – out for a stroll?'

Jack said he was in the area looking for work but had been let down by a farmer and was hoping to find somewhere that would take him on.

'Don't trust any of the farmers round here. Do you want a lift?'

'Where are you heading?'

'Back to my depot in Tengen. You're more than welcome to have a lift there but you'll struggle to get work: they're very fussy about who can work round there.'

'Why's that?'

'Tengen's right on the Swiss border, isn't it?'

Chapter 37

'Not like him to cut up so rough, is it, Barney?'

Barney Allen looked across the table at Piers Devereux and allowed himself a few moments before responding. He recalled Tom Gilbey's initial description of Piers: disobliging. Sometimes that was very much to the fore, like now.

'I think in the circumstances Jack can be excused for behaving so emotionally. I'm sure I would.'

'But he's in Switzerland now, isn't he? He ought to relax – take the air or whatever it is one's supposed to do there. What are the chances of him staying on our books?'

'A lot better than they were: Basil had the devil of a job to calm him down and now fortunately Noel Moore's looking after him. Jack's rather taken to him, maybe he prefers grammar school-educated Englishmen to us public-school ones, who knows? Can't say I blame him.'

'And this clinic?'

'They call it a sanitorium: apparently it's where rich Swiss women go when things become a bit too much for them. God knows what they get up to there and it cost a bloody fortune but Noel says Jack was close to having a nervous breakdown but after a month at this place he's as fit as a fiddle.'

'And he's happy to continue working for us?'

'Possibly: he's happy to remain in Bern for the time being, says he's now got nothing to go back to the United States for. Basil says we can't possibly send him back into Germany – not for a while anyway, but he gets the impression Jack may be rather sweet on Sophia – keeps asking about her, insisting we ought to bring her out.'

'Not yet I think is the correct answer, is it not, Barney? You say she's safe in Berlin?'

'For the time being, no one suspects her. As long as that remains the case then we'd be mad to get her out. We need her there. It's not as if the city's overcrowded with British agents, is it?'

'All in all, Barney, your wolf pack has been a resounding success, has it not? All the intelligence we received on that fighter plane and then Kimura passing on all the top-secret Japanese plans that Winston and Roosevelt were able to use to their advantage and the United States entering the war – and the ambassador persuading the Germans to declare war on the United States – that was a master stroke.'

He allowed a broad smile. 'Well done: all in all, I think we can be jolly proud of ourselves.'

'Of course – but at some price though, Piers. Poor old Werner – and now Kimura.'

Piers came and sat next to Barney and placed a consoling hand on his shoulder. 'I know, I know – but then when you consider the benefit to this country… nonetheless, not pleasant – but then it's part and parcel of this business, I'm afraid. Kimura's chum we brought over here…'

'Arno.'

'Does he know yet?'

'Not yet. I'm going to go up later in the week to tell him in person.'

–

'Wilhelm, but you'll call me Willi.'

The lorry swerved as Willi leaned over to shake his hand and then deliver a non-stop commentary. *See that farm there? He's a bastard, never pays us... I live the other side of Tengen, the poor area! My wife wants us to move but I tell her if she wasn't so lazy maybe we could afford to... Do you want to buy a hundred cigarettes? I have a box in the back... Did you hear about the Japanese?*

Jack said he hadn't and rather disconcertingly Willi turned round in his seat to more or less face him as he told him how it had been the first item on the news last night and again this morning: hundreds of Japanese aircraft had attacked the main American naval base on an island in the Pacific and destroyed their whole fleet! 'Can you believe that? Looks like the Americans have lost the war even before they've joined it!'

Jack felt nauseous and a cold tremor ran through him as he thought of his brother Tom. Did Willi know the name of this island, by any chance?

'They did give the name but I'm damned if I can remember it. To be honest with you I don't take much notice about the war: I just try and get on with my life.'

Jack didn't want to appear too interested and Willi seemed to be the kind of person prone to exaggeration, but he couldn't ignore the fact that less than a fortnight ago Tadashi had said the naval base at Pearl Harbor could be the target, although an unlikely one. The attack Willi was describing sounded like it could well be Pearl Harbor. Jack gripped the side of seat and felt the same sense of fear he'd experienced in Tadashi's apartment in Berlin – after all, hundreds of aircraft... destroying a whole fleet... it sounded ridiculous.

They passed a sign: *Schweiz 5.*

Switzerland was so close.

Willi had fallen silent but kept glancing at him. A mile further on he suddenly turned off the road and drove down a muddy track and only stopped when they were in a clearing. He turned to face Jack, looking at him in an accusing manner.

'Are you a Jew?'

'Pardon?'

'You're a fucking Jew, aren't you?'

'Of course not!'

'It's obvious you're here to cross the border – all that nonsense about looking for work… and dressed like you are: no one dressed like that sounds like you do. I'm not even sure you're German: I could turn you in and get a nice reward.' Willi folded his arms high on his chest and leaned back, pleased with himself. *There!*

Jack said nothing. The silence around them was excruciating and everything was absolutely still apart from the tops of the tall trees swaying and Willi's breathing.

'I promise you I'm not a Jew. I just came looking for work…'

Willi stared at him through half-closed eyes before laughing. 'What nonsense! People don't travel here for work without papers. But don't worry – finding me was your lucky day. I can get you over the border tonight, if you're interested?'

Jack shrugged. This could be a trap. He could feel his whole body trembling.

'But I have to take into account the risk I'm taking. If it's not worth my while then why should I bother?'

Jack shrugged again and asked Willi what he meant.

'I mean if you want to get into Switzerland tonight, I'll take you, but I want money. How much have you got?'

'A thousand Reichsmarks.'

'Don't be ridiculous. The price is two thousand five hundred.'

Jack said he didn't have that but could do fifteen hundred and Willi said that was still not enough.

'I can give you fifteen hundred and—'

'I told you that's not—'

'And Swiss Francs.'

Willi's eyes widened. 'How many?'

'Five hundred Reichsmarks' worth.'

Willi's eyes narrowed as he appeared to work out how much he'd be getting. He nodded and said fair enough but only because he liked him and he didn't look like a Jew even if he had driven a hard bargain. He slowly counted the money as Jack handed it over.

'Get in the back. I'll drive closer to the border and hide the lorry in the trees and then lead you to the border. I'll show you the route and then you're on your own. I promise you wouldn't find it without my help.'

Jack wasn't sure he trusted Willi but he was exhausted and couldn't see an alternative. But the German turned out to be as good as his word. Fifteen minutes later he and Willi were walking in the forest.

'That's the border over there. You could walk over it in five minutes from here but you'd never make it. We'll wait here an hour until it's even darker and then take a longer route: it will be an hour's walk and then you'll be on your own.'

It was nine o'clock when they came to the edge of the forest. Ahead of them the black fields were interrupted by small woods. 'Crawl across this field to that wood there, the long, narrow one to your right. The border runs through the middle and they rarely patrol inside it. In the middle is a metal fence with barbed wire on top. Climb over and you're in Switzerland. The nearest village is Bargen but it's not unknown for them to send people back so my advice is to head for Schaffhausen, further south. Good luck!'

When Jack turned round Willi's shadow was already hurrying back through the trees and Jack hesitated before moving into the field and then ran for a hundred metres or so before he remembered he was supposed to be crawling. Twenty minutes later he'd climbed over the fence into Switzerland and kept moving, heading south before finding a glade to hide in until the morning.

He walked into the centre of Schaffhausen just before ten and went into the first cafe he came to. There was a telephone booth at the back and he dialled the Bern number he'd memorised.

'Hello?'

'It's me – I'm in Switzerland.'

There was a pause, followed by a cough. 'Good Lord, is that really you, Jack?'

Jack said he very much hoped it was. A wave of exhaustion hit him and for some unaccountable reason he felt his eyes fill with tears.

'Thank heavens for that! I was quite worried after your last message when you said they were on to you: worried we'd lost you. Are you all right?'

Jack said he was, though he felt exhausted.

'Of course, of course... well, *grüezi* as we say in Switzerland: do you know where you are?' Basil Remington-Barber sounded distinctly relieved.

'A place called Schaffhausen.'

A brief pause. 'And I take it you're in one piece?'

Jack said he was.

'Well, that's a relief. Thank God you're all right: London will be delighted. I'll let them know right away. I'll send someone from Zurich to collect you.'

Jack gave him the name and address of the cafe and Basil said someone ought to be there in two hours.

'Has something happened with the Japanese – and the American Navy?'

'Bad show actually, Jack. Place called Pearl Harbor. I'll tell you all about it when we meet.'

–

Jack Miller was taken to Zurich on the Wednesday and arrived at the safe house on the southern outskirts of Bern late on the Thursday afternoon, 11 December. Basil Remington-Barber arranged for a doctor to check him over so it was early in the evening when he and Noel Moore sat down with him. The row began almost immediately.

I've been used – so have Tadashi and Sophia and God knows who else... it's obvious the British used the intelligence we passed on as a way of bringing the United States into the war and... how many were killed?

'They're saying over two thousand, Jack, but you really mustn't—'

'Mustn't what, Basil – get upset? You know who one of those casualties could be? And I'd have contributed to his death!'

'You're being very hasty, Jack, and, dare I say it, emotional. We just don't know all the facts and, in any case, escaping from Germany like that and the enormous pressure you've been under – you're clearly unwell, who wouldn't be in the circumstances. But Barney is insisting I start a proper debrief while events are still fresh in your mind, we—'

Jack Miller said – shouted – that until he knew one way or the other, he wasn't going to co-operate at all: not with a debrief, or with plans for the future, or with anything in fact. He wouldn't consider them until he was told one way or the other and he also wanted to know what the plans were for Sophia. If that didn't happen, he was minded to leave Switzerland and return to the States and who knows, write his memoirs perhaps?

Basil told him to calm down and Noel explained very calmly quite how hard it was to get out of Switzerland – almost as hard as it was to get into the country. 'It would have been a bit easier while you were the citizen of a neutral country, but now of course…'

'The United States is still a neutral country as far as Europe is concerned. It's only Japan—'

'I'm afraid that's no longer the case, Jack.'

Noel Moore looked across at Basil who raised his eyebrows and then glanced at the ground, clearly hoping Noel would continue.

'Basil?'

'Yes, well… we understand that this morning Hitler decided to declare war on the United States. Earlier this afternoon von Ribbentrop summoned the American *Chargé d'Affaires* in Berlin to tell him that as the United States had breached its neutrality with Germany, Germany now considered itself to be at war with the United States.'

'Germany declared war on us – are you sure?'

'I'm afraid so, yes.'

'Is Hitler mad?'

'Quite possibly: I can't for the life of me think why he'd play into Roosevelt's hands like that: can you?'

Jack Miller said no but then he remembered how he'd been told to instruct Kimura to get Ambassador Ōshima to persuade the Germans to join in any war against the United States. It appeared he'd succeeded, but felt no elation.

'How about you have a decent night's sleep and, in the morning, we can start the debrief and talk about the future and—'

'No. Until I find out, I'm not co-operating.'

-

When Ben Findlay arrived for work at the American Legation in Bern the following morning he was surprised to find the elderly English diplomat he'd met only a few weeks before sitting quietly in the corridor outside his office.

At first, he'd thought of Basil Remington-Barber as eccentric, possibly even slightly odd, but then it became clear he ran the British Intelligence operation in Switzerland and was an important contact. Although his cover was as a military attaché Findlay's real job was as an intelligence officer. He listened patiently as the Englishman explained the situation.

'It's not going to be easy to get this information quickly, Basil. As you can imagine it's utter chaos in Washington and… and now Germany's declared war on us we—'

'That is precisely the point though, Ben, is it not? The fact Germany has declared war on the United States means we're now allies: on the same team. We've been fighting pretty much on our own for two years and you're going to be relying on our advice and drawing on our experience, but that pulls two ways. The information I require is a priority: without it an important intelligence operation is on hold.'

'And you say he's an American citizen?'

'Yes.'

'I'll do what I can: I have a good contact at the Department of the Navy, I'll cable him today.'

'This morning, please, Ben.'

'It's still the middle of the night there.'

'Nonetheless. I'd appreciate an answer by tomorrow.'

'They're still counting the casualties, Basil, but I'm told over two thousand dead and rising and over a thousand injured and—'

'Tomorrow, please, Ben.'

—

Basil Remington–Barber had to give Ben Findlay his due: not only did he obtain the information but as soon as he did so he called Basil at his house late on the Friday night and offered to give the news to his fellow countryman in person. He felt it was his duty to do so.

Basil took the American diplomat to the safe house at nine o'clock on the Saturday morning. Noel Moore joined them in the lounge, sitting alongside Jack Miller on the sofa. Behind them a beautiful garden swept down to a small stream and the morning sun glinted through the trees, throwing a pleasant light into the room. The horizon was dominated by Mount Gurten, the snow on its peak shining like a beacon.

Basil made the introductions and Ben Findlay leaned over and shook Jack's hand and said he was from Oregon and Jack replied 'Pennsylvania' and then Basil spoke so softly Jack had to lean forward to catch what he was saying.

'Mr Findlay has been terribly helpful and has managed to obtain the information you requested Jack and... um... I'm afraid, Jack, that...'

And then young Ben Findlay took over, speaking in a firm voice, looking Jack Miller directly in the eye. 'I am very sorry to tell you that your brother, Lieutenant Tom Miller of the United States Navy, was killed at around eight in the morning Hawaii time on Sunday during the Japanese attack on Pearl Harbor.' He paused a moment. Jack's expression was unchanged though he remained noticeably still. 'Your brother was on the USS *Arizona* when it was attacked by Japanese aircraft. The ship subsequently sank with significant loss of life. I am sorry that your brother was one of more than eleven hundred men on board who died.'

Jack blinked, nodded, and then dropped his head and remained silent for a while. When he did look up, he said he was very grateful to Mr Findlay for the manner in which he'd passed on such awful news. As soon as he'd heard about Pearl Harbor, he'd had a dreadful feeling that Tom was amongst the casualties and the not knowing, the waiting…

Basil said he quite understood and Jack snapped he wasn't sure he did and then Ben Findlay left and Jack Miller told them he'd rather be on his own for the rest of the day. Basil said there was the matter of the debrief and discussing other— but Noel Moore said 'for heaven's sake, Basil' and Jack was already halfway out of the room and as he left it, slammed the door shut.

—

It was the following week before Barney Allen made it up to Leeds. He knew he ought to have gone there sooner but he procrastinated because he knew it was going to be so difficult.

He telephoned Arno's former professor at the Charité who was now a distinguished academic at Leeds University Medical School and the person who'd helped facilitate Arno's place. He explained the situation and the professor said he would arrange for the meeting to take place in his office.

Barney took the early morning train from Kings Cross and arrived at the medical school late morning. It was a long walk down corridors smelling of formaldehyde and then up a flight of stone stairs and through swing doors into an oak-panelled corridor smelling of polish to the professor's office. Arno Marcus was there and looked surprised when Barney Allen entered.

Barney had already told the professor that part of the conversation would need to be very confidential and he said of course he understood, so after a brief chat about how well Arno was doing he slipped out of the room.

'It's about Tadashi, isn't it?'

'It isn't good news, I'm afraid, Arno. We don't know exactly what happened but we do know that he came under suspicion sometime around the beginning of December. The American journalist you met – Jack – came under suspicion around the same time but he managed to get out of Berlin. Our information is – and this is not going to be pleasant, Arno – that Tadashi was arrested at the Japanese embassy and subsequently taken to the Gestapo headquarters on Prinz-Albrecht-Strasse and—'

'No!'

'We understand he was executed there. I'm most terribly sorry—'

Arno held up his hand for the Englishman to stop.

'When I left Berlin in February, I had a gut feeling I'd never see Tadashi again and I think I've been mourning him since then. He was a very complex man, you know; I think he felt what he was doing was wrong and he was very conflicted: his feelings for men, his spying for the British – his whole life was a battle of emotions… He told me once he'd never return to Japan. His dream was to come to England and we talked about that many times but maybe in his heart he knew it was never going to happen.'

He walked over to the window and Barney opened the door and told the professor to come back in. The professor put his arm round Arno's shoulder and spoke quietly with him in German and said how sorry he was and Arno was to stay with him and his wife for a few days and Arno replied that was most thoughtful but he would be fine and, in any case, he had a cardiology lecture that afternoon which he didn't want to miss.

–

Jack Miller's debrief was so unsatisfactory that Basil Remington-Barber didn't feel they could even begin discussing future plans. The American gave the impression of going through the motions and was largely unresponsive. He was slightly less hostile to Noel Moore, but even then he was mostly monosyllabic.

The only times when he was more expressive was when he complained – loudly and at length – about how he'd been used by the British and, it seemed, the Americans, and indirectly he'd probably contributed to the death of his brother. He'd then stayed in his room and hardly eaten, and after a few days they were concerned enough to call the doctor. Although the doctor was trusted by Remington-Barber – he used him to treat escaping RAF aircrew – there was a limit as to how much he'd tell him, though the doctor knew Jack had been operating clandestinely in Germany and when he asked how long and was told since before the war he said in that case he wasn't in the least bit surprised he was behaving like this.

'I'm surprised he functioned for as long as he did: must have bottled it all up.' The doctor suggested a spell at a sanatorium, one he could recommend. They'd be very discreet, he assured them, but perhaps if he wasn't left there on his own, just in case…

The spell in the sanatorium lasted a month and was a success. Jack Miller slept for most of the first week and by the end of the third week seemed much better. He'd become especially close to Noel Moore, with whom he felt able to discuss his feelings, and Noel turned out to be a good listener.

When they returned to Bern in January, Basil took Jack for a long walk on the banks of the Wohlensee, the large lake west of the city.

'You're a free man, Jack: if you want to go back to the United States, I'll do my best to get you to Portugal and you can catch a boat from Lisbon, though getting through France won't be without risks.'

'Or?'

'Or you can stay here and continue to work for us: think of yourself as a wolf who's roamed across the mountains and found a new den. I know you harbour a good deal of resentment, Jack, but as I've told you before – all of us have walk-on parts in this awful war: we have to accept that what we do can only be judged by its role in the great scheme of things.'

The American made an indistinct noise, as if yet to be convinced.

'And there's another thing: what will you do if you do return to the United States? Go back to your old life – join the army? That would be a terrible waste: you're a fine agent – bright, resourceful, brave. If you stay here and work with us – with Noel and I – then you'll be most effective against the Nazis and surely that would be the best way to avenge your brother's death.'

Jack said nothing and when Basil glanced at him the American's facial expression suggested he wasn't sure he saw things the same way.

'And Werner – and Tadashi: you'll be avenging them too.'

He noticed Jack nod in apparent agreement though Basil knew full well he'd not won him over quite yet. There was one other matter that needed to be addressed. They carried on walking, the path turning quite muddy. Basil waited for Jack to raise the subject.

'And Sophia?' When Jack asked the question, it was in a rather too matter-of-fact manner, a somewhat heavy-handed attempt to sound like a casual afterthought.

Basil had anticipated the question: he'd hoped Jack would ask it because he knew if and when he did it would mean he was more or less on board. He waited before answering: he wanted his response to appear spontaneous.

'I have a man in Berlin – the courier who collected your stuff from the kiosk and brought it here to Bern. He's watching Sophia – from a distance of course. He assures me she's safe.'

'Safe for how long, Basil? She can't stay there forever, can she?'

'She has to stay there for the time being, but if and when we need to, I promise we'll move heaven and earth to bring her out – and if you're here there's all the more chance we can pull that off, eh?'

They came to a bench and sat down despite the rain turning heavier and a low wind whipping off the surface. Jack was silent and Basil didn't want to push him. When he looked over, Jack was gazing in the direction of the Jura Mountains, just visible in the distance, frowning as if trying to make something out. When he finally spoke there was a trace of emotion in his voice, along with a steely determination too.

'As long as Sophia's in Germany I'm staying in Switzerland.'

Author's Note

Agent in Berlin is a work of fiction, so any similarities between characters in the book and real people are unintended and should be regarded as purely coincidental.

Inevitably there are a few exceptions to this, which will be obvious in most cases, though I've also featured some lesser-known real people either as characters in the book or by referring to them. Examples of this include Hans von Tschammer und Osten, the so-called Reichssportführer, and also Hiroshi Ōshima, the Japanese ambassador to Berlin.

There's a reference in Chapter 7 to a German Jewish athlete called Gretel Bergmann. Despite being the German women's record-holder at high jump she was not selected for the German team in the 1936 Berlin Olympics. Bergmann fled to the United States, where she lived to the age of 103.

The other references to the 1936 Berlin Olympics are all based on real events, people and locations at the Games – including the Italy v USA match. It was intriguing to combine my passion for football with my interest in the Second World War. The details about the different German clubs, their grounds and the Gauliga system are factually correct although I was flexible with the timing of one or two fixtures.

The match between Switzerland and Germany in Bern on 20 April 1941 did happen, as did the shock result of a 2–1 victory for the Swiss. After this game Goebbels is supposed to have said there'd be no further international sporting events where the result couldn't be guaranteed in Germany's favour.

Another very important true character referred to in the book is Frank Foley. Foley was a remarkable person. Throughout the

1930s – up until the outbreak of war – he was the head of the MI6 station in Berlin. As I say in the book, the Foreign Office and the British embassy in Berlin regarded espionage as a distasteful business and did their best to distance themselves from it. Frank Foley and his staff were based on Tiergartenstrasse, well away from the British embassy on Wilhelmstrasse, and were denied diplomatic status, which meant he'd have had no protection if he was caught by the Germans. Yet despite this he was a highly effective British agent and saved some ten thousand German Jews by issuing them with exit visas.

Although Ernst Scholz is a fictional character, Foley did recruit a senior Luftwaffe officer as an agent in 1938 but was ordered to drop him by the British embassy.

The war crime committed in Kielce in Chapter 20 (it also features in my novel *Prince of Spies*) is fictional, though typical of the atrocities carried out by the Nazis in Poland and elsewhere. Katzmann and Wittek – who are named in that chapter – are based on real people. In Kielce in 1946 forty-two Jews who'd survived the Holocaust and returned to the city were murdered during a pogrom carried out by locals.

The plot of *Agent in Berlin* is based around two true stories in the Second World War: the development of the Focke-Wulf 109 fighter plane and the events leading to the Japanese attack on Pearl Harbor in December 1941.

With the FW 109 I tried to avoid becoming too technical but hopefully the fundamentals and timeline of the plane's design, the locations and the RAF bombing raids are all correct. The aircraft's designer, Kurt Tank, is another person who actually existed. During 1941 there were a number of RAF raids on aircraft factories, especially in Bremen.

Likewise with the events leading up to (and including) Pearl Harbor. Inevitably when one delves into the highly secretive worlds of diplomacy and espionage even known facts can be controversial. It's still a matter of dispute as to how much the British and indeed President Roosevelt were aware of the Japanese plans before the attack on Pearl Harbor. There's certainly a school of thought that says Roosevelt was looking for a way into the war despite opposition to it in the US – and through the Purple intercepts was well aware of the Japanese plans. Likewise, Churchill was in no doubt it was in the United Kingdom's interests for the USA to join the war.

The RAF carried out a series of bombing missions over Hamburg in May 1940, all of which coincide with Jack Miller's visit to the city earlier that month.

In Chapter 16 there is a reference to the *Selbstschutz*. This organisation – of pro-Nazi ethnic Germans in Poland – did exist. In the same chapter there are references to two Polish cities: the city of Łódź was indeed renamed Litzmannstadt once the Nazis occupied Poland, while Wrocław in the west of Poland was called Breslau by the Germans.

Also in Chapter 16 Sophia and Barney meet at Wertheim's on Leipziger Platz. This was actually the largest department store in Europe at the time, though during 1939 it was taken from its Jewish owners and later renamed. The store was destroyed by Allied bombing in 1943.

There are a couple of references to the Jewish cemetery on Schönhauser Allee in Prenzlauer Berg. There was – and still is – such a cemetery there, which somehow continued to function during the war and was also a place where people hid.

When Ted Morris and Henry Adams meet for lunch in New York in Chapter 22 Adams makes a reference to a speech Hitler made earlier that year. Hitler's speech to the Reichstag included this threat: 'If the international Jewish financiers in and outside Europe should succeed in plunging the nations once more into a world war, then the result will not be the Bolshevization of the earth, and thus the victory of Jewry, but the annihilation of the Jewish race in Europe!'

Currencies and their relative value are tricky to get across in a novel. Broadly I've based £1 in 1938 being the equivalent of (just under) £69 in 2021 and $1 being worth $18.55 today. I also work on the basis of £1 (during the war) being worth around 12 Reichsmarks.

I'd like to express my sincere thanks and appreciation to the many people who've helped bring about the publication of this book. First and foremost, my agent Gordon Wise and his colleagues at Curtis Brown. Gordon has been enormously supportive over a number of years and continues to be an enormous help. My publishers Canelo couldn't have been more impressive with the manner in which they've handled the first of the Wolf Pack novels and before that the Prince series and the re-issuing of the Spy Masters novels. As ever Michael Bhaskar and Kit Nevile and indeed the whole team at Canelo have been thoroughly professional, supportive and encouraging throughout the writing and publication process. My thanks too to Jo Gledhill for her skilful copy-edit, and to everyone who helped me with aspects of the book and answered seemingly odd questions as I was writing it.

And finally to my family – especially my wife Sonia, my daughters and their partners and my grandsons – for their encouragement, understanding and love.

Alex Gerlis
London
July 2021